BRAIN GAMES®

CODE BREAKER

JUMBO EDITION

Publications International, Ltd.

Cover image: Shutterstock.com

Puzzle creators: Michael Adams, Cihan Altay, Chris Bolton, Myles Callum, Phillip Carter, Don Cook, Jeanette Dall, Mark Danna, Caroline Delbert, Josie Faulkner, Dave Green, Luke Haward, Rod Hines, Marilynn Huret, Mark Lebel, David Millar, Dan Moore, Michael Moreci, Elsa Neal, Alan Olschwang, Emily Rice, Stephen Ryder, Pete Sarjeant, Stephen Schaefer, Paul Seaburn, Fraser Simpson, Terry Stickels, Samuel Stoddard, Nicole Sulgit, Howard Tomlinson, Linda Washington, Wayne Robert Williams

Puzzle illustrators: Helem An, Chris Gattorna, Elizabeth Gerber, Pat Hagle, Robin Humer, Nicole H. Lee, Jay Sato, Shavan R. Spears, Jen Torche

Louis Weber, CEO
Publications International, Ltd.
8140 Lehigh Avenue
Morton Grove, IL 60053

ISBN: 978-1-64030-429-1

Manufactured in China.

8 7 6 5 4 3 2 1

Crack the Code

Cryptograms and codes have been around for centuries, confounding, testing, and entertaining those who take up their challenges. With *Brain Games® Jumbo Edition Code Breaker*, it's your turn. Pit yourself against more than 400 puzzles that test logic, language, and visual skills. Discover hidden messages by decrypting number and symbol-based codes!

If you get stuck, don't despair. Try another puzzle and come back to the one that's baffling you with a fresh eye later. There's an answer key in the back, just in case!

Are you ready to solve some codes?

Game On!

Solve this puzzle just as you would a sudoku puzzle. Use deductive logic to complete the grid so that each row, column, and 4-by-4 box contains the letters from the letters A E G M.

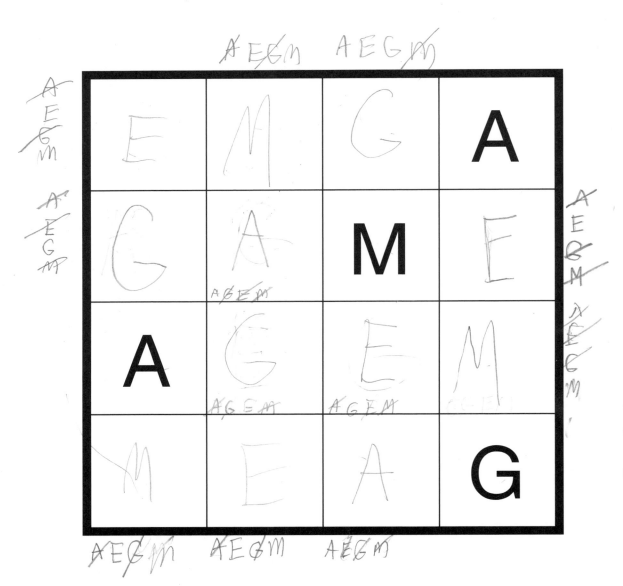

Answer on page 374.

Code-doku

Solve this puzzle just as you would a Sudoku puzzle. Use deductive logic to complete the grid so that each row, each column, and both diagonals contain each of the letters of the word MOUTH in some order. The solution is unique. We've inserted 6 letters to get you started.

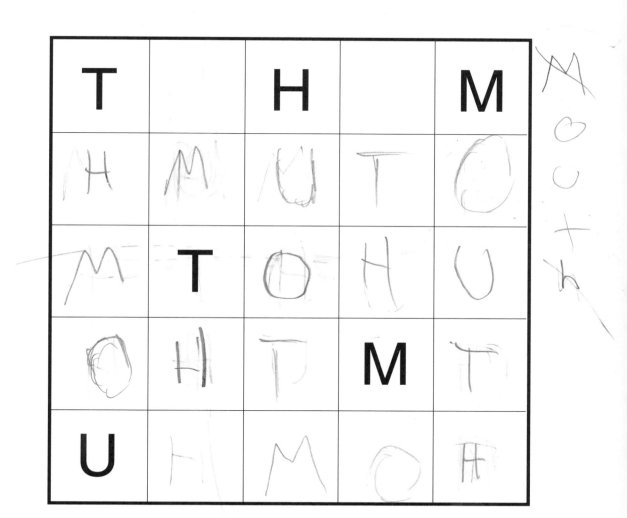

Answer on page 374.

An Actor's Bio

Cryptograms are messages in substitution code. Break the code to read the trivia question and answer. THE SMART CAT might become FVO QWGDF JGF if **F** is substituted for **T**, **V** for **H**, **O** for **E**, and so on.

LA ZRY MDWU-VR-MDWU REWDXE QRX "WDBVDTYE WRIXDFARIE" DYP "MRCE VRZY." LA DSER EVDXXAP TY "QDVLAX RQ VLA MXTPA." ZLR TE LA? EBAYWAX VXDWC

A B C D E F G H I J K L M N O P
Q R S T U V
X Z

A Place in the United States

Cryptograms are messages in substitution code. Break the code to read the message. THE SMART CAT might become FVO QWGDF JGF if **F** is substituted for **T**, **V** for **H**, **O** for **E**, and so on. The code is different for each cryptogram.

Hint: Look for repeated letters. E, T, A, O, N, R, and I are the most often used letters. A single letter is usually A or I; OF, IS, and IT are common 2-letter words; THE and AND are common 3-letter groups.

VLXZ VNT MXVD LJZ VLB AJVBFJD JQML JKU VLB EXZZNPQX RNVJKXMJG AJQUBK. FLJV XZ XV? ZV. GNPXZ

A B C D E F G H I J K L
M N O P Q R S T U V W X

Answers on page 374.

Petalgrams

Form six 7-letter words using the letters in each petal plus the F in the center. None of these words will begin with F. Then, form a 7-letter bonus word (beginning with F) using the first letter of each word you made plus the F.

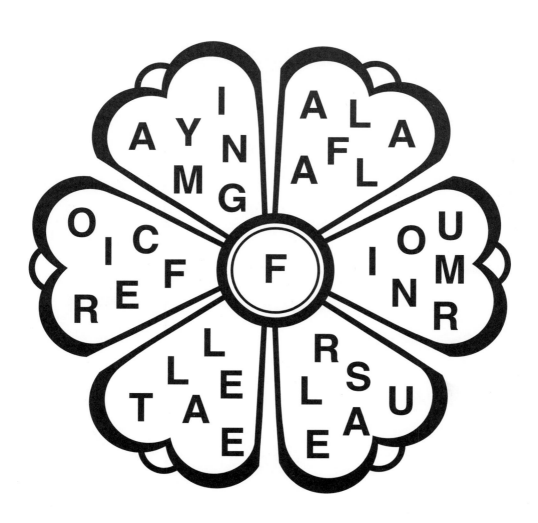

Answers on page 374.

Confused?

Every word listed below is contained within the group of letters. Words can be found in a straight line horizontally, vertically, or diagonally. They may read either forward or backward.

BEDLAM	JAMBALAYA	POTPOURRI
BROUHAHA	JUMBLE	PROBLEM
CHAOS	LABYRINTH	PUN
CLAMOR	MAZE	PUZZLE
CODE	MEDLEY	QUANDARY
CONUNDRUM	MELANGE	QUIZ
CRYPTOGRAM	MELEE	RABBLE
DILEMMA	MENAGERIE	RIGMAROLE
DIN	MIRE	RIOT
DISORDER	MISHMASH	RUBBLE
FRACAS	MIX-UP	RUMPUS
GUMBO	MOTLEY	SALMAGUNDI
HASH	MUDDLE	SHOCK
HODGEPODGE	OLIO	TOPSY-TURVY
HUBBUB	PASTICCIO	TUMULT
HURLY-BURLY	PASTICHE	TURMOIL
IMBROGLIO	POSER	UPROAR

```
T O P S Y T U R V Y M E L B O R P B U B B U H Z T
K C O H S A C A R F R E S O P J U M B L E H U I E
A H A H U O R B M E L E E E D O C O N U N D R U M
                                        L Q G
                                        Y A R
M E A H R E D R O S I D N U G A M L A S  B O M
I T S I Q U A N D A R Y M I X U P U N I  U B U
S A O                            P R      R M D
H T E                            M R      L U D
M L L   L A B Y R I N T H U Z    E U      Y G L
A U O   S Z L E H C I T S A P    D O      E M E
S M R   O M                      L P      G A I
H U A   A I                      E T      N Z M
E T M   H R L M A R G O T P Y R C Y O     A E B
U C G   C E A O T E I R E G A N E M P     L M R
N P I                                     E O O
A I R                                     M T G
E G D O P E G D O H D I L E M M A E L B B A R L L
J A M B A L A Y A S U P M U R L P U Z Z L E O E I
G L I O M R U T E L B B U R P A S T I C C I O Y O
```

Answers on page 374.

Zen in a Nutshell

Cryptograms are messages in substitution code. Break the code to read the humorous statement by David Bader. THE SMART CAT might become FVO QWGDF JGF if **F** is substituted for **T**, **V** for **H**, **O** for **E**, and so on.

"HK NKXK TUC. HK YUSKVRGIK KRYK RGZKX. OY ZNGZ YU IUSVROIGZKJ?"

2 Rules

Cryptograms are messages in substitution code. Break the code to read the message. THE SMART CAT might become FVO QWGDF JGF if **F** is substituted for **T**, **V** for **H**, **O** for **E**, and so on.

HNMFM TFM HIG FPQMK WGF PQHCJTHM KPAAMKK CO QCWM. OMSMF HMQQ MSMFLHNCOY LGP EOGI.

Answers on page 374.

Sum It Up

A message is hidden in these math problems. The answer to each problem has a letter. Write the letters above the blanks that correspond to each answer to find the secret message.

$3 \times 3 =$ **E** | $182 - 175 =$ **U** | $12 + 15 =$ **E**

$2 \times 3 =$ **T** | $19 - 7 =$ **M** | $6 \times 4 =$ **T**

$10 \times 2 =$ **Y** | $10 \div 5 =$ **H** | $11 \times 2 =$ **T**

$8 + 8 =$ **N** | $236 - 217 =$ **A** | $2 \times 2 =$ **F**

$100 \div 4 =$ **I** | $7 \times 3 =$ **A** | $5 \times 3 =$ **O**

$58 - 41 =$ **E** | $5 \times 2 =$ **C** | $25 \div 5 =$ **U**

$22 - 21 =$ **T** | $9 + 2 =$ **O** | $9 \times 2 =$ **D**

$78 \div 6 =$ **E** | $94 - 91 =$ **E** | $24 \div 3 =$ **R**

$13 \times 2 =$ **M** | $92 \div 4 =$ **A** | $7 + 7 =$ **S**

I 1 H 2 E 3 __4 __5 6 U 7 __8 __9 __10 __11

M 12 E 13 __14 __15 N 16 E 17 __18 __19 Y 20

__21 __22 __23 __24 25 M 26 __27

Answers on page 374.

One for the Ages

Betty, Billy, and Bobby were at Bonny's birthday party. They were all biting into the birthday cake, which was baked by Bonny's mom, Bunny, when Bonny whispered, "I probably shouldn't say this, but my mom is four times as old as I am." Bonny then added, "And I'm three years older than Billy." Bobby said, "In two years, I'll be twice as old as Billy is now." Betty said, "I'm two years younger than Bobby was a year ago." Billy said, "I'm really, really confused!" Just then, Bunny, Bonny's mom, came out of the house and said, "Bonny, I heard what you said about me. I just want all your friends to know that I'm very proud to look this good at 36." If Bonny's mom is telling the truth about her age, can you figure out how old all the kids are?

Betty: _____

Billy: _____

Bobby: _____

Bonny: _____

Answers on page 374.

Who's There?

Cryptograms are messages in substitution code. Break the code to read the meassage. THE SMART CAT might become FVO QWGDF JGF if **F** is substituted for **T**, **V** for **H**, **O** for **E**, and so on. The code is different for each cryptogram.

YVHH, MR M STHHVO BQV
YCGKN KDLWVC, YQX OMO
XGD TKEYVC BQV JQGKV?
—PTLVE BQDCWVC

Pardon My French

Cryptograms are messages in substitution code. Break the code to read the message. THE SMART CAT might become FVO QWGDF JGF if **F** is substituted for **T**, **V** for **H**, **O** for **E**, and so on.

EJPF'O FJK YXKHUJ YTX YRQQSK-QKQKK?
—SKERO UPXXTSS

Answers on page 374.

Cryptoquotes

Cryptograms are messages in substitution code. Break the code to read the historic quotes and their authors. THE SMART CAT might become FVO QWGDF JGF if **F** is substituted for **T**, **V** for **H**, **O** for **E**, and so on. The code is different for each cryptogram below.

1.

"WRLB, OZ XGRW BX XHFDRAYRD, OD SXB WRLB LHB CS OSYRDBERSB."

—ZFCSPAOS W. FXXDRYRAB

2.

"UOB LQ OACOGPYD QY BY URPO BVGB FVOA FO JYWO BY CRO OPOA BVO LACODBGIOD FRUU XO QYDDH."

—WGDI BFGRA

Answers on page 375.

Plus Code

Each set of letters represents a 5-letter word. To decipher each word, move either forward or backward in the alphabet the same number of letters for each letter given in a word. For example, if you move ahead 3 letters from each letter in ALQ, you'll discover the word DOT. (A + 3 letters = D; L + 3 letters = O; Q + 3 letters = T). When counting letters, keep in mind that the end of the alphabet connects with the beginning (Z + 4 letters = D). Use the alphabet line below to keep track of the number of moves you make.

1. **EJKNF** _____

2. **NGCXU** _____

3. **ZQZIO** _____

4. **ITUFQ** _____

5. **JGEIG** _____

6. **NTSNH** _____

7. **BLUFJ** _____

8. **SHGXL** _____

9. **HFHEC** _____

10. **GCGPI** _____

A B C D E F G H I J K L M N O P Q R S T U V W X Y Z

Answers on page 375.

Animal Riddles

Cryptograms are messages in substitution code. Break the code to read the riddles and their answers. THE SMART CAT might become FVO QWGDF JGF if **F** is substituted for **T**, **V** for **H**, **O** for **E**, and so on. The code is the same for both cryptograms.

1.

IOGN'V MEGTR GJB IOUNW GJB "PWB"
GEE QFWP?

G LWMPG IWGPUJY EUHVNUTR.

2.

IOK BUB NOW HQEUTW GPPWVN NOW
MUPB?

MWTGSVW UN IGV G PQMUJ.

Space-Savers

Two well-known proverbs are given below. No letter has been printed more than once in either of them, even if it appears in the proverb a number of times. For example: "RISEANDH" would be "RISE AND SHINE." Supply the missing letters and read the proverbs.

L O K B E F R Y U A P

W A S T E N O

Mind-Bender

We found this strange message carved on a rock in an ancient castle. Can you decipher it?

FLES TIFOM ARGAN ANASI ELF ITS

Answers on page 375.

Countdown

Cryptograms are messages in substitution code. Break the code to read the message. For example, THE SMART CAT might become FVO QWGDF JGF if **F** is substituted for **T, V** for **H, O** for **E,** and so on.

"ZJNX LXOBF, MSVXC CNX GNISBN FSV UANLQ;
PI DNBF LXOBF LX JVXHBNH."

　　　　　　　　— CJSRLU KNIINBUSX

"ZJNX LXOBF, MSVXC ISVB; ZJNX DNBF LXOBF
UZNLB."

　　　　　　　　— RLBQ CZLPX

Answers on page 375.

Letter Lesson

Cryptograms are messages in substitution code. Break the code to read the quote and its author. THE SMART CAT might become FVO QWGDF JGF if **F** is substituted for **T**, **V** for **H**, **O** for **E**, and so on.

"ULT, VU DUAEVPB, OBD EDOODJ TBVWB FLPO
CJDIMDUOEQ LWWMJP VP D. YCODJTYJX, OBD
PMWWDPPVLU JMUP OBMP: Y, L, V, X, B, U, J, P, O, M,
Q, W, C, A, E, F, T, Z, G, K, I, S, R. D KJDXLFVUYODP PL
JDFYJGYZEQ, OBYO YU VUXVNVXMYE PDUODUWD LC
YUQ EDUAOB VP JYJDEQ PDDU, VU TBVWB VO VP ULO OBD
KJDNYVEVUA WBYJYWODJ."

—DXAYJ YEEYU KLD

Bird Wisdom

Cryptograms are messages in substitution code. Break the code to read the message and answer. THE SMART CAT might become FVO QWGDF JGF if **F** is substituted for **T**, **V** for **H**, **O** for **E**, and so on. The code is the same for each cryptogram below.

1. F LNIV NM SXJ XFMV NG EAISX SEA NM SXJ
   LZGX.

2. LNIVG AO F OJFSXJI OKABH SADJSXJI.

3. SXJ JFIKR LNIV DJSG SXJ EAIC.

Answers on page 375.

Is That a Fact?

A cryptogram is a simple, scrambled alphabet code. Break the code to read the message. For example, I SEE TESS, in code, may be A DGG FGDD, where A = I, D = S, G = E, and F = T. Each cryptogram below uses a different code.

J QNLTAOLL TL YSS QTR HKOA TY YJEOL J HOOE
XSP RSLLTZ YS RS XPSG SAO OAV SX YKO
SXXTFO YS YKO SYKOP.

DQQN SX ZSXK ULJU QEQX SW AFR JOQ FX ULQ
OSCLU UOJBD, AFR TSMM CQU ORX FEQO SW
AFR YRHU HSU ULQOQ .

R XSTAOSEE IXZYSX ZE R QSXECP NKC XRTSE
QREV UCL NKSP UCL RXS WCZPW EZFVU-JZYS
BZOSE QSX KCLX .

Cryptoquote

Cryptograms are messages in substitution code. Break the code to read the message. THE SMART CAT might become FVO QWGDF JGF if **F** is substituted for **T**, **V** for **H**, **O** for **E**, and so on. Hint: In the cryptogram below, N equals G.

"BFS JDD QHFW KNNM RZ HZK EJMYKS— JZP OJSGA SAJS EJMYKS."

—UJWY SOJRZ

Instant Cure

Cryptograms are messages in substitution code. Break the code to read the message. THE SMART CAT might become FVO QWGDF JGF if **F** is substituted for **T**, **V** for **H**, **O** for **E**, and so on.

"XJOH D UAGT NF TAMUAY D MABGTH'U VPPAYT VH AKOYVUDAH, JO APPOYOT UA UABMJ–BK NF R– YVFZ."

—JOHHF FABHCNVH

Answers on page 375.

Word Columns

Find the hidden phrase by using the letters directly below each of the blank squares. Each letter is used only once.

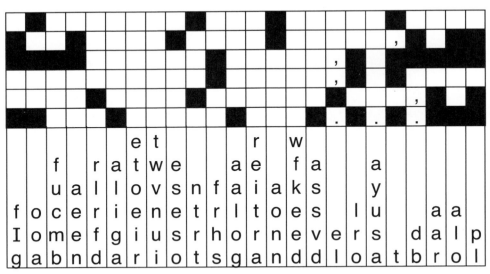

Word Columns

To find the statement, put the letters that appear in the bottom half of the puzzle into the column of boxes above them. The letters may not be listed in the exact order in which they appear in the boxes. Mark off used letters at the bottom. A letter may be used only once. The black squares represent the space between words.

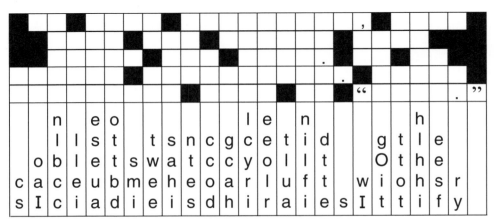

Answers on page 376.

World Capitals

Cryptograms are messages in substitution code. Break the code to read the message. For example, THE SMART CAT might become FVO QWGDF JGF if F is substituted for **T**, **V** for **H**, **O** for **E**, and so on. The code is the same for each.

1. FUBF, HFKSIT

2. URFMPEFBD, USOAOH

3. HOS AOBEN, NHANI

4. MINKF, OLTJR

5. COBLKIAO, UOKCNI

6. IDUROKAID, HOREOKBIHAU

7. DIAKNA, UJINH

8. RFPTF, GIJIH

9. UIHRNILF, MENBO

10. JEHFD JOHE, MIDCFANI

Answers on page 376.

Rules of Thumb

Cryptograms are messages in substitution code. Break the code to read the message. THE SMART CAT might become FVO QWGDF JGF if **F** is substituted for **T**, **V** for **H**, **O** for **E**, and so on. One code for all.

1. GQGPYL: WQG NOM GCMZFV PWMYJFL OJG GQGPYL WU WQG ZKGPZYG IZQHL NZP WP WQG NFMG-OSD RWWHGQ XZOIJ.

2. DWTGP PMFG: FWWT ZPWMQH OJG OZNFG ZQH USQH OJG KSIOSX. SU LWM IZQ'O OGFF RJW SO SV, SO'V LWM.

3. JWR OW XSA Z DPWDGP WSF-ZQH-KSQGYZP VZFZH HPGVVSQY: OJPGG DZPOV WSF, WQG DZPO KSQGYZP.

4. RJZO OW NPSQY OW VMXXGP IZXD? Z YWWH PMFG WU OJMXN: SU LWM IZPG ZNWMO OJG SOGX, FGZKG SO ZO JWXG.

Word Columns

Find the hidden phrase by using the letters directly below each of the blank squares. Each letter is used only once.

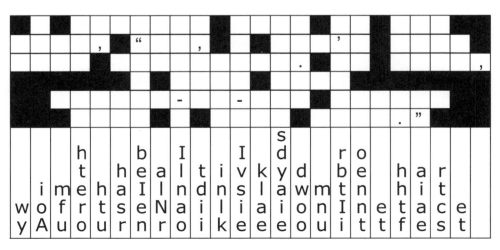

Answers on page 376.

Crypto-Animal Families

Cryptograms are messages in substitution code. Break the code to read the message. For example, THE SMART CAT might become FVO QWGDF JGF if **F** is substituted for **T, V** for **H, O** for **E,** and so on. Each Crypto-Family is a list of related words in code. Each family has its own code.

1. On the Farm

AMBANHD

CEFK

AEJ

MEGIH

CEEIH

OPANRBDC

IMHHS

IJBDH

GFTTBK

MEPDO

2. At the Zoo

EFAAGAGHIDJK

LEFMG

HFPNL

PFLIBBN

NONAEIMH

PGLFOOI

RNCLI

SIMPILGG

KMISNK

OFGM

3. In the Ocean

FLEPC

ICEP

AGBAPC

IAHKDBEJ

RMPNLHK

PMSIACB

MJIACB

IAEBTHIL

UCPPJTHIL

ILEBV

Answers on page 376.

Name Calling

Decipher the encoded word in the quip below using the numbers and letters on the phone pad. Remember that each number can stand for 3 or 4 possible letters.

Money is the root of all

9-3-2-5-8-4.

Famed Fabulist

Cryptograms are messages in substitution code. Break the code to read the message. THE SMART CAT might become FVO QWGDF JGF if **F** is substituted for **T**, **V** for **H**, **O** for **E**, and so on. The code is different for each cryptogram.

PCSO GLU KLO, QM PDLBSPSIU, L OALEN KCI ASENB

SU GSB-OSFPC HNUPJDM Q. H. LUHSNUP RDNNHN.

CSO OPIDSNO LDN OPSAA PLJRCP LO GIDLA

ANOOIUO. OIGN IT CSO GIOP TLGSASLD OPIDSNO

LDN "PCN PIDPISON LUB PCN CLDN" LUB "PCN QIM

KCI HDSNB KIAT." CN SO VUIKU LO LNOIW.

Answers on page 376.

Wacky Wordy

Can you "read" the phrase below?

BLOUNECMOEON

Classic Lit

Cryptograms are messages in substitution code. Break the code to read the quote and its author. THE SMART CAT might become FVO QWGDF JGF if **F** is substituted for **T**, **V** for **H**, **O** for **E**, and so on. Hint: Look for repeated letters. **E, T, A, O, N, R,** and **I** are the most often used letters. A single letter is usually **A** or **I; OF, IS,** and **IT** are common 2-letter words; **THE** and **AND** are common 3-letter groups.

"FC FT M CHYCR YAFLIHTMZZB MWJAPQZISUIS,
CRMC M TFAUZI KMA FA EPTTITTFPA PX M
UPPS XPHCYAI, KYTC DI FA QMAC PX M
QFXI."

—NMAI MYTCIA, *EHFSI MAS EHINYSFWI*

Answers on page 376.

Triangle Trial

How many triangles of any size are in the figure below?

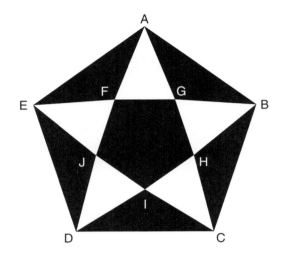

Name Calling

Decipher the encoded word in the quip below using the numbers and letters on the phone pad. Remember that each number can stand for 3 or 4 possible letters.

He who blows his stack only adds to the 9–6–7–5–3'–7 pollution.

Answers on page 377.

Acrostic Anagram

Unscramble the words below, then transfer the corresponding letters to the grid. A black square indicates the end of a word. When you're finished, you'll be rewarded with a quote by Agnes Repplier.

1. A C I N B
    —— —— —— —— ——
    10 30 35 40 12

2. M O P S Y C H I N
    —— —— —— —— —— —— —— —— ——
    36 42 50 4 8 74 21 69 18

3. E E L V L
    —— —— —— —— ——
    5 33 66 58 28

4. N P I Y T G
    —— —— —— —— —— ——
    15 49 1 67 55 20

5. A A W R D H E
    —— —— —— —— —— —— ——
    59 43 48 53 45 25 39

6. C A P N E
    —— —— —— —— ——
    29 6 64 71 75

7. I A L Z N F E I
    —— —— —— —— —— —— —— ——
    63 22 13 27 68 54 70 24

8. E H C O R
    —— —— —— —— ——
    52 57 62 44 2

9. O I A T A V R
    —— —— —— —— —— —— ——
    60 46 65 34 56 14 16

10. L I R Y W E A
    —— —— —— —— —— —— ——
    7 17 11 38 73 32 61

11. O B O E Z
    —— —— —— —— ——
    31 19 3 23 47

12. T P U U T O
    —— —— —— —— —— ——
    9 51 41 26 37 72

1 D	2 H	3 K	4 B	5 C	6 F		7 J	8 B	9 L		10 A	11 J	12 A	13 G	14 I	15 I		16 I	17 J
18 B	19 K	20 D	21 F	22 G	23 G	24 G		25 G		26 L	27 I	28 C	29 F	30 A	31 K	32 J	33 C		34 I
35 A	36 B	37 L	38 J	39 E	40 A	41 L	42 B		43 E	44 E	45 E		46 I	47 K	48 H	49 D		50 B	51 L
52 H	53 E		54 G	55 D		56 D	57 H	58 C		59 E	60 E	61 J		62 H	63 G		64 F	65 I	66 C
67 D	68 G	69 B	70 K	71 F	72 L	73 J	74 B	75 B									

Answers on page 377.

Wacky Wordy

Can you "read" the phrase below?

THEBLUEFACE

Crypto-Wisdom

Cryptograms are messages in substitution code. Break the code to read the message. THE SMART CAT might become FVO QWGDF JGF if **F** is substituted for **T**, **V** for **H**, **O** for **E**, and so on. The code is the same for each cryptogram.

Hint: Look for repeated letters. E, T, A, O, N, R, and I are the most often used letters. A single letter is usually A or I; OF, IS, and IT are common 2-letter words; THE and AND are common 3-letter words.

1.   I JGHHEKF MNGKC FINLCJM KG OGMM.

2.   I BCKKP MISCA EM I BCKKP CIJKCA.

3.   DEKA RGJAM HEKFCJ EK NLC LCIJN.

Acrostic Anagram

Unscramble the words below, then transfer the corresponding letters to the grid. A black square indicates the end of a word. When you're finished, you'll be rewarded with a quote by Agnes Repplier.

1. N I E I D O
   <u> </u> <u> </u> <u> </u> <u> </u> <u> </u> <u> </u>
   24 62 51 50 14 12

2. L F E R Y O W
   60 15 56 27 43 30 74

3. U U F R S O I
   20 54 2 5 38 63 58

4. S Y P W I
   1 3 45 17 46

5. N C U Y O T R
   53 19 57 32 4 49 16

6. C S O L O H
   9 37 11 13 47 55

7. E N O I M N E
   26 33 70 8 68 31 29

8. N S O E R
   22 35 71 66 73

9. R O O N D T A
   10 34 18 67 65 42 69

10. G I E E S
    23 52 36 7 64

11. I U N R E N O
    44 21 48 39 41 25 6

12. N I Y S H
    40 28 59 72 61

1 D	2 C	3 D	4 E	5 C	6 K	7 J		8 G	9 F		10 I	11 F	12 A		13 F	14 A	15 B	16 E	
17 D	18 I	19 E	20 C	21 K	22 H	23 J	24 A	25 K	26 G		27 B	28 L	29 G	30 B	31 G		32 E	33 G	
34 I	35 H	36 J		37 F	38 C	39 K	40 L	41 K	42 I	43 B	44 K	45 D		46 D	47 F	48 K			
49 E	50 A	51 A	52 J	53 E	54 C	55 F	56 B	57 E	58 C		59 L	60 B		61 L	62 A	63 C		64 J	65 I	66 H	67 I
	68 G	69 I		70 G	71 H	72 L	73 H	74 B										

Answers on page 377.

Acrostic Anagram

Unscramble the words below, then transfer the corresponding letters to the grid. When you're finished, you'll be rewarded with a quote from Denis Waitley.

1. A T R A A N A M C
   ___ ___ ___ ___ ___ ___ ___ ___ ___
   1 37 25 73 46 12 53 33 13

2. R B T E O E U T A H
   ___ ___ ___ ___ ___ ___ ___ ___ ___ ___
   26 2 15 59 6 41 17 47 52 62

3. F T E L E L A
   ___ ___ ___ ___ ___ ___ ___
   18 45 67 57 56 40 72

4. U B U C M S C
   ___ ___ ___ ___ ___ ___ ___
   54 65 69 31 29 61 74

5. E C H B N
   ___ ___ ___ ___ ___
   38 49 42 22 8

6. D A C E F A
   ___ ___ ___ ___ ___ ___
   58 20 21 3 43 28

7. G A E H G L
   ___ ___ ___ ___ ___ ___
   63 16 5 35 75 19

8. E E V N E N G C R C O
   ___ ___ ___ ___ ___ ___ ___ ___ ___ ___ ___
   10 51 66 48 70 44 14 23 4 68 55

9. P O N H E E L T E
   ___ ___ ___ ___ ___ ___ ___ ___ ___
   7 36 39 9 24 11 60 30 76

10. N Y E H H P
    ___ ___ ___ ___ ___ ___
    27 50 71 32 64 34

1 A	2 B	3 F	4 H	5 G	6 B		7 I	8 E	9 I		10 H	11 I	12 A	13 A	14 H	15 B	16 G	17 B	18 C
19 G		20 F	21 F	22 E	23 H	24 I	25 A		26 B	27 J	28 F		29 D	30 I	31 D	32 J	33 A	34 J	35 G
36 I	37 A	38 E	39 I	40 C		41 B	42 E	43 F		44 H	45 C	46 A	47 B	48 H	49 E		50 J	51 H	52 B
53 A	54 D	55 H	56 C	57 C		58 F	59 B	60 I	61 D		62 B	63 G	64 J		65 D	66 H	67 C	68 H	69 D
70 H	71 J	72 C	73 A	74 D	75 G	76 I												

Name Calling

Decipher the encoded word in the quip below using the numbers and letters on the phone pad. Remember that each number can stand for 3 or 4 possible letters.

It is difficult to make predictions, especially about the 3–8–8–8–7–3.

Wacky Wordy

Can you "read" the phrase below?

THE WHETHER

THE WEATHER

Answers on page 377.

Crypto-Game Families

Cryptograms are messages in substitution code. Break the code to read the message. THE SMART CAT might become FVO QWGDF JGF if **F** is substituted for **T**, **V** for **H**, **O** for **E**, and so on. The code is different for each crypto-game family.

1. Ball Games	2. Card Games	3. Board Games
ILKRNDILCC	SJAHBC	POKJJ
HFCF	CDREJC	JPBEIICK
SFCP	FAGIREPC	POKPLKBJ
MAFGJND	RKGKLOK	HFRFMFCA
BFCCNOILCC	BAGJDTTU	IENNCKJOSM
DNTTEK	RJKNUCABEOL	TEHKFUCSUK
PFFDILCC	FIMCJ	POSRKJKPOKPLKBJ
IFMMN	ECKJOL	MEBPOKKJS
ILKNILCC	LIPAOKAJC	PCDK
KFMMNA	SKRRKAKO	JFBBA

Answers on page 377.

Word Columns

Find the hidden quote and its author by using the letters directly above each of the blank squares. Each letter in a column is used only once in the squares below it.

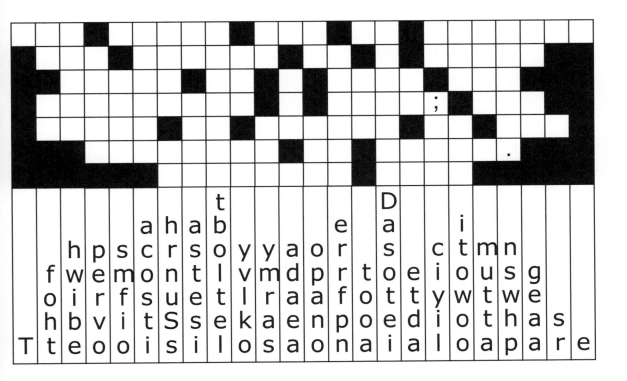

Answer on page 378.

Acrostic Anagram

Unscramble the words below, then transfer the corresponding letters to the grid. When you're finished, you'll be rewarded with a quote from Sir John Vanbrugh.

A. P A N I I A T D E C A T C
40 60 57 18 28 31 50 68 10 65 4 16 46

B. I E S P R H E D
64 25 34 36 70 51 23 20

F. I G S I N F H
73 56 32 48 58 14 42

C. S U E N S E S L F U
5 52 35 54 33 72 37 59 8 67

G. I N I T W T G
47 7 21 61 9 41 43

D. R U E V S Y
26 53 3 1 71 66

H. I W L W L O
17 49 29 62 45 13

E. D E O A R H F E
55 12 24 30 22 6 27 38

I. T R I S Y O R O
11 44 19 39 15 2 69 63

1 D	2 I	3 D	4 A	5 C	6 E		7 G	8 C		9 G	10 A	11 I		12 E	13 H	14 F
	15 I	16 A	17 H	18 A	19 I	20 B		21 G	22 E	23 B	24 E	25 B	26 D		27 A	
28 A	29 H	30 E	31 A	32 F	33 C	34 B	35 C		36 B	37 C		38 E	39 I	40 A	41 G	42 F
	43 G	44 I	45 H	46 A		47 G	48 F	49 H	50 A	51 B						
52 C	53 D	54 C	55 E	56 F	57 A	58 F	59 C	60 A	61 G	62 H	63 I		64 B	65 A	66 D	67 C
	68 A	69 I	70 B	71 D	72 C	73 F										

Answers on page 378.

Acrostic Anagram

Unscramble the words below, then transfer the corresponding letters to the grid. The end of a word is signified by a black square. When you're finished, you'll be rewarded with a quote from Simone Weil.

A. R E E O U C B N N C L T A A
   ‾ ‾ ‾ ‾ ‾ ‾ ‾ ‾ ‾ ‾ ‾ ‾ ‾ ‾
   56 66 3 52 14 59 35 60 19 71 9 26 27 41

B. R O E D S I S
   ‾ ‾ ‾ ‾ ‾ ‾ ‾
   47 30 74 69 12 34 68

F. A E E H F R R E T T
   ‾ ‾ ‾ ‾ ‾ ‾ ‾ ‾ ‾ ‾
   5 33 73 18 61 62 6 11 70 63

C. D I H F G O L S
   ‾ ‾ ‾ ‾ ‾ ‾ ‾ ‾
   44 51 8 42 38 55 13 57

G. F A T W S
   ‾ ‾ ‾ ‾ ‾
   58 46 22 29 21

D. R E R O N T H I
   ‾ ‾ ‾ ‾ ‾ ‾ ‾ ‾
   32 2 37 4 20 64 28 24

H. U E N E V
   ‾ ‾ ‾ ‾ ‾
   72 16 65 7 43

E. A R C A E H S E H T
   ‾ ‾ ‾ ‾ ‾ ‾ ‾ ‾ ‾ ‾
   54 23 48 45 17 1 10 40 25 36

I. T I T H W O U
   ‾ ‾ ‾ ‾ ‾ ‾ ‾
   53 50 39 15 31 67 49

1 E		2 D	3 A	4 D	5 F	6 F	7 H	8 C		9 A	10 E	11 F		12 B	13 C		14 A	15 I	16 H
	17 E	18 F	19 A	20 D	21 G	22 G	23 E	24 D	25 E	26 A	27 A	28 D		29 G	30 B		31 I	32 D	33 F
34 B	35 A	36 E		37 D	38 C		39 I	40 E	41 A		42 C	43 H	44 C	45 E	46 G	47 B	48 E	49 I	50 I
51 C	52 A		53 I	54 E	55 C	56 A	57 C		58 G	59 A		60 A	61 F	62 F	63 F		64 D	65 H
66 A	67 I	68 B	69 B	70 F	71 A	72 H	73 F	74 B									

Answers on page 378.

Big Top Code-doku

Solve this puzzle just as you would a sudoku. Use deductive logic to complete the grid so that each row, each column, and each 3-by-3 box contains each of the letters of the anagram MY CPA HERD in some order. The solution is unique. When you have completed the puzzle, read the shaded squares from left to right and top to bottm to reveal a phrase describing something you might see at the circus.

	D		C		P	M		
				H	R			
	E							
				E				A
P	H	A						
			A		M		D	
	C	Y				M		
	P			M	Y		C	
	R	H	P					

Hidden Message:

_____

_____

_____

Name Calling

Decipher the encoded word in the quip below using the numbers and letters on the phone pad. Remember that each number can stand for 3 or 4 possible letters.

8-4-2-8-6-7-9 goes to the player who makes the next-to-last mistake.

Answers on page 378.

Classic Lit

Cryptograms are messages in substitution code. Break the code to read the message. THE SMART CAT might become FVO QWGDF JGF if **F** is substituted for **T**, **V** for **H**, **O** for **E**, and so on. Hint: Look for repeated numbers. E, T, A, O, N, R, and I are the most often used letters. A single letter is usually A or I; OF, IS, and IT are common 2-letter words; THE and AND are common 3-letter words.

"6-3 6-20 13 3-8-25-3-18 25-1-6-12-9-8-20-13-26-26-2
13-23-10-1-15-17-26-9-19-21-9-19, 3-18-13-3 13
20-6-1-21-26-9 11-13-1 6-1 5-15-20-20-9-20-20-6-15-1
15-24 13 21-15-15-19 24-15-8-3-25-1-9, 11-25-20-3
4-9 6-1 17-13-1-3 15-24 13 17-6-24-9."
—14-13-1-9 13-25-20-3-9-1, *5-8-6-19-9 13-1-19*
5-8-9-14-25-19-6-23-9

Answer on page 378.

Word Columns

Find the hidden quote and its author by using the letters directly above each of the blank squares. Eac
letter in a column is used only once in the squares below it.

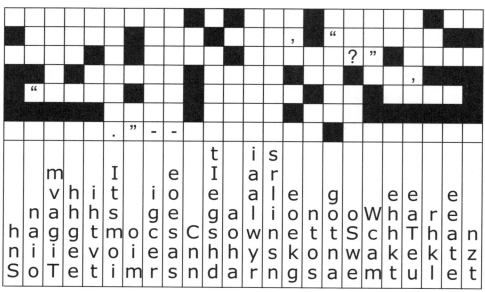

Wacky Wordy

Can you "read" the phrase below?

KNEE
SIGN

Answers on page 378.

Letterbox Colors

The letters in PINK can be found in boxes 1, 8, 16, and 19, but not necessarily in that order. Similarly, all letters in the colors listed below can be found in the boxes indicated. Your task is to insert all the letters of the alphabet into the boxes. If you do this correctly, the names of 2 more colors will be revealed in the shaded cells.

Hint: Look for words that share a single letter. For example, TAWNY shares a Y with GRAY and a T with TURQUOISE. By comparing the number lists, you can then deduce the values of these letters.

AZURE: 2, 6, 14, 21, 22

BEIGE: 4, 15, 19, 21

CREAM: 6, 7, 21, 22, 23

FAWN: 1, 6, 10, 17

GRAY: 6, 15, 22, 26

GREEN: 1, 15, 21, 22

JADE: 6, 12, 21, 25

KHAKI: 6, 8, 18, 19

MAUVE: 2, 6, 21, 23, 24

PINK: 1, 8, 16, 19

PURPLE: 2, 5, 16, 21, 22

RED: 21, 22, 25

SAXE: 6, 11, 13, 21

SILVER: 5, 13, 19, 21, 22, 24

TAWNY: 1, 6, 17, 20, 26

TURQUOISE: 2, 3, 9, 13, 19, 20, 21, 22

YELLOW: 3, 5, 17, 21, 26

1	2	3	4	5	6	7	8	9	10	11	12	13

14	15	16	17	18	19	20	21	22	23	24	25	26

Answer on page 378.

Fiery Lyrics

Cryptograms are messages in substitution code. Break the code to read the message. THE SMART CAT might become FVO QWGDF JGF if **F** is substituted for **T**, **V** for **H**, **O** for **E**, and so on.

ANS ARES AW NSKRAUAS RK ANVWODN; XW ARES

AW ZUJJWZ RX ANS ERVS. AVT XWZ ZS LUX WXJT

JWKS, UXI WOV JWFS HSLWES U MOXSVUJ GTVS.

Comedy Faster than a Speeding Bullet

Cryptograms are messages in substitution code. Break the code to read the message. THE SMART CAT might become FVO QWGDF JGF if **F** is substituted for **T**, **V** for **H**, **O** for **E**, and so on.

"FM BMLWZMH, FU IDN QDEEFP Z QKFEB, PTB

ADWFQB HDM'P TZRB Z LNM ZMH IDN HDM'P TZRB

Z LNM. FU IDN QDEEFP Z QKFEB, PTB ADWFQB

XFWW CZI 'CPDA, DK F'WW CZI CPDA ZLZFM.'"

—UKDE TFC "WFRB ZP PTB EBP" ABKUDKEZMQB FM

MBX IDKG, 1986

Answers on pages 378.

Acrostic Clues

Solve the clues below and then place the letters in their corresponding spots in the grid to reveal a historic quote. The letter in the upper-right corner of each grid square refers to the clue the letter comes from. A black square indicates the end of a word.

A.   Source of quote: 2 wds.

‾71‾ ‾41‾ ‾66‾ ‾33‾ ‾30‾ ‾74‾ ‾73‾ ‾24‾ ‾6‾ ‾31‾ ‾65‾ ‾8‾ ‾60‾ ‾61‾ ‾20‾

B.   James _____ Cooper

‾35‾ ‾11‾ ‾77‾ ‾1‾ ‾32‾ ‾81‾ ‾72‾ ‾58‾

F.   Legendary thief: 2 wds.

‾42‾ ‾22‾ ‾26‾ ‾9‾ ‾38‾ ‾64‾ ‾19‾ ‾69‾ ‾49‾

C.   Andalusian dance

‾57‾ ‾55‾ ‾78‾ ‾36‾ ‾28‾ ‾12‾ ‾18‾ ‾47‾

G.   Illicit liaison

‾63‾ ‾29‾ ‾21‾ ‾3‾ ‾75‾ ‾68‾

D.   Burial alternative

‾2‾ ‾23‾ ‾17‾ ‾14‾ ‾25‾ ‾59‾ ‾37‾ ‾15‾ ‾82‾

H.   Immunizing

‾56‾ ‾10‾ ‾67‾ ‾46‾ ‾50‾ ‾27‾ ‾7‾ ‾79‾ ‾5‾ ‾48‾ ‾76‾

E.   Ruby anniversary

‾40‾ ‾34‾ ‾16‾ ‾43‾ ‾80‾ ‾45‾ ‾52‾ ‾44‾

I.   Befuddle

‾51‾ ‾13‾ ‾4‾ ‾54‾ ‾53‾ ‾70‾ ‾62‾ ‾39‾

1 B		2 D	3 G	4 I		5 H	6 A	7 H	8 A	9 F	10 H	11 B		12 C	13 I		14 D	15 D	16 E
17 D		18 C	19 F	20 A	21 G	22 F	23 D	24 A	25 D	26 F	27 H	28 C		29 G	30 A	31 A	32 B	33 A	
34 E	35 B		36 C	37 D	38 F	39 I		40 E	41 A	42 F		43 E	44 E	45 E		46 H	47 C	48 H	49 F
50 H	51 I	52 E		53 I	54 I		55 C	56 H	57 C	58 B		59 D	60 A	61 A	62 I		63 G		64 F
65 A	66 A	67 H	68 G	69 F	70 I	71 A		72 B	73 A	74 A	75 G	76 H	77 B	78 C	79 H	80 E	81 B	82 D

Answers on page 379.

Code-doku

Solve this puzzle just as you would a sudoku. Use deductive logic to complete the grid so that each row, column, and 3-by-3 box contains the letters from the words PET SALMON. When you have completed the puzzle, read the shaded squares to reveal a great feat of exploration.

		L	T					P
			N					
		N					O	
		M					L	
	O			L	P	M		
	E			A	M			
					O			A
				N				S
S	P				A	T		

Hidden Message:

_____

_____

_____

Trick Question

Cryptograms are messages in substitution code. Break the code to read the message. THE SMART CAT might become FVO QWGDF JGF if **F** is substituted for **T**, **V** for **H**, **O** for **E**, and so on.

**SA WCLD XERLLTL NMSILX WN JLW NMSIL NSM, CNY
KN WCLD JLW GBGD NSM?**

Crypto-Quote

Cryptograms are messages in substitution code. Break the code to read the quote and its source. THE SMART CAT might become FVO QWGDF JGF if **F** is substituted for **T**, **V** for **H**, **O** for **E**, and so on.

"ACO RBHDA ILP JEDA BJFEHAILA ACBLK ER INN, IA NOIDA REH GHBAOHD AEPIM, BD AE DAHBF NILKVIKO SNOIL, AE NIM BA TIHO PEGL AE ACO TELO."

—OHLODA COJBLKGIM

Crypto-Wisdom

Cryptograms are messages in substitution code. Break the code to read the message. THE SMART CAT might become FVO QWGDF JGF if **F** is substituted for **T**, **V** for **H**, **O** for **E**, and so on. The code is different for each cryptogram.

1. FJCCM BL H DBLGLK JA OEK BDHNBIHOBJI.

2. HCB GDKIH HCLJM FEDAH PLIHFNBI LJ HCB NLHOCBJ LI HCFH RDA AIAFSSR CFTB HD BFH HCBP.

3. HBG'A IBDCLA AEFA FJJDLKMFAMBG MN FROFPN FJJDLKMFALH.

The Man with the Toothbrush Mustache

Cryptograms are messages in substitution code. Break the code to read the quote from Charlie Chaplin. THE SMART CAT might become FVO QWGDF JGF if **F** is substituted for **T**, **V** for **H**, **O** for **E**, and so on.

"ER GZZ EGVQ QP MRZX PVR GVPQMRD.
ER EGVQ QP ZOJR FW RGNM PQMRD'A
MGXXOVRAA, VPQ FW RGNM PQMRD'A
IOARDW."

Frankly, My Dear...

Cryptograms are messages in substitution code. Break the code to read the message. THE SMART CAT might become FVO QWGDF JGF if **F** is substituted for **T**, **V** for **H**, **O** for **E**, and so on.

"JQ CGPQ JOH YHFGV LYV OW JGDDQAQI
YAQ AOCJW (1934) WY G FJOMI ZJY
GIKOVQI OW, WQMMOAC JOK OW ZGH
WJQ ZOAAOC YL WJQ HWGWXQ WJGW
JGI KGWWQVQI, AYW YZAOAC OW. WJQ
YHFGV ZGH VQWXVAQI WY WJQ GFWYV'H
LGKOMT GLWQV JOH IQGWJ."

Answers on page 379.

Letterbox Valuables

The letters in ONYX can be found in boxes 6, 13, 19 and 22, but not necessarily in that order. Similarly, the letters in all the other valuables can be found in the boxes indicated. Your task is to insert all the letters of the alphabet into the boxes. If you do this correctly, the shaded cells will reveal two gem stones.

AQUAMARINE: 2, 4, 6, 7, 10, 11, 14, 25

BERYL: 4, 10, 12, 13, 17

CORAL: 2, 5, 10, 17, 22

EMERALD: 2, 3, 4, 10, 14, 17

FIRE OPAL: 2, 4, 10, 17, 20, 22, 23, 25

GARNET: 2, 4, 6, 10, 16, 18

IVORY: 9, 10, 13, 22, 25

JASPER: 1, 2, 4, 10, 21, 23

JEWELS: 1, 4, 17, 21, 26

KUNZITE: 4, 6, 8, 11, 15, 16, 25

ONYX: 6, 13, 19, 22

SAPPHIRE: 2, 4, 10, 21, 23, 24, 25

TOPAZ: 2, 15, 16, 22, 23

1	2	3	4	5	6	7	8	9	10	11	12	13

14	15	16	17	18	19	20	21	22	23	24	25	26

Answer on page 379.

Hashi

Each circle represents an island, with the number inside indicating the number of bridges connected to it. Draw bridges between islands using the number given. There can be no more than 2 bridges going in the same direction, and there must be a continuous path connecting all islands. Bridges can only be vertical or horizontal and may not cross islands or other bridges. We've drawn some bridges to get you started.

(2)——(4)   (3)   (3)
(2) (1)   (1)
(3)   (5)   (3)
(3)   (2)   (2)
(3) (3)   (2)
(2)   (2)   (2) (3)
(3) (6)   (3) (1)
(3) (1) (1)   (3) (3)
(2) (5)   (2)
(3) (3)   (2) (3) (1)

Crypto-botany

Cryptograms are messages in substitution code. Break the code to read the message. THE SMART CAT might become FVO QWGDF JGF if **F** is substituted for **T**, **V** for **H**, **O** for **E**, and so on.

RHIERH (name of plant)

RCOJO EJO IHJO UEJFORFON HP RHIERHON RCEB HP

EBW HRCOJ UOMORELDO. HJFMFBEDDW, KOHKDO

RCHVMCR RHIERHON XOJO KHFNHBHVN EBG MJOX

RCOI EN HJBEIOBRED KDEBRN. RCHIEN AOPPOJNHB

LOMEB RH MJHX RCOI FB 1781, LVR RCOW XOJOB'R

THBNFGOJOG RH LO OGFLDO VBRFD 1834.

RHIERHON CEUO EDNH LOOB TEDDOG MEJGOB

EKKDON, MHDG EKKDON, EBG DHUO EKKDON.

Answers on pages 379-380.

Name Calling

Decipher the encoded word in the quip below using the numbers and letters on the phone pad. Remember that each number can stand for 3 or 4 possible letters.

What food these

6-6-7-7-3-5-7 be!

What Did He Mean By That?

Cryptograms are messages in substitution code. Break the code to read the message. THE SMART CAT might become FVO QWGDF JGF if **F** is substituted for **T**, **V** for **H**, **O** for **E**, and so on.

ZIRP KOIKEO CYO AIPBOYOS AX PBIRO KCRRCJOR

IN RDYHKPFYO PBOX SI QIP FQSOYRPCQS, AFP

PBO KCRRCJOR PBCP AIPBOY ZO CYO PBIRO H SI

FQSOYRPCQS.

–ZCYV PLCHQ

Answers on page 380.

Word Columns

Find the hidden phrase by using the letters directly above each of the blank squares. Each letter is used only once. A black square indicates the end of a word.

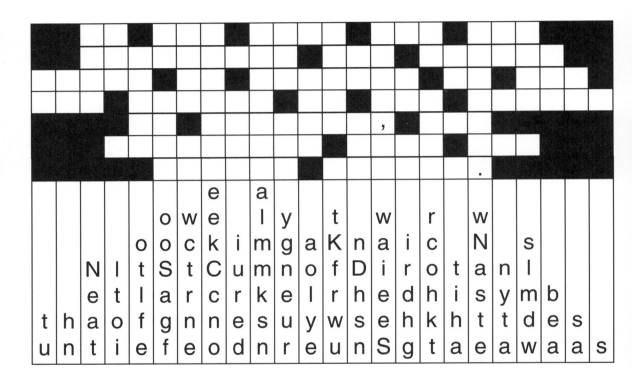

Answer on page 380.

Crypto-Logic

Each of the numbers in the sequence below represents a letter. Use the mathematical clues to determine which number stands for which letter, and then reveal the encrypted word.

4 9 3 1

Clues:

$S = 5$

$2S = I$

$I / 10 = T$

$S - T = N$

$N - A = T$

$3A = E$

Movie Title and Director Cryptogram

Cryptograms are messages in substitution code. Break the code to read 4 films and their directors. THE SMART CAT might become FVO QWGDF JGF if **F** is substituted for **T**, **V** for **H**, **O** for **E**, and so on.

1. *KMABL SJ KMABLFTIB:* **EPWATR LNBOLOMOV**

2. *BLT ILNKNKD:* **IBEKPTJ VGSANOV**

3. *ONBNQTK VEKT:* **MAIMK FTPPTI**

4. *AEDNKD SGPP:* **XEABNK IOMAITIT**

Answers on page 380.

The Sopranos

Solve the clues below, then transfer the corresponding letters to the grid. A black square indicates the end of a word. When you're finished, you'll be rewarded with a quote from "The Sopranos."

A. Television show and source of quote: 2 wds.

   $\overline{71}$ $\overline{13}$ $\overline{28}$ $\overline{41}$ $\overline{94}$ $\overline{42}$ $\overline{17}$ $\overline{96}$ $\overline{11}$ $\overline{50}$ $\overline{111}$

B. MSG, for example

   $\overline{105}$ $\overline{33}$ $\overline{87}$ $\overline{102}$ $\overline{68}$ $\overline{35}$ $\overline{22}$ $\overline{14}$

C. Corrado's nickname

   $\overline{85}$ $\overline{77}$ $\overline{57}$ $\overline{5}$ $\overline{80}$ $\overline{24}$

D. Tapped

   $\overline{97}$ $\overline{18}$ $\overline{75}$ $\overline{78}$ $\overline{89}$ $\overline{107}$

E. Tony's sister

   $\overline{61}$ $\overline{2}$ $\overline{8}$ $\overline{91}$ $\overline{112}$ $\overline{73}$

F. Aggressively hostile

   $\overline{27}$ $\overline{10}$ $\overline{16}$ $\overline{30}$ $\overline{115}$ $\overline{20}$ $\overline{12}$

G. Dr. Melfi, for one

   $\overline{99}$ $\overline{37}$ $\overline{72}$ $\overline{56}$ $\overline{47}$ $\overline{95}$

H. Eviscerated

   $\overline{64}$ $\overline{86}$ $\overline{51}$ $\overline{55}$ $\overline{46}$ $\overline{90}$

I. Real-life mob family

   $\overline{88}$ $\overline{113}$ $\overline{110}$ $\overline{76}$ $\overline{100}$ $\overline{25}$ $\overline{93}$

J. Stupid, incompetent person

— — — — — —
79 40 44 81 1 36

K. Criminal

— — — — — —
60 67 92 4 74 34

L. Late-nighter: 2 wds.

— — — — — — — —
106 108 9 39 48 70 52 19

M. Blood feud

— — — — — — — —
83 26 32 63 21 101 38 109

N. Desire for fame or power

— — — — — — — —
43 15 66 45 69 7 98 54

O. Fixed up

— — — — — — — — —
29 65 49 103 6 53 59 84 116

P. Common flowering plant

— — — — — — — —
58 23 114 31 104 82 62 3

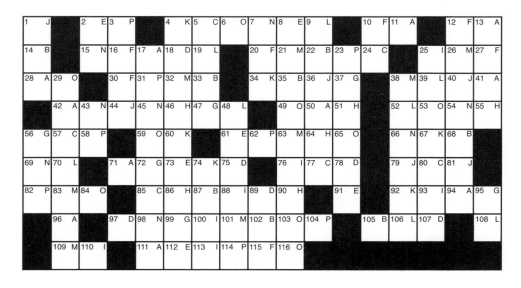

Code-doku

Solve this puzzle just as you would a sudoku. Use deductive logic to complete the grid so that each row, each column, and each 3-by-3 box contains each of the letters ABCDEGIMR in some order. When you have completed the puzzle, unscramble the letters to reveal an English university town.

	B		D				A	
	A	I				E		R
G	R		I		B			M
			A	R				E
	M	B	E		D		G	
A			B	M			R	
E			G		A			B
B		M			I	C		
	I						D	

Answer: _____

Cross Count

All the letters of the alphabet have been assigned a value from 1 to 9, as demonstrated in the box below. Fill in the grid with common English words so that the rows and columns add up correctly.

1	2	3	4	5	6	7	8	9
A	B	C	D	E	F	G	H	I
J	K	L	M	N	O	P	Q	R
S	T	U	V	W	X	Y	Z	

^{2}t				17
	^{1}a			17
a	^{3}c	^{9}		18
			^{4}m	15
9	18	28	12	

Answer on page 380.

Crypto-Logic

Each of the numbers in the sequence below represents a letter. Use the mathematical clues to determine which number stands for which letter and reveal the encrypted word.

Hint: Remember that a / indicates divided by, and that all sums in parentheses must be done first.

6 4 9 1 5 7

Clues:

$A = 8$

$A / B = 4$

$A / 2B = 2I$

$4I = E$

$1 \frac{1}{2} E = G$

$G + E = R$

$R / 2 = U$

$R - 1 = N$

$N - 2I = S$

Name Calling

Decipher the encoded word in the quip below using the numbers and letters on the phone pad. Remember that each number can stand for 3 or 4 possible letters.

Not to have 3-3-5-8 7-2-4-6 is not to have been 4-8-6-2-6.

Answers on page 380.

Code-doku

Solve this puzzle just as you would a sudoku. Use deductive logic to complete the grid so that each row, each column, and each 3-by-3 box contains each of the letters ABCEKLPRU in some order. When you have completed the puzzle, unscramble the letters to reveal a Nobel Prize-winning author.

		L					E	
E				B				U
C		P	R		U			K
	P		E		B		C	L
		B				P		
R	A		P		K		U	
U			C		L	K		E
P				K				C
	C							

Hidden Name: _____

Answer on page 381.

Cross Count

All the letters of the alphabet have been assigned values from 1 to 9, as demonstrated in the box below. Fill in the grid with English words so that the rows and columns add up correctly.

1	2	3	4	5	6	7	8	9
a	b	c	d	e	f	g	h	i
j	k	l	m	n	o	p	q	r
s	t	u	v	w	x	y	z	

	³c		²	7
a		⁹	¹	14
				17
	³		p	12
4	12	20	14	

Answer on page 381.

Word Columns

Find the hidden punny question and answer by using the letters directly below each of the blank squares. Each letter is used only once. A black square or end of a line indicates the end of a word.

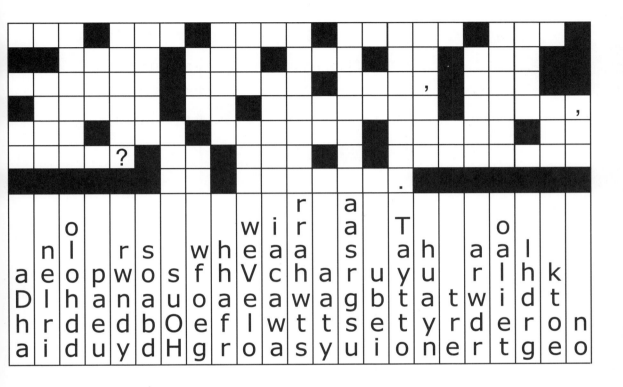

Answer on page 381.

Record High

Cryptograms are messages in substitution code. Break the code to read a quote from the film *High Fidelity* and who spoke it. For example, THE SMART CAT might become FVO QWGDF JGF if **F** is substituted for **T**, **V** for **H**, **O** for **E**, and so on.

QZM (RZDC KOHIKU): "CZT, GDS EIUYCX ZL I XZZA
KZEJYBIGYZC GIJS YH I PSQV HOMGBS IQG. EICV
AZH ICA AZC'GH. LYQHG ZL IBB, VZO'QS OHYCX
HZESZCS SBHS'H JZSGQV GZ SFJQSHH DZT VZO
LSSB. GDYH YH I ASBYKIGS GDYCX."

Revolutionary Crypto-quote

Cryptograms are messages in substitution code. Break the code to read the quote and its source. THE SMART CAT might become FVO QWGDF JGF if **F** is substituted for **T**, **V** for **H**, **O** for **E**, and so on.

"D KNT BMKR MSBTP TPMGFL CTOMXTI BLT BVGBL."

—Q. N. KTPNP

Answers on page 381.

Code-doku

Solve this puzzle just as you would a sudoku. Use deductive logic to complete the grid so that each row, each column, and each 3-by-3 box contains each of the letters ACEILNRST in some order. When you have completed the puzzle, unscramble those 9 letters to reveal a single reed woodwind instrument (in its plural form), popularized by Artie Shaw.

S			N					T
I	N						C	R
			S	C	L			
A	C		R		S		L	E
				I				
T	S		L		C		N	I
			A	E	T			
C	E						S	N
R								L

Answer: _____

Answer on page 381

Cross Count

All the letters of the alphabet have been assigned a value from 1 to 9, as demonstrated in the box below. Fill in the grid with common English words so that the rows and columns add up correctly.

1	2	3	4	5	6	7	8	9
A	B	C	D	E	F	G	H	I
J	K	L	M	N	O	P	Q	R
S	T	U	V	W	X	Y	Z	

2			7	27
	o			24
				14
p			n	16
19	21	19	22	

Answer on page 381.

Word Columns

Find the hidden quote from Joseph Addison by using the letters directly below each of the blank squares. Each letter is used only once. A black square indicates the end of a word.

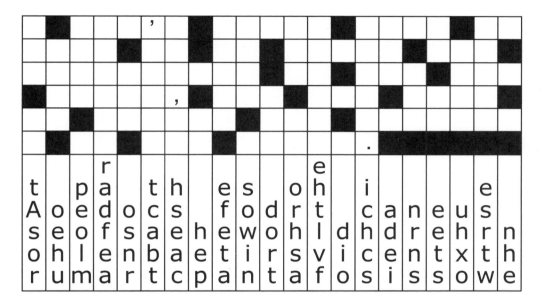

Maiden Voyage

Cryptograms are messages in substitution code. Break the code to read the movie fact. THE SMART CAT might become FVO QWGDF JGF if **F** is substituted for **T**, **V** for **H**, **O** for **E**, and so on.

CZXY KIZRGV VX KQIMLGEUGZP, YXPV XC VQG

LGKXZ XM VQG PQUR TIP GUVQGZ ZGKXMPVZFKVGL

OS XZ FMLGZ VQG PFRGZJUPUXM XC VQG XZUHUMIE

KXYRIMUGP VQIV CFZMUPQGL VQG *VUVIMUK.*

Answers on page 381.

Code-doku

Solve this puzzle just as you would a sudoku. Use deductive logic to complete the grid so that each row, column, and 3-by-3 box contains the letters from the words WAR BY POND. When you have completed the puzzle, read the shaded squares to reveal a hidden message.

B				W		O		
	P							
	A					Y		
R			N				A	
		Y						
		O	B	R				
P				B	N		D	R
	W					P		
	O			P		N		B

Hidden Message: _____

Answer on page 381.

Codeword

The letters of the alphabet are hidden in code: Each is represented by a random number from 1 through 26. With the letters already given, complete the crossword puzzle with English words and break the code.

15	11	24	24	16	■	4	11	21	16	24	20	14
9	■	20	■	13	■	17	■	■	17	■	12	■
10	■	4	■	14	■	13	■	10	24	26	20	7
11	19	9	15	11	13	14	9	■	25	■	23	■
2	■	26	■	22	■	11	■	14	16	21	9	15
2	14	9	12	9	19	2	6	■	18	■	■	16
20	■	15	■	15	■	■	■	25	■	15	■	7
19	■	■	17	■	20	22	26	20	26	11	20	19
24	5	9	10	9	■	26	■	19	■	10	■	26
■	20	■	9	■	12	20	2	20	26	16	19	11
3	11	25	25	6	■	11	■	24	■	13	■	22
■	1	■	17	■	■	19	■	11	■	9	■	5
8	17	20	14	11	24	6	■	2	26	6	4	24

A B C D E F G H I J K L M N O P Q R S T U V W X Y Z

1	2	3	4	5	6	7	8	9	10	11	12	13

14	15	16	17	18	19	20	21	22	23	24	25	26
				X	N	A					F	

Answers on page 382.

Mastermind

The goal of this puzzle is to replace the question marks with a correct sequence of numbers. The numbers you need for the answer are contained in the rows above the question marks. Follow these 2 guides: A black dot indicates that a number needed for the solution is in that row and in the correct position; a white dot means that a number needed for the solution is in that row but in the wrong position. Numbers do not appear more than once in the solution, and the solution never begins with 0.

$$2 \quad 1 \quad 7 \quad \bigcirc \quad \bigcirc$$

$$9 \quad 3 \quad 8 \quad \bullet$$

$$7 \quad 4 \quad 5 \quad \bigcirc$$

$$4 \quad 0 \quad 1 \quad \bigcirc$$

$$\overline{? \quad ? \quad ?}$$

Unconventional Genius

Cryptograms are messages in substitution code. Break the code to read the movie quote. THE SMART CAT might become FVO QWGDF JGF if **F** is substituted for **T**, **V** for **H**, **O** for **E**, and so on.

"TO TSTTQ QGVQOU UQME GMRH VQU GMWH Q
FSP SR AXSASGQBHU. OSL DHZHC WDSV VXQB
OSL'CH NSDDQ NHB."

Answers on page 382.

Codeword

The letters of the alphabet are hidden in code: Each is represented by a random number from 1 through 26. With the letters already given, complete the crossword puzzle with English words and break the code.

15	10	17	11	11	18	▪	▪	12	▪	6	2	12
▪	17	▪	▪	17	▪	16	5	4	24	23	▪	2
12	17	5	17	3	3	17	▪	12	▪	5	▪	15
▪	15	▪	▪	19	▪	4	▪	4	10	21	17	15
11	23	5	12	23	4	21	23	▪	▪	2	▪	2
▪	13	▪	▪	21	▪	15	▪	17	▪	16	▪	10
2	15	15	7	23	15	▪	23	13	3	17	22	23
13	▪	21	▪	22	▪	26	▪	21	▪	▪	23	▪
1	▪	5	▪	▪	8	17	21	26	23	5	23	22
23	14	2	21	15	▪	21	▪	23	▪	▪	11	▪
5	▪	6	▪	21	▪	23	13	9	17	18	23	22
13	▪	23	25	7	4	10	▪	17	▪	▪	13	▪
17	20	13	▪	8	▪	▪	17	8	21	7	15	23

A B C D E F G H I J K L M N O P Q R S T U V W X Y Z

1	2	3	4	5	6	7	8	9	10	11	12	13

14	15	16	17	18	19	20	21	22	23	24	25	26
	S		O	K								

Answers on page 382.

Crypto-group: Comic Book Heroes

Cryptograms are messages in substitution code. Break the code to read the message. THE SMART CAT might become FVO QWGDF JGF if **F** is substituted for **T**, **V** for **H**, **O** for **E**, and so on.

SLBXLV

RLKPRPYNT

STLOA FNRMF

NKMV CNIB

OJOTMHI

Crypto-Logic

Each of the numbers in the sequence below represents a letter. Use the mathematical clues to determine which number stands for which letter and reveal the encrypted word.
Hint: Remember that a / indicates divided by, and that all sums in parentheses must be done first.

8 6 5 1 3 2 9 4

Clues:

$F = 10$

$F - T - U - I = 4$

T, U and I are all letters in the encrypted word

$U < I$

$T > I$

$Y + C = F$

$3Y = 4T$

$S = 1\frac{1}{3}C$

$S - T = R$

$9R = P = 5N$

Answers on page 382.

Code-doku

Solve this puzzle just as you would a sudoku. Use deductive logic to complete the grid so that each row, each column, and each 3-by-3 box contains each of the letters ADEGIMNRS in some order. When you have completed the puzzle, unscramble those 9 letters to reveal an inspiration for Australian-Aboriginal artwork.

A			I			R	N	
	M		D				A	S
N	R		G		E	D		
D			S				G	
	A				D			R
S		G	R		A	M		
R	M							N
		A					I	
I				M		G	A	

Answer: _____

Answer on page 382.

Code-doku

Solve this puzzle just as you would a sudoku. Use deductive logic to complete the grid so that each row, each column, and each 3-by-3 box contains each of the letters EHJLNORTY in some order. When you have completed the puzzle, unscramble those 9 letters to reveal America's tenth president.

	H						E	
		R				N		Y
O			R		H			T
R				Y	O			N
			N		L		O	
E			T		J			
N			O		E			H
H		T	Y			J		
	R						L	

Hidden Name: _____

Answer on page 382.

Word Columns

Find the humorous statement by using the letters directly below each of the blank squares. Each letter is used only once. A black square indicates the end of a word.

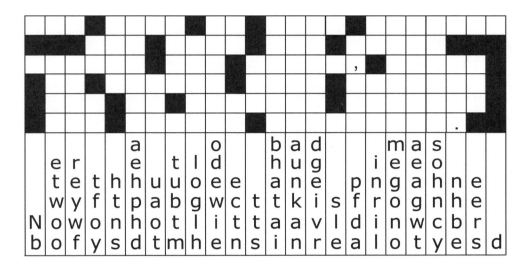

Best Day Ever

Cryptograms are messages in substitution code. Break the code to read the movie fact. THE SMART CAT might become FVO QWGDF JGF if **F** is substituted for **T**, **V** for **H**, **O** for **E**, and so on.

DYPWQSKPD SIE AIU QPC TVMFOS VQ

HWQJUWCIAQOE, HOQQUEMZIQVI, RWC

VQ APPSUCPGX, VMMVQPVU. RVMM

FWYYIE AIU RVCCOQ RE CKO DYPWQSKPD

CAVGO SWYVQD UKPPCVQD.

Answers on page 382.

Party Time

Cryptograms are messages in substitution code. Break the code to read the humorous message. THE SMART CAT might become FVO QWGDF JGF if **F** is substituted for **T**, **V** for **H**, **O** for **E**, and so on.

OUCUSNM JXOEHSXFNM PXBWSUO DUSU XRCXEUV

EH N GNSEA. UXROEUXR ONXV XE DHWMV IU

SUMNEXCUMA UNOA EH NEEURV. OFJWIUSE ONXV

JU'V FHKU, IWE EJUSU DNO OHKUEJXRB JU JNV

EH PXRXOJ PXSOE. VS. TUQAMM DNO HP EDH

KXRVO . . .

Maxims to Ponder

Cryptograms are messages in substitution code. Break the code to read the message. THE SMART CAT might become FVO QWGDF JGF if **F** is substituted for **T**, **V** for **H**, **O** for **E**, and so on. The code is the same for each of these cryptograms.

1. RHDKRQ FHJ QYHO TVC ZRHQRKQ WYP'C DRC QVLIRW MPCY SRC RPDMPRQ.

2. PRNRO HODVR ZMCX H QBYVQR ZXY MQ BHLIMPD JYVO BHOHLXVCR.

3. PRNRO FYYP H ZRORZYKE.

Codeword

The letters of the alphabet are hidden in code: Each is represented by a random number from 1 through 26. With the letters already given, complete the crossword puzzle with English words and break the code.

2	6	23	26	15		23	11	16	7	23	14	16
6		16		1		10			2		16	
17		2		11		22		12	14	8	14	18
23	15	15	2	4	9	2	2		19		26	
4		22		22		5		12	2	4	3	23
18	14	4	21	1	26	23	11		11			4
14		2		15				9		9		14
24			20		23	13	1	23	11	14	1	10
2	18	15	2	11		1		18		24		22
	13		15		7	14	21	7	4	2	18	18
4	1	11	18	2		16		14		11		14
	23		23			7		4		15		15
23	15	22	10	14	25	2		21	23	18	18	3

A B C D E F G H I J K L M N O P Q R S T U V W X Y Z

1	2	3	4	5	6	7	8	9	10	11	12	13
U			N									

14	15	16	17	18	19	20	21	22	23	24	25	26
		C										

Answers on page 383.

Codeword

The letters of the alphabet are hidden in code: Each is represented by a random number from 1 through 26. With the letters already given, complete the crossword puzzle with English words and break the code.

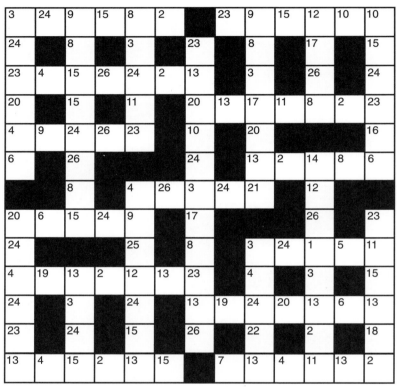

A B C D E F G H I J K L M N O P Q R S T U V W X Y Z

1	2	3	4	5	6	7	8	9	10	11	12	13
		M			Y	B						

14	15	16	17	18	19	20	21	22	23	24	25	26

Answers on page 383.

Crypto-Logic

Each of the numbers in the sequence below represents a letter. Use the mathematical clues to determine which number stands for which letter and reveal the encrypted word. There are more clues than you'll need.

1 4 7 1 6 8 9 6 3

Clues:

N is the fourth prime.
A is a double square.
D is spatial.
Twelve U's in an hour.
O is quadrilateral.

C is unity.
L is the first non-prime odd one (other than C).
E is the best when it comes to a die.
S is dichotomy.

Mastermind

The goal of this puzzle is to replace the question marks with a correct sequence of numbers. The numbers you need for the answer are contained in the rows above the question marks. Follow these 2 guides: A black dot indicates that a number needed for the solution is in that row and in the correct position; a white dot means that a number needed for the solution is in that row but in the wrong position. Numbers do not appear more than once in the solution, and the solution never begins with 0.

9 1 3 2 ● ●
9 7 1 0 ○ ○ ○
5 3 2 4 ○
8 0 7 6 ○ ○
_____
? ? ? ?

Answers on page 383.

Acrostic

Solve the clues below, and then place the letters in their corresponding spots in the grid to reveal a quote from H.L. Mencken. The letter in the upper-right corner of each grid square refers to the clue the letter comes from. A black square indicates the end of a word.

A. Lepidopter

‾‾ ‾‾ ‾‾ ‾‾
21 121 94 2

B. Memorial inscription

‾‾ ‾‾ ‾‾ ‾‾ ‾‾ ‾‾ ‾‾
131 90 12 114 5 70 32

C. For lack of his love Echo died

‾‾ ‾‾ ‾‾ ‾‾ ‾‾ ‾‾ ‾‾ ‾‾ ‾‾
17 127 93 67 51 124 40 77 82

D. Map

‾‾ ‾‾ ‾‾ ‾‾ ‾‾
6 44 57 63 71

E. Treat with obsequious deference

‾‾ ‾‾ ‾‾ ‾‾ ‾‾ ‾‾
130 26 39 81 102 46

F. Without difficulty

‾‾ ‾‾ ‾‾ ‾‾ ‾‾ ‾‾
98 10 126 113 29 24

G. Caught

‾‾ ‾‾ ‾‾ ‾‾ ‾‾ ‾‾
53 66 108 110 16 23

H. Spoiler

‾‾ ‾‾ ‾‾ ‾‾ ‾‾ ‾‾ ‾‾
64 109 123 91 49 59 119

I. Tax

‾‾ ‾‾ ‾‾ ‾‾ ‾‾ ‾‾
72 84 105 35 99 7

J. Famous

‾‾ ‾‾ ‾‾ ‾‾ ‾‾
103 38 1 56 50

K. Church collection

‾‾ ‾‾ ‾‾ ‾‾ ‾‾ ‾‾ ‾‾ ‾‾ ‾‾
107 61 25 45 101 116 92 19 75

L. Optimistic

$\overline{78}$ $\overline{47}$ $\overline{34}$ $\overline{115}$

M. Incensed

$\overline{83}$ $\overline{106}$ $\overline{118}$ $\overline{8}$ $\overline{69}$

N. Throwing

$\overline{11}$ $\overline{62}$ $\overline{88}$ $\overline{58}$ $\overline{80}$ $\overline{73}$ $\overline{104}$

O. Fresh; vigorous

$\overline{87}$ $\overline{76}$ $\overline{122}$ $\overline{96}$ $\overline{13}$ $\overline{42}$ $\overline{89}$ $\overline{30}$

P. Long-limbed and slender

$\overline{27}$ $\overline{14}$ $\overline{60}$ $\overline{74}$ $\overline{120}$

Q. Moral

$\overline{20}$ $\overline{31}$ $\overline{97}$ $\overline{111}$ $\overline{68}$ $\overline{129}$ $\overline{86}$

R. Propose to give

$\overline{85}$ $\overline{37}$ $\overline{18}$ $\overline{4}$ $\overline{128}$ $\overline{22}$ $\overline{48}$

S. Missed the mark

$\overline{41}$ $\overline{15}$ $\overline{3}$ $\overline{36}$ $\overline{52}$ $\overline{9}$ $\overline{54}$ $\overline{43}$

T. Without due consideration

$\overline{55}$ $\overline{28}$ $\overline{79}$ $\overline{117}$ $\overline{112}$ $\overline{65}$

U. Bonds

$\overline{100}$ $\overline{125}$ $\overline{33}$ $\overline{95}$

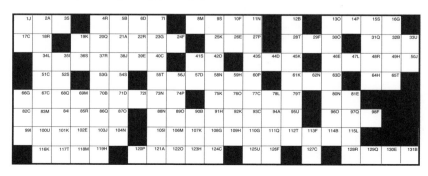

1J	2A	3S		4R	5B	6D	7I		8M	9S	10F	11N		12B		13O	14P	15S	16G
17C	18R		19K	20Q	21A	22R	23G	24F		25K	26E	27P		28T	29F	30O		31Q	32B	33U
	34L	35I	36S	37R	38J	39E	40C		41S	42O		43S	44D	45K		46E	47L	48R	49H	50J
	51C	52S		53G	54S		55T	56J	57D	58N	59H	60P		61K	62N	63D		64H	65T
66G	67C	68Q	69M	70B	71D	72I	73N	74P		75K	76O	77C	78L	79T		80N	81E		
82C	83M	84I	85R	86Q	87O		88N	89O	90B	91H	92K	93C	94A	95U		96O	97Q	98F	
99I	100U	101K	102E	103J	104N		105I	106M	107K	108G	109H	110G	111Q	112T	113F	114B	115L		
	116K	117T	118M	119H		120P	121A	122O	123H	124C		125U	126F		127C		128R	129Q	130E	131B

Answers on page 383.

Name Calling

Decipher the encoded words in the quip below using the numbers and letters on the phone pad. Remember that each number can stand for 3 or 4 possible letters.

Ask about your 6-3-4-4-4-2-6-7-7, then 2-8-9 the 4-6-8-7-3.

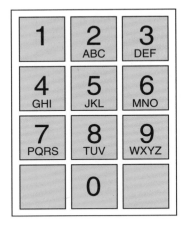

Crypto-group: European Cities

Cryptograms are messages in substitution code. Break the code to reveal 5 European cities. THE SMART CAT might become FVO QWGDF JGF if **F** is substituted for **T**, **V** for **H**, **O** for **E**, and so on.

KNOT

PMKRMK

SEAOTPMKE

QTKNOT

STAPNK

Answers on page 383.

Cross Count

All the letters of the alphabet have been assigned a value from 1 to 9, as demonstrated in the box below. Fill in the grid with common English words so that the rows and columns add up correctly.

1	2	3	4	5	6	7	8	9
A	B	C	D	E	F	G	H	I
J	K	L	M	N	O	P	Q	R
S	T	U	V	W	X	Y	Z	

⁶	a			20
		⁶	e	15
		⁶	²t	16
²	⁶	²		15
10	17	23	16	

Answer on page 383.

Life's Little Mysteries

Cryptograms are messages in substitution code. Break the code to read the humorous observations. THE SMART CAT might become FVO QWGDF JGF if **F** is substituted for **T**, **V** for **H**, **O** for **E**, and so on. The code is the same for each of the cryptograms.

1.   YCXQJ DAOJP HNJU YUQ HG GX IOG UT "Q"
     HT GCJ YXAN "PHQI"?

2.   HB QYHWWHTF HQ QX FXXN BXA KXOA
     BHFOAJ, CXY DXWJ YCUPJQ UAJ QX BUG?

3.   YCUG CUIIJTQ HB KXO FJG QDUAJN CUPB GX
     NJUGC GYHDJ?

Mastermind

The goal of this puzzle is to replace the question marks with a correct sequence of numbers. The numbers you need for the answer are contained in the rows above the question marks. Follow these 2 guides: A black dot indicates that a number needed for the solution is in that row and in the correct position; a white dot means that a number needed for the solution is in that row but in the wrong position. Numbers do not appear more than once in the solution, and the solution never begins with 0.

4 2 9 0 ● ●

6 8 7 5 ○

3 1 2 9 ●

8 6 3 1 ○

? ? ? ?

Answers on pages 383-384.

Code-doku

Solve this puzzle just as you would a sudoku. Use deductive logic to complete the grid so that each row, column, and 3-by-3 box contains the letters from the words GEM PLANTS. When you have completed the puzzle, the shaded squares can be read to reveal a hidden message regarding exploration.

				T	P			
	T					N	S	M
P	E							
		L						
A							L	
E			L			G		M
		T	S	A		L		G
	M				G			A
								S

Hidden Message: _____

Answer on page 384.

Code-doku

Solve this puzzle just as you would a sudoku. Use deductive logic to complete the grid so that each row, column, and 3-by-3 box contains the letters from the words PICK FERNS. When you have completed the puzzle, read the shaded squares to reveal a hidden message.

					S		E	R
S						K		F
C								
R		C				P	K	
			K					
	F		I					
P		E		S		C		
K			N		P			I
		N	C	E				

Hidden Message: _____

Answer on page 384.

Codeword

The letters of the alphabet are hidden in code: Each is represented by a random number from 1 through 26. With the letters already given, complete the crossword puzzle with English words and break the code.

	10	17	19	26	2	15	10	19	24	9	26	
14		10		15		24		14		10		13
21		15		3	26	6	20	2		13	21	23
19	21	7	22	21		5		21		26		24
19		24		2		20		5	26	13	21	19
26	1	26	2	16	24	13	26					12
6		2		26				5		5		26
18					6	24	15	21	19	10	20	2
26	10	13	26	11		19		2		2		17
2		16		20		13		2	24	21	25	10
26	8	21		16	2	26	11	21		4		15
11		23		7		17		23		20		11
	16	17	21	13	26	3	24	13	19	26	11	

A B C D E F G H I J K L M N O P Q R S T U V W X Y Z

1	2	3	4	5	6	7	8	9	10	11	12	13
	R	F						V			Z	

14	15	16	17	18	19	20	21	22	23	24	25	26
				P			O					E

Answers on page 384.

A World Upside-Down

Solve the clues below, and then place the letters in their corresponding spots in the grid to reveal a quote from "Spider-Man." The letter in the upper-right corner of each grid square refers to the clue the letter comes from. A black square indicates the end of a word.

A. Peter Parker player: 2 wds.

    ___ ___ ___ ___ ___ ___ ___ ___ ___ ___ ___ ___
    1   51 77 59 89 39 23 45 84 47 15 13

B. Battled

    ___ ___ ___ ___ ___ ___
    83 64 74 49 42 50

C. Peter's love interest: 2 wds.

    ___ ___ ___ ___ ___ ___ ___ ___
    22 27 60 12 73 21 48 43

D. Hard, chewy candy

    ___ ___ ___ ___ ___ ___
    100 35 65 54 30 72

E. Sandman actor Thomas Haden _____

    ___ ___ ___ ___ ___ ___
    79 18 91 7   92 26

F. Spider-Man villain: 2 wds.

    ___ ___ ___ ___ ___ ___ ___ ___ ___ ___ ___
    29 81 5   19 33 96 46 52 85 98 41

G. _____ space (area not covered by print)

    ___ ___ ___ ___ ___
    17 93 67 63 82

H. Like Peter and clue C, for example

  16 86 38 97 36 2 61 14 56 57 68

I. Sincere and honorable

  58 88 95 11 44 9

J. Spider-Man co-creator: 2 wds.

  4 76 40 28 69 53 78

K. Common street service, back in the day: 2 wds.

  31 37 101 8 62 10 70 24 3

L. Ringleader

  66 90 20 25 87 55

M. Disney musical classic

  71 94 99 34 80 75 32 6

1 A	2 H	3 K	4 J	5 F		6 M	7 E	8 K		9 I	10 K	11 I		12 C	13 A	14 H	15 A	16 H		17 G	18 E	19 F
20 L		21 C		22 C	23 A	24 K		25 L	26 E	27 C	28 J	29 F	30 D	31 K		32 M	33 F	34 M	35 D		36 H	37 K
38 H		39 A	40 J	41 F		42 B	43 C	44 I		45 A	46 F	47 A	48 C	49 B		50 B	51 A		52 F	53 J		54 D
55 L	56 H		57 H	58 I	59 A		60 C	61 H	62 K	63 G		64 B	65 D		66 L	67 G	68 H		69 J	70 K	71 M	72 D
	73 C	74 B	75 M	76 J		77 A	78 J		79 E	80 M	81 F	82 G	83 B	84 A	85 F		86 H	87 L	88 I		89 A	90 L
91 E		92 E	93 G	94 M	95 I	96 F	97 H		98 F	99 M	100 D	101 K										

Answers on page 384.

Codeword

The letters of the alphabet are hidden in code: Each is represented by a random number from 1 through 26. With the letters already given, complete the crossword puzzle with English words and break the code.

1	2	3	4	5	6	7	8	9	10	11	12	13
								D				

14	15	16	17	18	19	20	21	22	23	24	25	26
	Q									W		

Answers on page 384.

Number Code: 5 Months

First, solve each of the arithmetic problems. Then, find the corresponding letter in the number code at right. Write the letter for that number on the second dash. Reading down the column of letters will reveal the hidden words.

1. 15+10= ___ ___

   3+16= ___ ___

   4+8= ___ ___

2. 2+ 4= ___ ___

   7+6=___ ___

   14+7=___ ___

   6+6= ___ ___

3. 1+5= ___ ___

   11+2= ___ ___

   6+2= ___ ___

   5+6= ___ ___

4. 4+ 15= ___ ___

   12+14= ___ ___

   8+1= ___ ___

   9+8= ___ ___

   6+15= ___ ___

5. 12+13= ___ ___

   3+16= ___ ___

   2+7= ___ ___

   7+8= ___ ___

   15+8= ___ ___

Code

1	Z	14	T
2	K	15	C
3	Q	16	W
4	S	17	I
5	D	18	X
6	J	19	A
7	B	20	V
8	N	21	L
9	R	22	G
10	O	23	H
11	E	24	F
12	Y	25	M
13	U	26	P

Answers on page 384.

Shrouded Summary

Hidden in the word search below is a synopsis of a well-known story. The words listed below are anagrams of the actual words you need to find; in the word search they are presented in an order that will make more sense. The words may be vertical, horizontal, or diagonal. As a bonus, can you name the novel and its author?

ANT SMOG (7)

BIZARRE ABS (10)

INN OVEREAT (10)

OUTSTRIP ISSUE (13)

PIG MUD CRAYON (5,7)

RIP ONCE (7)

THUNDERY TOADS (8,5)

```
O V S A N T A S N V A S N
V O U T S T R P E N S U E
E F P O R C I N E E U V U
R S E O C Q E C W L W E M
E A R U B R R L I S S U E
A U S M A I A W U M S N D
T L T T R A Z Y U P E U Z
L D I E B G E A O N C E A
D O T I A E M G R N J D R
N F I G R O U P S R Y E R
A G O C I M A N Y D L D E
O V U F Z A R M Y A X N P
F B S P E D F N O O K A L
S C A E S T O A D N U R Q
A U P G H M D H P K G T I
U M H Z D E N D A R T S H
L E N W I G Z S T N U L T
```

Answers on pages 385.

Beauty Products

The letters in BLUSHER can be found in boxes 6, 7, 8, 13, 17, 22, and 23 but not necessarily in that order. Similarly, the letters in all the other beauty products can be found in the boxes indicated. Your task is to insert all the letters of the alphabet into the boxes. If you do this correctly, the shaded cells will reveal the name of a beauty treatment.

Hint: Compare COMB and COMPACT to get the value of B, then COMB and MASCARA for the value of O.

Unused letters: J, Q, X
BLUSHER: 6, 7, 8, 13, 17, 22, 23
COLD CREAM: 1, 2, 5, 7, 8, 16, 20, 22
COMB: 1, 5, 13, 16
COMPACT: 1, 2, 5, 9, 12, 16
EYELINER: 3, 4, 7, 8, 18, 22
HAND LOTION: 2, 3, 4, 9, 16, 20, 22, 23
LIPSTICK: 4, 5, 9, 12, 15, 17, 22
MAKEUP: 1, 2, 6, 8, 12, 15
MASCARA: 1, 2, 5, 7, 17
POWDER PUFF: 6, 7, 8, 11, 12, 14, 16, 20
ROUGE: 6, 7, 8, 16, 21
SHAMPOO: 1, 2, 12, 16, 17, 23
TONER: 3, 7, 8, 9, 16
TWEEZERS: 7, 8, 9, 10, 11, 17
VANISHING CREAM: 1, 2, 3, 4, 5, 7, 8, 17, 19, 21, 23

1	2	3	4	5	6	7	8	9	10	11	12	13

14	15	16	17	18	19	20	21	22	23	24	25	26
										J	Q	X

Answer on page 385.

Titan of Terror

Cryptograms are messages in substitution code. Break the code to read the quote from Alfred Hitchcock. THE SMART CAT might become FVO QWGDF JGF if **F** is substituted for **T**, **V** for **H**, **O** for **E**, and so on.

WUPFHK IOSXIXLXN JWB TLS LTUR SIH AWBSHF LP

BMBDHTBH, CMS SIH AWHBSFL LP JOSSR FHSLFSB.

SL W JLAWT JIL XLADUWOTHK SIWS SIH BILJHF

BXHTH OT *DBRXIL* BL PFOYISHTHK IHF KWMYISHF

SIWS SIH YOFU JLMUK TL ULTYHF BILJHF, IH BWOK,

"SIHT AWKWA, O BMYYHBS RLM IWZH IHF KFR-

XUHWTHK."

Mastermind

The goal of this puzzle is to replace the question marks with a correct sequence of numbers. The numbers you need for the answer are contained in the rows above the question marks. Follow these 2 guides: A black dot indicates that a number needed for the solution is in that row and in the correct position; a white dot means that a number needed for the solution is in that row but in the wrong position. Numbers do not appear more than once in the solution, and the solution never begins with 0.

```
6  9  4  1   ●
8  2  3  5   ●
6  4  7  0   ● ○
8  5  9  1     ○
_____
?  ?  ?  ?
```

Answers on page 385.

Codeword

The letters of the alphabet are hidden in code: Each is represented by a random number from 1 through 26. With the letters already given, complete the crossword puzzle with English words and the names of baseball players and break the code.

	23		5		23		20		13		3	
26	17	19	17	8	9	1	17		17	19	14	8
	21		5		10		13		8		4	
5	4	26	17	20	17		4	21	26	10	8	26
		24		5		21		14		1		
20	4	2	17	6	10	16		7	1	22	10	20
	5			21		7				21		
15	10	8	10	16		19	14	16	21	10	8	8
	16		12		25		16		4			
23	17	19	17	21	17		16	1	11	10	16	17
	8		8		18		1		1		17	
23	4	25	10		4	11	10	16	23	4	13	10
	16		20		4		16		10		5	

A B C D E F G H I J K L M N O P Q R S T U V W X Y Z

1	2	3	4	5	6	7	8	9	10	11	12	13
							T					

14	15	16	17	18	19	20	21	22	23	24	25	26
U					B							

Answers on page 385.

Gemstones

The letters in AGATE can be found in boxes 1, 2, 5, and 6 but not necessarily in that order. Similarly, the letters in all the other gemstones can be found in the boxes indicated. Your task is to insert all the letters of the alphabet into the boxes. If you do this correctly, the shaded cells will reveal the name of another gemstone.

Hint: Compare AGATE and ALEXANDRITE to get the value of G, then AGATE and TOPAZ for the value of E.

Unused letters: V, W

AGATE: 1, 2, 5, 6

ALEXANDRITE: 2, 3, 4, 5, 6, 8, 16, 17, 23

BERYL: 3, 5, 10, 11, 23

CITRINE: 3, 4, 5, 6, 17, 20

DIAMOND: 2, 4, 14, 16, 17, 18

FIRE OPAL: 2, 3, 5, 14, 17, 19, 21, 23

GIRASOL: 1, 2, 3, 14, 15, 17, 23

JACINTH: 2, 4, 6, 12, 17, 20, 22

JASPER: 2, 3, 5, 15, 19, 22

KUNZITE: 4, 5, 6, 7, 9, 13, 17

ONYX: 4, 8, 10, 14

RUBY: 3, 9, 10, 11

TOPAZ: 2, 6, 7, 14, 19

TURQUOISE: 3, 5, 6, 9, 14, 15, 17, 24

ZIRCON: 3, 4, 7, 14, 17, 20

1	2	3	4	5	6	7	8	9	10	11	12	13
14	15	16	17	18	19	20	21	22	23	24	25	26
											V	W

Answer on page 385.

Timeless Truths

A cryptogram is a simple, scrambled alphabet code. Break the code to read the message. For example: I SEE TESS, in code, may be A DGG FGDD, where **A** = **I**, **D** = **S**, **G** = **E**, and **F** = **T**. Each cryptogram below uses a different code.

1.

LYTAVUCHCPB: UWA XCPA LVU FX ELDCPB KFI UWCPD KFI'TA OFPBAY XFV HFEAUWCPB LOO KFIV OCXA UWLU KFI PATAV WALVY FX ZAXFVA.

2.

"SR HSNH OKRG TKKO QKJ TKKO'G GNXR GRRXG YRVHSRJ LJNVGR YKJ JRCNJO, MEH SR VG GEJR KQ MKHS VY HSR RYO."
—CVWWVNZ LRYY

Answers on page 385.

Wise Words

Cryptograms are messages in substitution code. Break the code to read the message. THE SMART CAT might become FVO QWGDF JGF if **F** is substituted for **T**, **V** for **H**, **O** for **E**, and so on. The code is different for each cryptogram.

1.

JIRY IB VR GCQ EIFGE—ZSQH ZQ CQGMS G MQCYGAH GUQ ZQ EAWQ YI RYAMW YI AY.

2.

YZV YZPGWB KCBY UVCUSV JQGY YC AGCJ QTV GCGV CM YZVPT IFBPGVBB.

3.

EYQRUEX UC UAMYCCUJSL QY QRL ABE ZRY PYLC EYQ RBGL QY PY UQ RUACLSV.

4.

EFVAUVAY GBOO VX GVXB; SOCAAVAY GBOO VX GVXBN; MHVAY GBOO VX GVXBXE CAM PBXE HR COO.

5.

JIX LZY BFFT JIXK WFZC ZMIAF NZRFK OS JIX WIDC JIXK LWOY XT.

6.

YBWWRYY NY QJGPNJV ZIR KNEERMRJWR HRZPRRJ WGMJRMNJV SRGSTR LJK VRZZNJV ZIRO NJ DGBM WGMJRM.

Answers on page 385.

Searching for Evidence

ACROSS

1. Guitarist at Woodstock
5. Cabinet department
10. Dieter's choice
14. Declare as true
15. National rival
16. Egg on
17. Phobia start
18. Baseball squads
19. Regatta squad
20. The crime took place in New York City at the _____
23. Buddhism type
24. Century 21's field
25. AARP member, often
29. New Age singer of "Orinoco Flow"
31. Where the victim was forced to take a _____ drug
33. More ready to be picked
38. Put down
39. Trap
41. Ankle-length 68-Across
42. "Let's hear _____ our next contestant"
44. Right before being _____
46. Running track shape
48. Lorraine neighbor
49. Drill sergeant's instruction
53. Heat organization: abbr.
54. By a woman wearing _____
59. "The doctor _____"
60. Renter's paper
61. Multipatient hospital room
64. Lead-in for Romeo

65. Rarin' to go
66. Lots
67. States
68. Woman's garment
69. Not-quite-final program version

DOWN

1. Airline code for a Florida city
2. "_____ had it up to here!"
3. Desktop bar
4. Pressing need?
5. Camping lights
6. Man in the moon?
7. Reception performers
8. Portent
9. Prayer beads
10. St. _____ (Caribbean island)
11. Swashbuckling Flynn
12. Ticket seller
13. Filled with gossip
21. Its logo was a green alligator
22. Rip
25. Protection purchase, perhaps: abbr.
26. Q.E.D. word: Lat.
27. Babe in the woods
28. _____ -European
29. Modern letter: hyph.
30. Geek
32. '60s teen idol Paul
34. Little devils
35. John Phillips was one
36. Co. man
37. Hitchhiker's hope

40. Facilitators
43. Parks on a bus
45. Jai _____
47. Kind of threat
49. Opera parts
50. Unit with T as its symbol
51. Enlighten
52. Pavlova and others
53. They might smell a rat

55. King with three daughters
56. Beep
57. Q-tip, e.g.
58. Can't stand
62. Decompose
63. The crime was solved by finding traces of _____ contained in each theme answer of 20-, 31-, 44-, and 54-Across

Answers on page 386.

Batteries Not Included

Cryptograms are messages in substitution code. Break the code to read the message. THE SMART CAT might become FVO QWGDF JGF if **F** is substituted for **T**, **V** for **H**, **O** for **E**, and so on. The code is the same for each cryptogram.

Hint: Look for repeated letters. E, T, A, O, N, R, and I are the most often used letters.

1.   **VJOT QVVTOSPH NTZCGNTU.**

2.   **CVT JLPH QV UGNTXITU.**

3.   **QV VTTL JL IW.**

4.   **QWJGU XJLIQXI YGIM VEGL.**

5.   **QFFPH JLPH IJ QKKTXITU QNTQ.**

6.   **HJC OCVI ST FNTVTLI IJ YGL.**

7.   **MQNOKCP JN KQIQP GK VYQPPJYTU.**

8.   **LJ FCNXMQVT LTXTVVQNH!**

Answers on page 386.

Codeword

The letters of the alphabet are hidden in code: Each is represented by a random number from 1 through 26. With the letters already given, complete the crossword puzzle with English words and break the code.

16	23	1	1	2	5	15	25	5		25	13	5	15	12
12						8		25		10				13
2			12	13	14	17	8	19	13	1				19
23						7		2		18				11
15	8	9	8	14	22		8	22	14	2	5	25	17	
8							14		5			21		
14	2	21	25	18	15	7	8	9	13	22	25	16		
22							15		15		5			3
	13	9	1		25	10	12	8	26	8	15			23
		2		24			2		2					2
		5		2			14		14		26	25	15	
26		25		23		24		6			13			8
2			15	5	25	25		9	25	14	15	8	2	14
4			15		13			16			20			22
18		13	17	12	25	5	25		15		25			

A B C D E F G H I J K L M N O P Q R S T U V W X Y Z

1	2	3	4	5	6	7	8	9	10	11	12	13
P								M				A

14	15	16	17	18	19	20	21	22	23	24	25	26

Answers on page 386.

Codeword

The letters of the alphabet are hidden in code: Each is represented by a random number from 1 through 26. With the letters already given, complete the crossword puzzle with English words and break the code.

1	2	3	4	5	6	7	8	9	10	11	12	13
		L										E

14	15	16	17	18	19	20	21	22	23	24	25	26
						I						V

Answers on page 386.

Ancient Wisdom

Cryptograms are messages in substitution code. Break the code to read the message. THE SMART CAT might become FVO QWGDF JGF if **F** is substituted for **T**, **V** for **H**, **O** for **E**, and so on.

"KXVVXI C MPCAYRM DPVB C TJCD VBCR C LXKKJX DPVBYNV."

—EBPRXOX LIYQXIK

Grape Expectations

Cryptograms are messages in substitution code. Break the code to read the quote and its source. THE SMART CAT might become FVO QWGDF JGF if **F** is substituted for **T**, **V** for **H**, **O** for **E**, and so on.

"DFOVUVGGVO UJHFW, AJS LVOF PYIFW DFZDGF XYDDT."

—YGFCYOQFH MGFPVOK

Answers on page 386.

Shoes

The letters in BOOT can be found in boxes 3, 12, and 22 but not necessarily in that order. Similarly, the letters in all the other types of shoes can be found in the boxes indicated. Your task is to insert all the letters of the alphabet into the boxes. If you do this correctly, the shaded cells will reveal the name of another type of shoe.

Hint: Compare MULE and PUMP to get the value of P, then PUMP and MOCCASIN for the values of M and U.

Unused letters: J, Q

BOOT: 3, 12, 22

BROGUE: 3, 4, 10, 12, 16, 18

CHOPINE: 1, 3, 7, 9, 11, 15, 16

GYM SHOE: 3, 4, 5, 15, 16, 17, 24

LOAFER: 2, 3, 6, 10, 13, 16

MOCCASIN: 1, 3, 5, 6, 7, 9, 17

MULE: 2, 16, 17, 18

OVERSHOE: 3, 5, 10, 15, 16, 19

OXFORD: 3, 8, 10, 13, 23

PUMP: 11, 17, 18

SANDAL: 2, 5, 6, 9, 23

SLIPPER: 2, 5, 7, 10, 11, 16

SNEAKER: 5, 6, 9, 10, 14, 16

WEDGE: 4, 16, 21, 23

ZORI: 3, 7, 10, 20

1	2	3	4	5	6	7	8	9	10	11	12	13
14	15	16	17	18	19	20	21	22	23	24	25	26
											J	Q

Answer on page 386.

Women's Jobs

The letters in ARCHER can be found in boxes 1, 5, 6, 8, and 20 but not necessarily in that order. Similarly, the letters in all the other jobs can be found in the boxes indicated. Your task is to insert all the letters of the alphabet into the boxes. If you do this correctly, the shaded cells will reveal the name of Holly's job.

Hint: Compare ARCHER and CARPENTER to get the value of H, then KING and KNIGHT for the value of T.

Unused letters: J, Q, Y, Z

(Anne) ARCHER: 1, 5, 6, 8, 20

(Anita) BAKER: 5, 6, 8, 13, 15

(Barbara) BOXER: 5, 6, 7, 12, 13

(Brett) BUTLER: 2, 4, 5, 6, 13, 16

(Karen) CARPENTER: 3, 4, 5, 6, 8, 20, 22

(Minnie) DRIVER: 5, 6, 10, 17, 18

(Frances) FARMER: 5, 6, 8, 19, 21

(Carole) KING: 3, 14, 15, 17

(Gladys) KNIGHT: 1, 3, 4, 14, 15, 17

(Natalie) MERCHANT: 1, 3, 4, 5, 6, 8, 20, 21

(Sue) MILLER: 5, 6, 16, 17, 21

(Katherine Ann) PORTER: 4, 5, 6, 12, 22

(Victoria) PRINCIPAL: 3, 6, 8, 16, 17, 20, 22

(Cybill) SHEPHERD: 1, 5, 6, 9, 18, 22

(Sigourney) WEAVER: 5, 6, 8, 10, 11

1	2	3	4	5	6	7	8	9	10	11	12	13

14	15	16	17	18	19	20	21	22	23	24	25	26
									J	Q	Y	Z

Answer on page 386.

Code-doku

Solve this puzzle just as you would a sudoku. Use deductive logic to complete the grid so that each row, column, and 3-by-3 box contains the letters ABDIRSTUY.

When you have completed the puzzle, unscramble those 9 letters to reveal a word used to define surreal humor.

A		T	D					B
D				R		I		
	D		B					T
	I		Y					A
	R			S		U		
Y		B	A					
				U		S		
		R					B	

Answer: _____

Answer on page 386.

Word Columns

Find the hidden phrase by using the letters directly above each of the blank squares. Each letter is used only once. A black square indicates the end of a word.

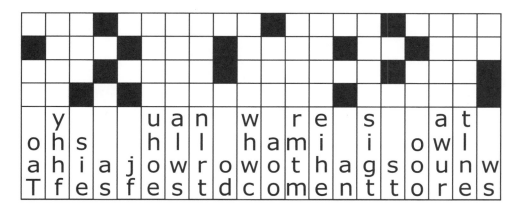

Missing Connections

It's a crossword without the clues! Use the letters below to fill in the empty spaces in the crossword grid. When you are finished, you'll have words that read both across and down, crossword-style.

A A B C D E E E E G H

H I I K L N N N P P P

R T T T T W Y

Answers on page 386.

Cryptograms are messages in substitution code. Break the code to read the message. THE SMART CAT might become FVO QWGDF JGF if **F** is substituted for **T**, **V** for **H**, **O** for **E**, and so on. The code is the same for each cryptogram.

Hint: Look for repeated letters. E, T, A, O, N, R, and I are the most often used letters. A single letter is usually A or I; OF, IS, and IT are common 2-letter words; THE and AND are common 3-letter groups.

1. "SGO PK MGCO VXBB WM X 'IEWBPWJD'? WM BKKTN BWTC WM'N UWJWNGCP. SGO WNJ'M WM X 'IEWBM'?"

—ACZZO NCWJUCBP

2. X UZCEPWXJ NBWL WN SGCJ OKE NXO KJC MGWJD IEM HCXJ OKEZ HKMGCZ.

3. GCZ YKVXIEBXZO SXN XN IXP XN, BWTC, SGXMCYCZ.

4. "W LBXJMCP NKHC IWZP NCCP. X IWZP DZCS. JKS W PKJ'M TJKS SGXM MK UCCP WM."

—NMCYCJ SZWDGM

5. SGCZC PK UKZCNM ZXJDCZN DK MK DCM XSXO UZKH WM XBB?

Answers on page 387.

Can you "read" the phrase below?

ANOTHERONETHING

Wacky Wordy

Can you "read" the phrase below?

DGOEE

Answers on page 387.

Acrostic Anagram

Unscramble the words below, then transfer the corresponding letters to the grid. The end of a word is signified by a black square. When you're finished, you'll be rewarded with a quote from Will Rogers.

1. Y A Y N W A
    62 29 68 66 5 10

2. T C R I A C
    67 40 4 30 56 15

3. Y W T E A R
    48 22 14 43 50 59

4. E W R T O
    11 39 65 53 46

5. I C A N H
    36 12 31 16 42

6. N Y A N S O
    34 6 26 60 54 8

7. Z O E O N
    28 21 2 63 37

8. Y I U T I L T
    3 23 18 58 20 51 47

9. E D H A E V
    52 64 13 33 45 27

10. A N K L F
    38 19 49 35 55

11. U O A Y T L
    57 9 1 25 61 7

12. D I V V I
    44 41 17 24 32

1 K	2 G	3 H		4 B	5 A	6 F	7 K		8 F	9 K	10 A		11 D	12 E	13 I	14 C		15 B	16 E
17 L	18 H	19 J	20 H	21 G	22 C	23 H	24 L	25 K	26 F		27 I	28 G	29 A	30 B		31 E	32 L	33 I	34 F
35 J	36 E	37 G		38 J	39 D	40 B		41 L	42 E		43 C	44 L	45 I	46 D	47 H		48 C	49 J	50 C
	51 H	52 I	53 I	54 F		55 J	56 B	57 K	58 H		59 C	60 F	61 K		62 A		63 G	64 D	65 D
	66 A	67 B	68 A														

Answers on page 387.

Acrostic Anagram

Unscramble the words below, then transfer the corresponding letters to the grid. When you're finished, you'll be rewarded with a quote from Agnes Repplier.

1. T   N   E   D   S   R
    ── ── ── ── ── ──
    18 7   30 9   61 54

2. B   D   D   N   E   R   A
    ── ── ── ── ── ── ──
    36 48 27 39 73 45 43

3. S   L   S   A   C   P
    ── ── ── ── ── ──
    29 52 71 69 46 11

4. G   B   N   U   R   E   L
    ── ── ── ── ── ── ──
    6   2   13 40 62 67 5

5. O   E   H   N   Y
    ── ── ── ── ──
    17 23 50 59 35

6. F   I   E   N   R   E
    ── ── ── ── ── ──
    26 53 56 31 60 25

7. N   U   G   I   S   H   R
    ── ── ── ── ── ── ──
    57 64 41 1   15 75 76

8. M   I   N   N   R   O   G
    ── ── ── ── ── ── ──
    3   4   32 28 38 65 10

9. A   Y   R   G   N
    ── ── ── ── ──
    19 72 16 37 63

10. N   I   I   A   D   D   S
    ── ── ── ── ── ── ──
    51 74 55 21 42 58 20

11. T   S   L   A   I   E   D
    ── ── ── ── ── ── ──
    66 44 22 49 8   24 14

12. I   N   R   E   O   T
    ── ── ── ── ── ──
    33 68 12 47 34 70

1 G	2 D	3 H	4 H	5 D		6 D	7 A	8 M	9 A	10 H	11 C		12 N	13 D	14 M	15 G	16 I	17 E	18 A
	19 I	20 L	21 L		22 M	23 E	24 M	25 F	26 F	27 B	28 H	29 C	30 A		31 F	32 H	33 N	34 N	35 E
	36 B	37 I	38 H	39 B	40 D	41 G		42 L		43 B	44 M	45 B	46 C	47 N	48 B		49 M	50 E	51 L
	52 C	53 F	54 A	55 L		56 F	57 G	58 L	59 E	60 F	61 A	62 D	63 I		64 G	65 H	66 M	67 D	68 N
69 C	70 N	71 C	72 I	73 B	74 L	75 G	76 G											

Answers on page 387.

Word Columns

Find the hidden humorous statement by using the letters directly below each of the blank squares. Each letter is used once. A black square indicates the end of a word.

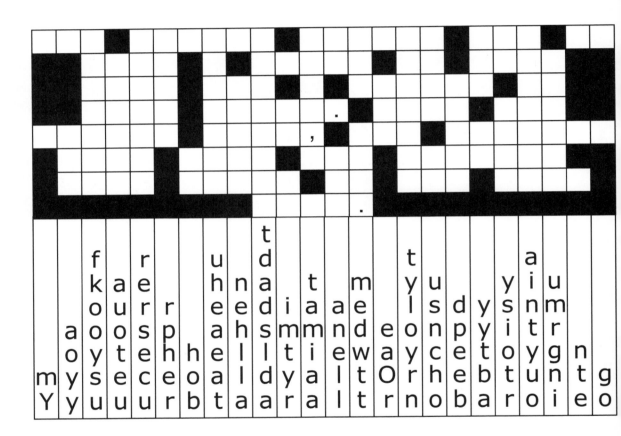

Answer on page 387.

Code-doku

Solve this puzzle just as you would a sudoku. Use deductive logic to complete the grid so that each row, column, and 3-by-3 box contains the letters from the words WASN'T HELD. When you have completed the puzzle, read the shaded squares to reveal a hidden message.

	L	T						P
		N						
	N					O		
	M					L		
O				L	P	M		
E			A	M				
				O				A
		N						S
S	P			A	T			

Hidden Message:

_____

_____

_____

Name Calling

Decipher the encoded word in the quip below using the numbers and letters on the phone pad. Remember that each number can stand for 3 or 4 possible letters.

My poor mind works like lightning: one 2-7-4-5-5-4-2-6-8 flash and it is gone!

Answers on page 387.

Queen of Song

Cryptograms are messages in substitution code. Break the code to read the message. THE SMART CAT might become FVO QWGDF JGF if **F** is substituted for **T**, **V** for **H**, **O** for **E**, and so on.

HSSM KXRWVHJMSO DFT RYXJRHHT VJMEEL

MDMJOB, EFJH RYMT MTL FRYHJ PMWW

ZHJKFJEHJ. YHJ TXNQTMEH DMB "KXJBR

SMOL FK BFTV."

Cryptogram

Cryptograms are messages in substitution code. Break the code to read the message. THE SMART CAT might become FVO QWGDF JGF if **F** is substituted for **T**, **V** for **H**, **O** for **E**, and so on.

"OUMH KUM KRXARMF RE DGXN,

KRMVHOXN BXCM FEOH DMAKEHXGGN XHF

AYPPMF UVK HXCM ETT RUM DVXHE."

Answers on page 387

Code-doku

Solve this puzzle just as you would a sudoku. Use deductive logic to complete the grid so that each row, column, and 3-by-3 box contains the letters A D E I L O S T V. When you have completed the puzzle, unscramble the letters to reveal a word used to define interlocking joints used in woodworking.

	D						A	
		S				L		V
O			S		D			T
			A	V	O			L
			L		I			
A				T				
L			O		A			D
D		T				E		
	S							O

Answer: _____

Answer on page 387.

Acrostic Anagram

Unscramble the words below, then transfer the corresponding letters to the grid. When you're finished, you'll be rewarded with a quote from James Thomson.

A. T S S A R E L E B H
   46 7 31 20 16 40 60 61 38 12

B. E O E M R E R M T H T
   50 51 41 28 1 26 8 47 69 37 14

C. E O E R O G S F
   58 71 3 52 30 23 63 49

D. O Y F I R F T
   24 45 34 44 70 65 48

E. S I A N H A U T E A
   18 27 55 57 29 42 9 32 6 67

F. C I F A O T N
   5 54 66 33 43 2 21

H. N U K H C Y
   25 19 13 72 36 62

G. H U U C E N
   15 68 10 59 56 17

I. O I D E D W W
   53 35 11 64 39 4 22

1 B	2 F	3 C	4 I		5 F	6 E	7 A	8 B		9 E	10 G	11 I		12 A	13 H	14 B	15 G		16 A
17 G	18 E		19 H	20 A	21 F	22 I		23 C	24 D		25 H	26 B	27 E	28 B	29 E	30 C	31 A		32 E
33 F	34 D	35 I	36 H	37 B	38 A		39 I	40 A	41 B	42 E		43 F	44 D		45 D	46 A	47 B	48 D	49 C
	50 B	51 B	52 C		53 I	54 F	55 E	56 G	57 E	58 C	59 G	60 A		61 A	62 H	63 C		64 I	65 D
	66 F	67 E	68 G	69 B	70 D	71 C	72 H										

114

The First Lady of Cinema

Cryptograms are messages in substitution code. Break the code to read the message. THE SMART CAT might become FVO QWGDF JGF if **F** is substituted for **T**, **V** for **H**, **O** for **E**, and so on.

"NPL JDUQ MPRC YS MPR NBKJM NKMP ORUMPRBJ NPRS LYZ EUS TRDM MPRC YHRB MPR PRUX NKMP U JDRXWRPUCCRB?"

Wise Words from a *Star Wars* Queen

Cryptograms are messages in substitution code. Break the code to read the message. THE SMART CAT might become FVO QWGDF JGF if **F** is substituted for **T**, **V** for **H**, **O** for **E**, and so on.

"GYN PNMG HXOG XPFEG PNDIR ZODNIAM KDGY TFEO HXONIGM DM GYXG IF LXGGNO KYXG TFE AF, GYNT YXQN GF JNNH VFQDIR TFE."

Answers on page 388.

Code-doku

Solve this puzzle just as you would a sudoku. Use deductive logic to complete the grid so that each row, each column, and each 3-by-3 box contains the letters BDEGHINRU. When you have completed the puzzle, unscramble those 9 letters to reveal the home of the military tattoo in the United Kingdom.

	H	E		B		R		
	D		G					I
N			I				E	H
D	N				I			
	I	D	H	E				R
	H	G					I	B
G					B	H		U
R			I		D			
	B		N			I		

Answer: _____

Codeword

The letters of the alphabet are hidden in code: Each is represented by a random number from 1 through 26. With the letters already given, complete the crossword puzzle with English words and break the code.

20	10	7	11	10		9	17	19	18	2	9	17
10		10		18		1			10		2	
4		26		25		17		9	19	24	9	11
16	6	2	12	3	9	7	14		19		10	
1		17		24		23		9	24	1	6	11
10	11	11	24	19	9	17	8		1			1
9		9		10				24		23		17
17			15		10	8	24	25	9	2	23	17
19	17	20	22	11		17		9		11		9
	5		6		10	11	25	2	19	10	9	17
10	22	13	2	6		25		4		23		6
	2		24			24		10		2		17
22	25	21	19	24	6	9		7	24	11	17	19

A B C D E F G H I J K L M N O P Q R S T U V W X Y Z

1	2	3	4	5	6	7	8	9	10	11	12	13

14	15	16	17	18	19	20	21	22	23	24	25	26
	J		E									

Answers on page 388.

Name Calling

Decipher the encoded words in the quip below using the numbers and letters on the phone pad. Each number can stand for 3 or 4 possible letters.

"7-8-7-4" and "7-8-5-5" are 9-7-4-8-8-3-6 on the 3-6-6-7 of 7-8-2-2-3-7-7.

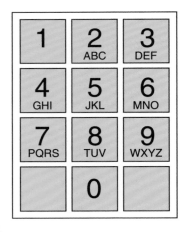

Name Calling

Decipher the encoded words in the quip below using the numbers and letters on the phone pad. Each number can stand for 3 or 4 possible letters.

A 7-3-7-7-4-6-4-7-8, confronted with two bad choices, 2-4-6-6-7-3-7 both.

Answers on page 388.

Acrostic Anagram

Unscramble the words below, then transfer the corresponding letters to the grid. When you're finished, you'll be rewarded with a quote from George F. Will.

A. C   A   R   B   E   C   I
    ―   ―   ―   ―   ―   ―   ―
    61 49 69 21 55 63 52

B. V   R   T   E   E   I   I   P   E   T
    ―   ―   ―   ―   ―   ―   ―   ―   ―   ―
    6   59 47 37 62 29 12 43 17 39

C. S   E   H   G   U   S   D. T   E   N   I   T   Y
    ―   ―   ―   ―   ―   ―   ―   ―   ―   ―   ―   ―
    70 5   11 36 73 46   18 24 50 10 42 3

E. O   R   V   O   Y   J   S   E
    ―   ―   ―   ―   ―   ―   ―   ―
    71 40 48 67 7   20 27 32

F. L   O   I   A   G   A   N   A   N   T   I   V
    ―   ―   ―   ―   ―   ―   ―   ―   ―   ―   ―   ―
    64 16 30 23 45 41 35 1   4   44 51 14

G. B   E   I   L   N   V   E   A
    ―   ―   ―   ―   ―   ―   ―   ―
    54 72 60 34 25 9   28 31

H. N   E   O   B   G   E   D   L
    ―   ―   ―   ―   ―   ―   ―   ―
    68 15 53 8   19 65 57 22

I. L   W   E   L   O   R   F   O
    ―   ―   ―   ―   ―   ―   ―   ―
    2   13 58 38 66 33 56 26

1 F	2 I		3 D	4 F	5 C	6 B		7 E	8 H	9 G		10 D	11 C		12 B	13 I					
14 F	15 H	16 F	17 B	18 D	19 H		20 E	21 A	22 H	23 F	24 D	25 G	26 I	27 E					
28 G	29 B	30 F	31 G	32 E		33 I	34 G	35 F	36 C		37 B	38 I	39 B	40 E	41 F	42 D	43 B	44 D	45 F
	46 C	47 B	48 E	49 A	50 D	51 F	52 A	53 H	54 G		55 A	56 I						
57 H	58 I	59 B	60 G	61 A	62 B	63 A	64 F	65 H		66 I	67 E		68 H	69 A		70 C	71 E	72 G	73 C

Answers on page 388.

119

The Greatest

Cryptograms are messages in substitution code. Break the code to read the message. THE SMART CAT might become FVO QWGDF JGF if **F** is substituted for **T**, **V** for **H**, **O** for **E**, and so on.

> "E QET YFC KLZYM VFZ YCIGX VFZ MEQZ EV ULUVR
>
> EM FZ XLX EV VYZTVR FEM YEMVZX VFLIVR RZEIM
>
> CU FLM GLUZ."

Breaking the Baseball Color Line

Cryptograms are messages in substitution code. Break the code to read the message. THE SMART CAT might become FVO QWGDF JGF if **F** is substituted for **T**, **V** for **H**, **O** for **E**, and so on.

> "ATU QVSTA BJ UKUQM FWUQVPFH AB JVQIA-PRFII
>
> PVAVOUHITVZ VI ATU WBIA VWZBQAFHA VIIYU BJ
>
> BYQ AVWU."

Answers on page 388.

Word Columns

Find the hidden quote by using the letters directly above each of the blank squares. Each letter is used only once. A black square indicates the end of a word.

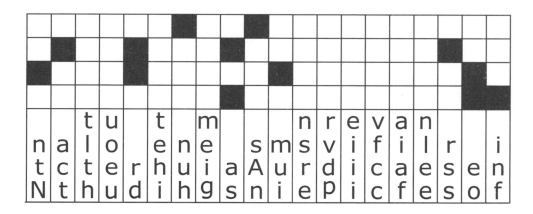

Dial Tone

Decipher the encoded words in the quip below using the numbers and letters on the phone pad. Remember that each number can stand for 3 or 4 possible letters.

We waited for 4 hours for tickets to the hottest show on 2-7-6-2-3-9-2-9.

Answers on page 388.

Codeword

The letters of the alphabet are hidden in code: Each is represented by a random number from 1 through 26. With the letters already given, complete the crossword puzzle with English words and break the code.

1	2	3	4	5	6	7	8	9	10	11	12	13
										S		A

14	15	16	17	18	19	20	21	22	23	24	25	26
Y						E						

Answers on page 389.

Code-doku

Solve this puzzle just as you would a sudoku. Use deductive logic to complete the grid so that each row, column, and 3-by-3 box contains the letters from the words OAF ETHICS. When you have completed the puzzle, read the shaded squares to reveal a well-known saying.

		A			O		C	H
		S	C				E	
							O	
O			I		A		T	
H		F	E					
						O		
T	O			F				E
C				E				I
A						T		

Hidden Saying: _____

Answer on page 389.

123

Acrostic Anagram

Unscramble the words below, then transfer the corresponding letters to the grid. The end of a word is signified by a black square. When you're finished, you'll be rewarded with a quote from Virginia Woolf.

A. E   P   E   E   D   A   R   R   P   S   S   N
    —   —   —   —   —   —   —   —   —   —   —   —
    14 48 18 10 52 39 57 32 12 71 25 30

B. S   U   F   O   L   O   H   S   P   E
    —   —   —   —   —   —   —   —   —   —
    67 27 38 5   70 55 9   36 47 43

C. N   I   O   S   M   O   T
    —   —   —   —   —   —   —
    40 64 50 24 11 60 19

D. O   O   O   N   N   T   P
    —   —   —   —   —   —   —
    63 16 53 1   31 41 65

E. A   A   N   A   P   T   O   I   T   D
    —   —   —   —   —   —   —   —   —   —
    66 3   26 58 69 45 54 21 34 7

F. R   E   D   H   A   F   E   O
    —   —   —   —   —   —   —   —
    17 22 72 28 51 59 68 61

G. R   U   N   O   L   A   Y   E   V   S
    —   —   —   —   —   —   —   —   —   —
    15 13 46 6   23 2   35 20 44 49

H. S   F   D   I   U   D   F   E
    —   —   —   —   —   —   —   —
    8   33 37 42 62 29 4   56

1 D	2 G		3 E	4 H	5 B	6 G	7 E	8 H		9 B	10 A	11 C	12 A		13 G		14 A	15 G	16 D
17 F	18 A	19 C	20 G	21 E	22 F	23 G		24 C	25 A		26 E	27 B	28 F	29 H	30 A		31 D	32 A	
33 H	34 E	35 G	36 B		37 H	38 B	39 A	40 C		41 D	42 H		43 B	44 G	45 E	46 G	47 B	48 A	49 G
	50 C	51 F	52 A	53 D		54 E	55 B		56 H	57 A	58 E	59 F	60 C	61 F		62 H	63 D	64 C	65 D
66 E		67 B	68 F	69 E	70 B	71 A	72 F												

Answers on page 389.

The Big Dipper

Cryptograms are messages in substitution code. Break the code to read the message. THE SMART CAT might become FVO QWGDF JGF if **F** is substituted for **T**, **V** for **H**, **O** for **E**, and so on.

"VWHK JAR LA ARX XWHDH PKE EA XWH XWFKLB
JAR'DH BRQQABHE XA EA, QHAQCH TFHV JAR PB
BHCYFBW."

Who Is…?

Cryptograms are messages in substitution code. Break the code to read a fact about Alex Trebek. THE SMART CAT might become FVO QWGDF JGF if **F** is substituted for **T**, **V** for **H**, **O** for **E**, and so on.

KD 1997, ZF ZYGLFJ "HZFFN YP PYILWDF" HZKNF
CUL GURUX LYYX YTFI "RFYCUIJB!" LZF GHKLQZFIYY
HUG UD UCIKN PYYNG' JUB RYXF.

Answers on page 389.

Codeword

The letters of the alphabet are hidden in code: Each is represented by a random number from 1 through 26. With the letters already given, complete the crossword puzzle with English words and break the code.

20	14	7	18	4	16	■	17	■	13	■	14	■
14	■	21	■	■	14	16	16	14	25	18	3	10
3	15	6	■	■	25	■	21	■	14	■	24	■
4	■	3	14	16	7	21	3	■	3	15	18	19
14	■	18	■	■	14	■	6	■	6	■	25	■
19	14	11	18	25	■	16	19	18	3	21	17	22
■	■	■	8	■	12	■	11	■	18	■	■	■
14	3	24	18	19	4	17	■	14	9	14	7	18
■	15	■	20	■	21	■	22	■	■	25	■	20
10	25	21	16	■	5	18	14	19	15	10	■	13
■	9	■	19	■	5	■	23	■	■	2	18	18
26	14	19	14	16	18	3	15	■	■	4	■	25
■	11	■	25	■	17	■	1	22	21	19	19	17

A B C D E F G H I J K L M N O P Q R S T U V W X Y Z

1	2	3	4	5	6	7	8	9	10	11	12	13
												B

14	15	16	17	18	19	20	21	22	23	24	25	26
										G		

Answers on page 389.

Name Calling

Cryptograms are messages in substitution code. Break the code to read the message. THE SMART CAT might become FVO QWGDF JGF if **F** is substituted for **T**, **V** for **H**, **O** for **E**, and so on.

America had often been discovered before 2-6-5-8-6-2-8-7, but it had always been hushed up.

Crack the Code

Determine the value of the symbols and replace the question mark with the correct number. The question mark is the sum of the symbols, diagonally.

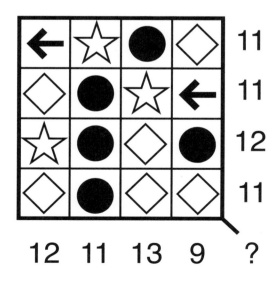

Answers on page 389.

Acrostic

Solve the clues below, and then place the letters in their corresponding spots in the grid to reveal a historic quote. The letter in the upper-right corner of each grid square refers to the clue the letter comes from. A black square indicates the end of a word.

A.   Renaissance artist, inventor, and author of quote: 3 wds.

$\overline{25}$ $\overline{49}$ $\overline{28}$ $\overline{17}$ $\overline{72}$ $\overline{6}$ $\overline{8}$ $\overline{20}$ $\overline{59}$ $\overline{53}$ $\overline{10}$ $\overline{79}$ $\overline{73}$ $\overline{63}$ $\overline{41}$

B.   Absent-minded fantasies

$\overline{14}$ $\overline{1}$ $\overline{33}$ $\overline{74}$ $\overline{32}$ $\overline{13}$ $\overline{23}$ $\overline{21}$ $\overline{62}$

C.   Plunged

$\overline{70}$ $\overline{11}$ $\overline{40}$ $\overline{3}$ $\overline{19}$

F.   Mushroom, e.g.

$\overline{84}$ $\overline{58}$ $\overline{51}$ $\overline{18}$ $\overline{68}$ $\overline{71}$

D.   Fully owned, as in stock options

$\overline{30}$ $\overline{5}$ $\overline{27}$ $\overline{47}$ $\overline{46}$ $\overline{37}$

G.   Breaks up

$\overline{12}$ $\overline{39}$ $\overline{78}$ $\overline{45}$ $\overline{76}$ $\overline{54}$ $\overline{44}$ $\overline{75}$

E.   Type of computer

$\overline{42}$ $\overline{50}$ $\overline{2}$ $\overline{15}$ $\overline{80}$ $\overline{64}$ $\overline{77}$

H.   Most breezy

$\overline{48}$ $\overline{16}$ $\overline{69}$ $\overline{38}$ $\overline{9}$ $\overline{29}$ $\overline{26}$ $\overline{57}$

I.   In an obnoxious manner

$\overline{67}$ $\overline{66}$ $\overline{22}$ $\overline{82}$ $\overline{36}$ $\overline{81}$ $\overline{35}$ $\overline{4}$ $\overline{31}$ $\overline{24}$ $\overline{55}$

J.   To a great extent

$\overline{60}$ $\overline{52}$ $\overline{34}$ $\overline{61}$ $\overline{65}$ $\overline{56}$ $\overline{43}$ $\overline{83}$ $\overline{7}$

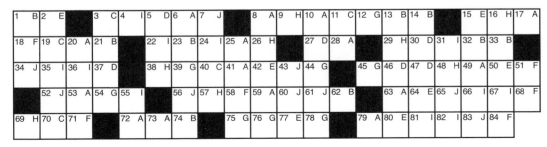

Answers on page 389.

Acrostic Anagram

Unscramble the words below, then transfer the corresponding letters to the grid. The end of a word is signified by a black square. When you're finished, you'll be rewarded with a quote from Voltaire.

A. A   M   B   E   A   C   R
   ___ ___ ___ ___ ___ ___ ___
   69 70 26 56 11   6 34

B. N   H   A   X   T   A   R
   ___ ___ ___ ___ ___ ___ ___
   46 23 40 68 33 35 51

C. D   H   M   A   E   M   W
   ___ ___ ___ ___ ___ ___ ___
   45 59 39 20 36 21 32

D. E   R   S   W   N   S   E   T
   ___ ___ ___ ___ ___ ___ ___ ___
   64 50 53 47 18 14 57 44

E. N   H   E   T   N   T   I   S
   ___ ___ ___ ___ ___ ___ ___ ___
   54 42 25 29 28   3 55 31

F. A   C   A   T   S   T   R   A   C
   ___ ___ ___ ___ ___ ___ ___ ___ ___
   67 22 66 12 73 27 48   1 17

G. S   S   T   A   I   R   L   M   A
   ___ ___ ___ ___ ___ ___ ___ ___ ___
   60   7 15 13 10 52 19 41 61

H. D   H   O   D   A   H   E   T   E
   ___ ___ ___ ___ ___ ___ ___ ___ ___
   49 63 37 38 72 65 58   9   8

I. D   N   H   O   W   S   I   K   O
   ___ ___ ___ ___ ___ ___ ___ ___ ___
    2 30   5 24   4 43 62 71 16

1 F	2 I	3 E		4 I	5 I	6 A	7 G	8 H		9 H	10 G	11 A	12 F	13 G	14 D	15 G	16 I	17 F	18 D
19 G		20 C	21 C		22 F	23 B	24 I		25 E		26 A	27 F	28 E	29 E	30 I	31 E		32 C	33 B
34 A	35 B	36 C		37 H	38 H	39 C	40 B		41 G	42 E	43 I	44 D		45 C	46 B	47 D	48 F	49 H
50 D	51 B	52 G	53 D	54 E	55 E		56 A	57 D	58 H		59 C	60 G	61 G		62 I	63 H		64 D	65 H
66 F	67 F	68 B	69 A	70 A	71 I	72 H	73 F											

Answers on page 389.

Headline Hoots

Cryptograms are messages in substitution code. Break the code to read the message. THE SMART CAT might become FVO QWGDF JGF if **F** is substituted for **T**, **V** for **H**, **O** for **E**, and so on.

1. BL YIGBDV BYU'I YVIIRVH FMBQDRT BI PET REYI
    E SCBRV.

2. FMVVU PEGT CEKBUZ XAIIAP YQGEJVH.

3. YIARVU JEBUIBUZ LAMUH XT IGVV.

4. LVHVGER EZVUIY GEBH ZMU YCAJ, LBUH
    SVEJAUY.

Answers on page 390.

Name Calling

Decipher the encoded word in the quip below using the numbers and letters on the phone pad. Remember that each number can stand for 3 or 4 possible letters.

The sea has a soothing effect. Did you ever see a 6-3-7-8-6-8-7 clam?

Mastermind

The goal of this puzzle is to replace the question marks with a correct sequence of numbers. The numbers you need for the answer are contained in the rows above the question marks. Follow these 2 guides: A black dot indicates that a number needed for the solution is in that row and in the correct position; a white dot means that a number needed for the solution is in that row but in the wrong position. Numbers do not appear more than once in the solution, and the solution never begins with 0.

9 2 6 4 ○ ○

1 4 9 3 ○ ○

3 6 2 7 ○ ○

4 5 7 2 ○ ○

5 9 4 8 ○ ○

? ? ? ?

Answers on page 390.

Codeword

The letters of the alphabet are hidden in code: Each is represented by a random number from 1 through 26. With the letters already given, complete the crossword puzzle with English words and break the code.

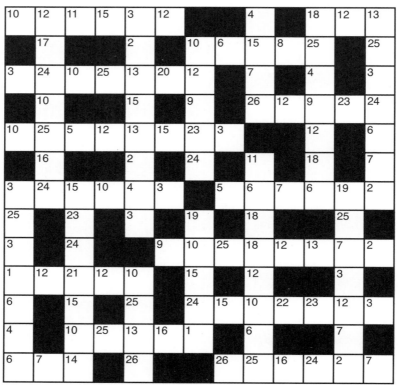

A B C D E F G H I J K L M N O P Q R S T U V W X Y Z

1	2	3	4	5	6	7	8	9	10	11	12	13
									R			

14	15	16	17	18	19	20	21	22	23	24	25	26

Answers on page 390.

Codeword

The letters of the alphabet are hidden in code: Each is represented by a random number from 1 through 26. With the letters already given, complete the crossword puzzle with English words and break the code.

4	10	15	2	23	14	■	6	9	7	13	3	17
2	■	2	■	2	■	■	■	12	■	2	■	26
24	2	12	2	19	3	23	■	15	3	23	11	4
3	■	3	■	15	■	9	■	3	■	6	■	7
21	7	14	19	3	■	7	12	14	23	2	15	12
17	■	■	■	3	■	18	■	■	■	13	■	8
■	■	23	9	14	3	■	26	2	23	16	■	■
10	■	10	■	■	■	4	■	14	■	■	■	20
26	2	21	10	10	16	2	■	24	10	5	3	23
2	■	21	■	12	■	26	■	7	■	3	■	3
25	9	7	11	17	■	26	3	23	1	2	14	3
9	■	12	■	3	■	■	■	2	■	17	■	18
3	23	17	2	11	18	■	22	21	2	11	21	5

A B C D E F G H I J K L M N O P Q R S T U V W X Y Z

1	2	3	4	5	6	7	8	9	10	11	12	13
	A	E		Y						T		

14	15	16	17	18	19	20	21	22	23	24	25	26
			S									

Answers on page 390.

Kitchen

The letters in BREAD BOX can be found in boxes 4, 5, 6, 7, 8, 14, and 21 but not necessarily in that order. Similarly, the letters in all the other kitchen items can be found in the boxes indicated. Your task i to insert all the letters of the alphabet into the boxes. If you do this correctly, the shaded cells will reveal the name of another kitchen item.

Hint: Compare OVEN and STOVE to get the value of N, then SINK and DISHWASHER for the value of

Unused letter: Q

BREAD BOX: 4, 5, 6, 7, 8, 14, 21

COFFEEPOT: 1, 3, 5, 12, 14, 16

DISHWASHER: 6, 7, 8, 9, 14, 15, 18, 25

FAUCET: 1, 2, 6, 12, 14, 16

FREEZER: 7, 10, 14, 16

GRIDDLE: 7, 8, 14, 20, 22, 25

JARS: 6, 7, 9, 23

JUICER: 1, 2, 7, 14, 23, 25

MICROWAVE: 1, 5, 6, 7, 11, 14, 18, 19, 25

OVEN: 5, 11, 14, 17

PANTRY: 3, 6, 7, 12, 17, 24

RANGE: 6, 7, 14, 17, 22

SINK: 9, 13, 17, 25

STOVE: 5, 9, 11, 12, 14

TEAKETTLE: 6, 12, 13, 14, 20

1	2	3	4	5	6	7	8	9	10	11	12	13

14	15	16	17	18	19	20	21	22	23	24	25	26
												Q

Answer on page 390.

Acrostic

Solve the clues below, and then place the letters in their corresponding spots in the grid to reveal a quote by Nancy Reagan. The letter in the upper-right corner of each grid square refers to the clue the letter comes from. A black square indicates the end of a word.

A. Dishes, silverware, glasses, etc.

$\overline{65}$ $\overline{5}$ $\overline{17}$ $\overline{32}$ $\overline{12}$ $\overline{2}$ $\overline{13}$ $\overline{70}$ $\overline{15}$

B. Break one's word?

$\overline{33}$ $\overline{20}$ $\overline{55}$ $\overline{58}$ $\overline{30}$ $\overline{26}$ $\overline{67}$ $\overline{57}$ $\overline{69}$

C. _____ and crannies

$\overline{6}$ $\overline{27}$ $\overline{3}$ $\overline{11}$ $\overline{8}$

D. With deliberation

$\overline{35}$ $\overline{61}$ $\overline{37}$ $\overline{29}$ $\overline{50}$ $\overline{40}$ $\overline{19}$ $\overline{31}$ $\overline{52}$

E. Uninterrupted

$\overline{23}$ $\overline{29}$ $\overline{25}$ $\overline{68}$ $\overline{7}$ $\overline{48}$ $\overline{56}$ $\overline{64}$ $\overline{54}$ $\overline{42}$

F. New neighbor party

$\overline{43}$ $\overline{21}$ $\overline{22}$ $\overline{36}$ $\overline{59}$ $\overline{66}$ $\overline{1}$ $\overline{38}$ $\overline{4}$ $\overline{10}$ $\overline{62}$ $\overline{41}$

G. French vegetable stew

$\overline{60}$ $\overline{24}$ $\overline{14}$ $\overline{16}$ $\overline{28}$ $\overline{53}$ $\overline{47}$ $\overline{45}$ $\overline{9}$ $\overline{51}$ $\overline{44}$

H. Solemn vows

$\overline{34}$ $\overline{18}$ $\overline{49}$ $\overline{63}$ $\overline{46}$

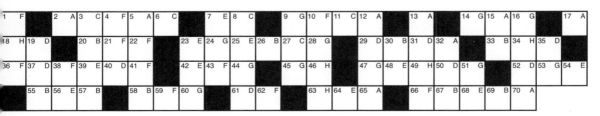

Answers on page 390.

Code-doku

Solve this puzzle just as you would a sudoku puzzle. Use deductive logic to complete the grid so that each row, column, and 3-by-3 box contains the letters from the word PONYTAILS.

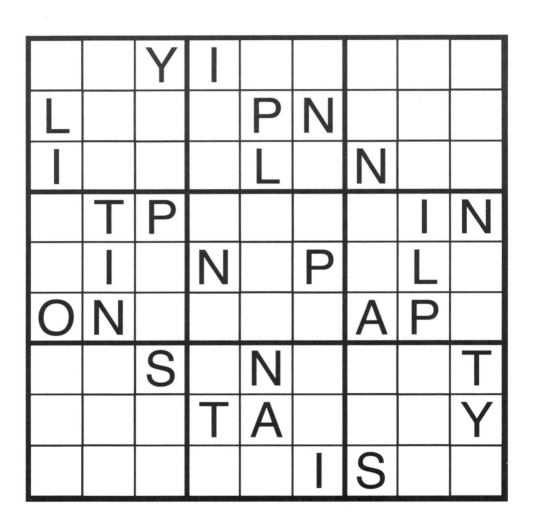

Answer on page 390

French Women

The letters in BRIGITTE can be found in boxes 3, 4, 5, 6, 7, and 23 but not necessarily in that order. Similarly, the letters in the other names of French women can be found in the boxes indicated. Your task is to insert all the letters of the alphabet into the boxes. If you do this correctly, the shaded cells will reveal another French female name.

Hint: Compare YVONNE AND YVETTE to get the value of T, then YVETTE and VALERIE for the value of Y.

Unused letters: K, W, and X

BRIGITTE: 3, 4, 5, 6, 7, 23

CLAUDETTE: 2, 5, 7, 9, 12, 14, 15

FRANCOISE: 2, 3, 4, 5, 10, 11, 15, 16, 20

GISELLE: 4, 5, 10, 12, 23

HELENE: 5, 12, 20, 22

JACQUELINE: 2, 4, 5, 9, 12, 13, 15, 19, 20

JEANNE: 2, 5, 13, 20

MONIQUE: 1, 4, 5, 9, 11, 19, 20

PAULETTE: 2, 5, 7, 9, 12, 21

SIMONE: 1, 4, 5, 10, 11, 20

SOPHIE: 4, 5, 10, 11, 21, 22

SUZETTE: 5, 7, 8, 9, 10

VALERIE: 2, 3, 4, 5, 12, 18

YVETTE: 5, 7, 17, 18

YVONNE: 5, 11, 17, 18, 20

1	2	3	4	5	6	7	8	9	10	11	12	13

14	15	16	17	18	19	20	21	22	23	24	25	26
										K	W	X

Answer on page 390.

Codeword

The letters of the alphabet are hidden in code: Each is represented by a random number from 1 through 26. With the letters already given, complete the crossword puzzle with English words and break the code.

13	16	14	14	13	20	22	2		8	11	15	20
25		20		11		3		9		21		2
22	11	21		22	16	8	8	2		21	25	7
4		14		20		11		3		20		11
	6	23	22	2	11	22		7	23	14	11	12
		25						6				23
17	23	22	25	2	6		5	20	22	7	20	14
23				3					14			
19	11	11	18	2		9	23	15	22	20	10	
24		15		21		14		23		11		10
16	14	22		20	18	23	25	8		2	1	25
20		20		18		10		21		11		23
19	20	14	11		26	11	22	19	23	8	20	19

A B C D E F G H I J K L M N O P Q R S T U V W X Y Z

1	2	3	4	5	6	7	8	9	10	11	12	13
										O		

14	15	16	17	18	19	20	21	22	23	24	25	26
R					Z	E						

Answers on page 390.

Dial Tone

Decipher the encoded words in the statement below using the numbers and letters on the phone pad. Remember that each number can stand for 3 or 4 possible letters.

After breaking up with your boyfriend, comfort foods such as 4-2-3 2-7-3-2-6 can really help!

Altared States

Cryptograms are messages in substitution code. Break the code to read the hidden quote and its source below. THE SMART CAT might become FVO QWGDF JGF if **F** is substituted for **T**, **V** for **H**, **O** for **E**, and so on.

"W EPHR DRWAI BQKKWRU. WM'C CP IKRQM MP XWAU MJQM PAR CORLWQE ORKCPA ZPT NQAM MP QAAPZ XPK MJR KRCM PX ZPTK EWXR."

—KWMQ KTUARK

Answers on page 390.

Code-doku

Solve this puzzle just as you would a sudoku. Use deductive logic to complete the grid so that each row, column, and 3-by-3 box contains the letters from the word SUNBATHER.

	H						N	
B			A			U		
E		U	R			S		
			U	N		S	R	
S	U	T		E	A			
	N			U		H		A
		A		H				T
	E					U		

Answer on page 391.

Stores

The letters in ANTIQUE can be found in boxes 2, 6, 7, 8, 9, 10, and 14 but not necessarily in that order. Similarly, the letters in all the other types of stores can be found in the boxes indicated. Your task is to insert all the letters of the alphabet into the boxes. If you do this correctly, the shaded cells will reveal the name of another type of store.

Hint: Compare PET and PACKAGE to get the value of T, then PET and SHOE for the values of P and E.

Unused letters: X and Z

ANTIQUE: 2, 6, 7, 8, 9, 10, 14

BOOK: 5, 18, 19

CANDY: 1, 4, 7, 10, 12

CLOTHING: 2, 4, 5, 7, 8, 15, 16, 23

CONVENIENCE: 2, 4, 5, 7, 9, 22

DEPARTMENT: 1, 7, 8, 9, 10, 20, 21, 24

DRUG: 1, 6, 21, 23

FURNITURE: 2, 6, 7, 8, 9, 17, 21

GENERAL: 7, 9, 10, 15, 21, 23

GROCERY: 4, 5, 9, 12, 21, 23

HARDWARE: 1, 9, 10, 13, 16, 21

JEWELRY: 9, 11, 12, 13, 15, 21

PACKAGE: 4, 9, 10, 19, 20, 23

PET: 8, 9, 20

SHOE: 3, 5, 9, 16

1	2	3	4	5	6	7	8	9	10	11	12	13

14	15	16	17	18	19	20	21	22	23	24	25	26
											X	Z

Answer on page 391.

Beyond *Clueless*

Cryptograms are messages in substitution code. Break the code to read the quote and its source. THE SMART CAT might become FVO QWGDF JGF if **F** is substituted for **T**, **V** for **H**, **O** for **E**, and so on.

"U YAF'B TGFB BA LK MFATF GH BNK GKVAHQUBN
RNURM, LDB UB'H XDF BA SDB AF BNK LAABH GFY
QGMKDS GFY GRB EUMK G BADWN WUVE."

—GEURUG HUECKVHBAFK

Good Eats Up North

Cryptograms are messages in substitution code. Break the code to read the food fact. THE SMART CAT might become FVO QWGDF JGF if **F** is substituted for **T**, **V** for **H**, **O** for **E**, and so on.

ZHNELTU, O ZHZNKOG IHYRHGE RHHP LT IOTOPO,
LB RGUTIV RGLUB EHZZUP MLEV RGUBV IVUUBU
INGPB, EVUT IHQUGUP MLEV CGHMT WGOQX.

Answers on page 391.

Codeword

The letters of the alphabet are hidden in code: Each is represented by a random number from 1 through 26. With the letters already given, complete the crossword puzzle with English words and break the code.

17	16	11	22	25	14	■	15	8	13	18	2	25
16	■	9	■	16	■	14	■	14	■	25	■	13
21	14	5	13	17	2	25	■	24	8	16	17	3
13	■	14	■	3	■	16	■	14	■	11	■	14
9	14	8	12	14	■	22	2	8	2	19	16	25
6	■	■	15	■	14	■	■	14	■	■	14	20
■	21	16	13	19	15	■	26	1	16	19	14	■
10	■	11	■	■	■	26	■	16	■	■	■	19
2	9	15	13	23	11	14	■	19	25	14	22	15
19	■	24	■	11	■	9	■	13	■	4	■	8
22	8	13	7	14	■	17	1	14	21	13	19	14
14	■	15	■	14	■	1	■	8	■	19	■	2
8	13	19	13	9	6	■	19	20	19	15	14	21

A B C D E F G H I J K L M N O P Q R S T U V W X Y Z

1	2	3	4	5	6	7	8	9	10	11	12	13
								N	U			

14	15	16	17	18	19	20	21	22	23	24	25	26
E									Q			

Answer on page 391.

Shrouded Summary

Hidden in the word search is a summary of a well-known novel. The words listed below are anagrams of the actual words you need to find; in the word search the actual words are presented in an order that will make more sense. The numbers in parentheses reveal how many letters are in each new word. Words can be found in a straight line horizontally, vertically, or diagonally. They may read either forward or backward. As a bonus, can you name the novel and its author?

DERIVATIVE JUNGLE NUN (8, 11)

HARMONIC PORT HOP (15)

MAST SINCE (9)

SAD IVORY (8)

STASIS (6)

VALOR MUSE (9)

```
A N T H R O P O M O R P H I C L
O D R E M I U P S M D O L G R S
I A V T A M T E C O N S C T R U
A S C I T N A M E S D I P I S C
N S G E S L I G A S E D O E I U
S I M O D O T E M R P O R I N E
I S D I D U R N T U V T L A B L
R T E E T D O Y A L O E R M A G
N A A L I Q U P D U T E L N I N
A D M I N U V E V N I A M O Q U
I S M U S E I D E L I N E V U J
V H A R M O N I N V L R S E D S
O N O S T R U D T A U L L A M C
R C O N S E Q A U L T D U I S A
Y U T E I R U R R O E S S E C U
S N U T L A B O I R U K M N U L
L A P A E I A T N U R P R O I D
D E R I V A T K G E N T O F I C
```

Answers on page 391.

Code-doku

Solve this puzzle just as you would a sudoku. Use deductive logic to complete the grid so that each row, column, and 3-by-3 box contains the letters from the words FUN MOVIES.

		S	N	U	E			
		M	F					
F		E				S		
			O	M				F
V	N					S	I	
M			I	N				
		V				O		M
				U	E			
		S	M	N	I			

Answer on page 391.

Word Columns

Find the hidden humorous observation by using the letters directly below each of the blank squares. Each letter is used only once. A black square or the end of the line indicates the end of a word.

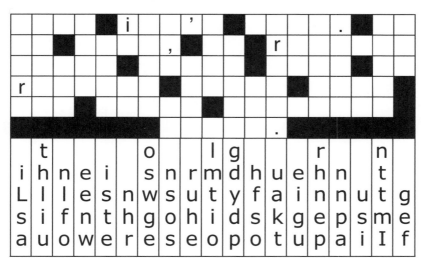

Word Columns

Find the hidden phrase by using the letters directly below each of the blank squares. Each letter is used only once. A black square or the end of the line indicates the end of a word.

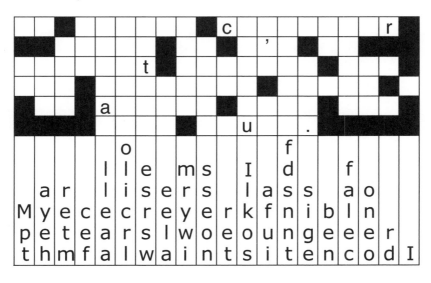

Answers on page 391.

Grid Fill

To complete this puzzle, place the given letters and words into the shapes in this grid. Words and letters will run across, down, and wrap around each shape. When the grid is filled, each row will contain one part of the following names: JESSICA SIMPSON, EVE, MISSY ELLIOTT, NELLY FURTADO

1. **J, Y**
2. **CA, EL, LP, OL, RI, SY, TS, TT**
3. **ADO, SIM, SON**
4. **LINE**
5. **FUMES, SIEVE**

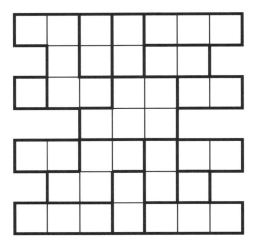

About One of Her Own

Cryptograms are messages in substitution code. Break the code to reveal the quote and its author. THE SMART CAT might become FVO QWGDF JGF if **F** is substituted for **T**, **V** for **H**, **O** for **E**, and so on.

"D'B ZRON VW JRX VZRV, DF CNFNTRQ, PWBNQJ
VRMN VZNPJNQONJ VWW JNTDWSJQX. ERJDIRQQX,
VZNX RTN CNFNVDI HTNRMJ LZW JKNFB R IWSKQN
WH ZWSTJ DF ZRDT RFB PRMNSK."

—TNENIIR TWPDYF

Answers on pages 391-392.

Out of Africa

The letters in BOTSWANA can be found in boxes 2, 4, 5, 9, 17, 21, and 24, but not necessarily in that order. Similarly, the letters in all these words can be found in the boxes indicated. Your task is to insert all the letters of the alphabet into the boxes. If you do this correctly, the shaded cells will reveal what ties these words together.

Hint: Compare LIBYA and MALI to get the value of M, then MALI to CHAD to get the value of A.

Unused letter: X

BOTSWANA 2, 4, 5, 9, 17, 21, 24

BURKINA FASO 2, 3, 4, 6, 7, 9, 13, 17, 21, 25

CHAD 1, 10, 17, 18

CONGO 1, 2, 4, 15

DJIBOUTI 2, 3, 5, 7, 14, 18, 21

EGYPT 5, 8, 11, 15, 16

GAMBIA 7, 15, 17, 21, 23

IVORY COAST 1, 2, 5, 6, 7, 9, 11, 17, 19

KENYA 4, 8, 11, 13, 17

LIBYA 7, 11, 17, 21, 22

MALI 7, 17, 22, 23

MOZAMBIQUE 2, 3, 7, 8, 12, 17, 20, 21, 23

UGANDA 3, 4, 15, 17, 18

ZAMBIA 7, 12, 17, 21, 23

1	2	3	4	5	6	7	8	9	10	11	12	13

14	15	16	17	18	19	20	21	22	23	24	25	26
												X

Answer on page 392.

It's a Fortnight

The letters in ARBOR can be found in boxes 2, 6, 11, and 22, but not necessarily in that order. Similarly, the letters in all these words can be found in the boxes indicated. Your task is to insert all the letters of the alphabet into the boxes. If you do this correctly, the shaded cells will reveal another word related to the theme.

Hint: Compare LEAP and MEMORIAL to get the value of P, then LEAP to LABOR to get the value of E.

Unused letters: J, Q, and Z

ARBOR 2, 6, 11, 22

BOXING 2, 8, 10, 19, 21, 22

CANADA 5, 6, 10, 14

FLAG 6, 17, 21, 23

GROUNDHOG 2, 5, 9, 10, 11, 15, 21

HIGH HOLY 2, 7, 8, 15, 17, 21

LABOR 2, 6, 11, 17, 22

LEAP 4, 6, 13, 17

MEMORIAL 2, 3, 4, 6, 8, 11, 17

NEW YEAR'S 1, 4, 6, 7, 10, 11, 16

PRESIDENTS 1, 4, 5, 8, 10, 11, 12, 13

ST. PATRICK'S 1, 6, 8, 11, 12, 13, 14, 18

VALENTINES 1, 4, 6, 8, 10, 12, 17, 20

VETERANS 1, 4, 6, 10, 11, 12, 20

1	2	3	4	5	6	7	8	9	10	11	12	13

14	15	16	17	18	19	20	21	22	23	24	25	26
										J	Q	Z

Answer on page 392.

Codeword

The letters of the alphabet are hidden in code: Each is represented by a random number from 1 through 26. With the letters already given, complete the crossword puzzle with English words and break the code.

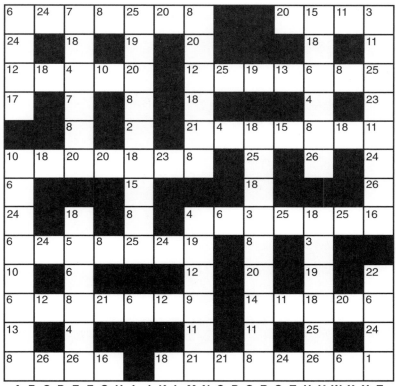

6	24	7	8	25	20	8			20	15	11	3
24		18		19		20				18		11
12	18	4	10	20		12	25	19	13	6	8	25
17		7		8		18				4		23
		8		2		21	4	18	15	8	18	11
10	18	20	20	18	23	8		25		26		24
6				15				18				26
24		18		8		4	6	3	25	18	25	16
6	24	5	8	25	24	19		8		3		
10		6				12		20		19		22
6	12	8	21	6	12	9		14	11	18	20	6
13		4				11		11		25		24
8	26	26	16		18	21	21	8	24	26	6	1

A B C D E F G H I J K L M N O P Q R S T U V W X Y Z

1	2	3	4	5	6	7	8	9	10	11	12	13
X				F	I		M					

14	15	16	17	18	19	20	21	22	23	24	25	26
								J				

Answers on page 392.

Happy Christmas

The letters in SNOW can be found in boxes 6, 7, 12, and 16, but not necessarily in that order. Similarly, the letters in all the other words can be found in the boxes indicated. Your task is to insert all the letters of the alphabet into the boxes. If you do this correctly, the shaded cells will reveal another word associated with Christmas.

ADVENT: 4, 6, 8, 13, 14, 20

BAUBLES: 7, 8, 9, 11, 18, 20

BLAZING FIRE: 1, 5, 6, 8, 9, 11, 17, 20, 25, 26

CHOCOLATE: 2, 4, 8, 9, 12, 20, 24

CRACKERS: 7, 8, 20, 22, 24, 26

FAIRY: 3, 5, 20, 25, 26

HOLLY: 2, 3, 9, 12

JINGLE BELLS: 1, 5, 6, 7, 8, 9, 11, 21

LIQUEURS: 5, 7, 8, 9, 18, 23, 26

MISTLETOE: 4, 5, 7, 8, 9, 12, 19

PRESENTS: 4, 6, 7, 8, 10, 26

REINDEER: 5, 6, 8, 13, 26

SNOW: 6, 7, 12, 16

XMAS LIGHTS: 1, 2, 4, 5, 7, 9, 15, 19, 20

YULE LOG: 1, 3, 8, 9, 12, 18

1	2	3	4	5	6	7	8	9	10	11	12	13

14	15	16	17	18	19	20	21	22	23	24	25	26

Answer on page 392.

Codeword

The letters of the alphabet are hidden in code: Each is represented by a random number from 1 through 26. With the letters already given, complete the crossword puzzle with English words and break the code. Once you have completed the grid, unscramble the letters found in the gray cells to reveal the name of a hockey prize.

6	18	15	18	24	2		2	11	6	17	20	1
18			21		23		18		18		6	
9	17	22	24	23	12	16	24		7	6	23	10
16			16				11		18		9	
18	4	18	1		7		12		18	21	23	13
19			18	22	16	2	16	1	13		7	
1	25	14			1		3			10	17	17
	22		16	12	2	6	8	7	18			24
11	23	12	10		23		18		12	18	23	2
	2		22		12			26				23
13	18	13	17		24	23	6	6	14	16	12	10
	23		17		18		18		13			17
5	8	1	1	18	7		7	18	18	25	18	12

A B C D E F G H I J K L M N O P Q R S T U V W X Y Z

1	2	3	4	5	6	7	8	9	10	11	12	13
S				F		D						

14	15	16	17	18	19	20	21	22	23	24	25	26
					W							

Answers on page 392.

Cryptogram

Cryptograms are messages in substitution code. Break the code to read a movie quote from Billy Crystal. THE SMART CAT might become FVO QWGDF JGF if **F** is substituted for **T**, **V** for **H**, **O** for **E**, and so on.

"T WLXV OVKV QJZTYOQ EVWLMBV GOVZ SJM
KVLFTAV SJM GLZQ QJ BCVZN QOV KVBQ JI SJMK
FTIV GTQO BJXVEJNS, SJM GLZQ QOV KVBQ JI
SJMK FTIV QJ BQLKQ LB BJJZ LB CJBBTEFV."

Grid Fill

To complete this puzzle, place the given letters and words into the shapes in this grid. Words and letters will run across, down, and wrap around each shape. When the grid is filled, each row will contain one of the following words: access, aching, cloths, erodes, kettle, league, sprint.

1. **L, S, T**
2. **AG, SS, TI**
3. **ACE, ODE, SUE**
4. **ETCH, LORE, SACK**
5. **LENGTH, PRINCE**

Answers on page 392.

Have a Ball

The letters in BASKET can be found in boxes 5, 6, 7, 8, 10, and 24, but not necessarily in that order. Similarly, the letters in all these words can be found in the boxes indicated. Your task is to insert all the letters of the alphabet into the boxes. If you do this correctly, the shaded cells will reveal another "ball" term.

Hint: Compare FOOT and MATZO to get the value of F, then FOOT to SNOW to get the value of O and T.

Unused letter: X

BASKET: 5, 6, 7, 8, 10, 24

BILLIARD: 3, 7, 8, 9, 21, 23

CRYSTAL: 1, 3, 6, 8, 9, 24, 25

EIGHT: 5, 14, 17, 21, 24

FOOT: 13, 22, 24

JUMP: 2, 16, 18, 20

KNUCKLE: 1, 2, 5, 9, 10, 19

MATZO: 8, 11, 13, 20, 24

MEDICINE: 1, 5, 19, 20, 21, 23

PING PONG: 13, 17, 18, 19, 21

RACQUET: 1, 2, 3, 5, 8, 12, 24

SNOW: 6, 13, 15, 19

SOCCER: 1, 3, 5, 6, 13

TENNIS: 5, 6, 19, 21, 24

VOLLEY: 4, 5, 9, 13, 25

1	2	3	4	5	6	7	8	9	10	11	12	13

14	15	16	17	18	19	20	21	22	23	24	25	26
												X

Answer on page 392.

Codeword

The letters of the alphabet are hidden in code: Each is represented by a random number from 1 through 26. With the letters already given, complete the crossword puzzle with English words and break the code.

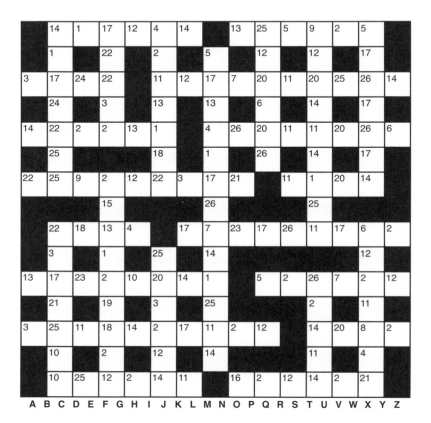

1	2	3	4	5	6	7	8	9	10	11	12	13
H			K									

14	15	16	17	18	19	20	21	22	23	24	25	26
				U				P				

Answers on page 392.

Acrostic

Solve the clues below, and then place the letters in their corresponding spots in the grid to reveal a quote from Abraham Lincoln. The letter in the upper-right corner of each grid square refers to the clue the letter comes from. A black square indicates the end of a word.

A. Cause for revolution

___ ___ ___ ___ ___ ___ ___
66 58 45 55 38 16 26

B. Insect repellant

___ ___ ___ ___ ___ ___ ___ ___
73 6   60 28 25 9   68 18

C. "Nonsense!"

___ ___ ___ ___ ___
20 43 8   37 1

D. "Separate but equal" policy struck down in 1954

___ ___ ___ ___ ___ ___ ___ ___ ___ ___ ___
64 11 12 52 69 36 15 14 47 51 76

E. Obviously

___ ___ ___ ___ ___ ___ ___ ___ ___
3   10 72 39 19 23 50 34 5

F. Type of auto accident: 3 wds.

___ ___ ___ ___ ___ ___ ___ ___
30 59 65 57 48 33 74 7   4

G. Abe's pad, for a while: 2 wds.

___ ___ ___ ___ ___ ___ ___ ___ ___ ___
56 40 31 24 17 71 13 53 61 35

H. Grant's presidency, numerically

___ ___ ___ ___ ___ ___ ___ ___ ___ ___
41 42 49 2   27 29 63 32 44 21

I. Able to float

___ ___ ___ ___ ___ ___ ___
62 75 67 46 22 54 70

1 C	2 H	3 E	4 F	■	5 E	6 B	7 F	■	8 C	9 B	10 E	11 D	■	12 D	13 G	14 D	■	15 D	16 A	■	17 G	18 B
19 E	20 C	21 H	22 I	23 E	24 G	■	25 B	26 A	■	27 H	28 B	29 H	■	30 F	31 G	32 H	33 F	■	34 E	35 G	36 D	■
37 C	38 A	39 E	■	40 G	41 H	■	42 H	43 C	■	44 H	45 A	46 I	47 D	48 F	49 H	■	50 E	51 D	■	52 D	53 G	54 I
■	55 A	56 G	57 F	58 A	■	59 F	60 B	61 G	■	62 I	63 H	64 D	65 F	■	66 A	67 I	■	68 B	69 D	70 I	■	71 G
72 E	73 B	■	74 F	75 I	76 D																	

Answers on page 393.

Code-doku

Solve this puzzle just as you would a sudoku. Use deductive logic to complete the grid so that each row, each column, and each 3-by-3 box contains each of the letters ACEFIORST in some order. The solution is unique. When you have completed the puzzle, unscramble those 9 letters to reveal "buildings used for manufacturing."

	F	E	T					I
T					I	E	C	
A				F			S	
I		A		E				
		C	S	T			I	O
	R	A				C	F	
		F	R					
					A		E	
O		I		C	F	R		S

Answer: _____

Answer on page 393.

Mastermind

The goal of this puzzle is to replace the question marks with a correct sequence of letters. The letters you need for the answer are contained in the rows above the question marks. Follow these 2 guides: A black dot indicates that a letter needed for the solution is in that row and in the correct position; a white dot means that a letter needed for the solution is in that row but in the wrong position. Letters do not appear more than once in the solution.

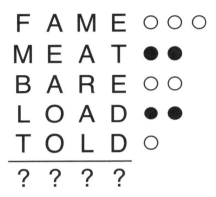

Mastermind

The goal of this puzzle is to replace the question marks with a correct sequence of letters. The letters you need for the answer are contained in the rows above the question marks. Follow these 2 guides: A black dot indicates that a letter needed for the solution is in that row and in the correct position; a white dot means that a letter needed for the solution is in that row but in the wrong position. Letters do not appear more than once in the solution.

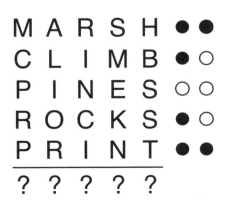

Answers on page 393.

Order in the Court

The letters in ACQUITTAL can be found in boxes 1, 3, 4, 5, 14, 15, and 20, but not necessarily in that order. Similarly, the letters in all these words can be found in the boxes indicated. Your task is to insert all the letters of the alphabet into the boxes. If you do this correctly, the shaded cells will reveal another legal term.

Hint: Compare BAILIFF and PLAINTIFF to get the value of B, then BAILIFF to ACQUITTAL to get the value of F.

ACQUITTAL 1, 3, 4, 5, 14, 15, 20

BAILIFF 3, 4, 5, 17, 21

CASE 4, 6, 7, 20

COURTROOM 1, 2, 12, 14, 18, 20

DOCKET 1, 7, 16, 18, 20, 26

EXECUTION 1, 3, 7, 9, 11, 14, 18, 20

GAVEL 4, 5, 7, 22, 24

HUNG JURY 2, 10, 11, 13, 14, 22, 23

JUDGE 7, 10, 14, 16, 22

LAWYER 2, 4, 5, 7, 13, 25

OBJECTION 1, 3, 7, 10, 11, 17, 18, 20

OYEZ 7, 8, 13, 18

PLAINTIFF 1, 3, 4, 5, 11, 19, 21

VERDICTS 1, 2, 3, 6, 7, 16, 20, 24

1	2	3	4	5	6	7	8	9	10	11	12	13

14	15	16	17	18	19	20	21	22	23	24	25	26

Answer on page 393.

Codeword

The letters of the alphabet are hidden in code: Each is represented by a random number from 1 through 26. With the letters already given, complete the crossword puzzle with English words and break the code.

A B C D E F G H I J K L M N O P Q R S T U V W X Y Z

1	2	3	4	5	6	7	8	9	10	11	12	13

14	15	16	17	18	19	20	21	22	23	24	25	26
H		T	K	I					U			

Answers on page 393.

Code-doku

Solve this puzzle just as you would a sudoku. Use deductive logic to complete the grid so that each row, column, and 3-by-3 box contains the letters from the word MICROWAVE.

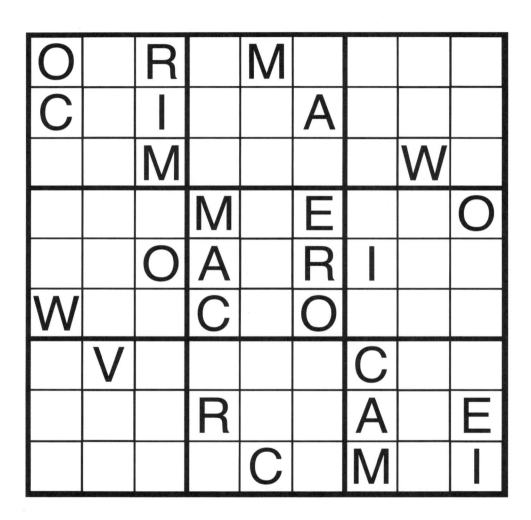

Answer on page 393.

Calcu-doku

Use arithmetic and deductive logic to complete the grid so that each row and column contains the numbers 1 through 6 in some order. Numbers in each outlined set of squares combine to produce the number in the top corner using the mathematical sign indicated.

1−	3+		11+	15×	
	8×			5−	
5−		90×		7+	3+
20×					
3÷	15×		24×		20×
		4+		2	

Answer on page 393.

Trade Secret

Cryptograms are messages in substitution code. Break the code to read the message. THE SMART CAT might become FVO QWGDF JGF if **F** is substituted for **T**, **V** for **H**, **O** for **E**, and so on.

JKGE JZCPEW, JZTGRKJRAG PJCGCP VXJ GEZ *AZS*

MXJH GCQZT, KTZB QKWGCLWZ BCTFKCTZT SEZA

TEZ DCTCGZB JZTGRKJRAGT. GEZ BCTFKCTZ HCG

CAPWKBZB GSZWDZ SCFT, JKNNZJ PZQZAG GX

PJZRGZ SJCAHWZT, LEXAM ZMZFWRTTZT, RAB

"NRB PWXGEZT VJXQ GEJCVG TEXLT."

Sight Unseen

Cryptograms are messages in substitution code. Break the code to read the message. THE SMART CAT might become FVO QWGDF JGF if **F** is substituted for **T**, **V** for **H**, **O** for **E**, and so on.

"S WKFH GL SGVHBHNV SG VWH PBKGY

TKGALG; S OBHZHB EGGKVEBKU RLGYHBN,

USQH JKUU LZ KJHBSTK LB JKYLGGK."

—TLUEJGSNV GLBJKG TWKY

Thirteen States?

The letters in ARIZONA can be found in boxes 3, 5, 6, 9, 11, and 23, but not necessarily in that order. Similarly, the letters in all these words can be found in the boxes indicated. Your task is to insert all the letters of the alphabet into the boxes. If you do this correctly, the shaded cells will reveal another state.

Hint: Compare FLORIDA to IDAHO to get the value of H, then IDAHO to ARIZONA to get the value of D.

Unused letter: Q

ARIZONA: 3, 5, 6, 9, 11, 23

NEW JERSEY: 1, 2, 6, 16, 18, 21, 23

TEXAS: 8, 11, 16, 18, 20

FLORIDA: 3, 5, 10, 11, 19, 23, 24

IDAHO: 3, 5, 10, 11, 25

ALABAMA: 4, 11, 19, 22

KENTUCKY: 2, 6, 8, 13, 15, 16, 17

OKLAHOMA: 3, 4, 11, 13, 19, 25

OREGON: 3, 6, 7, 16, 23

VERMONT: 3, 4, 6, 8, 14, 16, 23

PENNSYLVANIA: 2, 5, 6, 11, 12, 14, 16, 18, 19

WISCONSIN: 1, 3, 5, 6, 17, 18

1	2	3	4	5	6	7	8	9	10	11	12	13

14	15	16	17	18	19	20	21	22	23	24	25	26
												Q

Answer on page 393.

What's That?

Decipher this sentence to create a phrase common in everyday English.

It is highly inadvisable to use a calculator or other device, including fingers, to enumerate a certain avian species while they are not yet in existence.

Symbol Solution

Which symbol should replace the question mark?

‡ § ≠ ✿ ☼ Γ Δ & ◄ ‡ § ≠ ✿ ☼ Γ Δ & ‡ § ≠ ✿
☼ Γ Δ ‡ § ≠ ✿ ☼ Γ ‡ § ≠ ✿ **?** ‡ § ≠ ✿ ‡ § ≠ ‡ §

a. Δ   b. ☼   c. &   d. ‡   e. Γ

Answers on pages 393-394.

Code-doku

Solve this puzzle just as you would a sudoku. Use deductive logic to complete the grid so that each row, column, and 3-by-3 box contains the letters from the words DAIRY BELT. When you have completed the puzzle, read the shaded squares from left to right and top to bottom to reveal a hidden message regarding something to do in New York City.

I			E		R	L		
	A	R						B
		E				T		
		A						
		B	T					
	I			L		B	E	
E					T	A	R	
			Y					
B			L	E				

Hidden Message: _____

Answer on page 394.

Mastermind

The goal of this puzzle is to replace the question marks with a correct sequence of letters. The letters you will need for the answer are contained in the rows above the question marks. Follow these 2 guides: A black dot indicates that a letter needed for the solution is in that row and in the correct position; a white dot means that a letter needed for the solution is in that row but in the wrong position. Letters do not appear more than once in the solution.

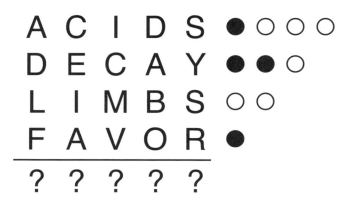

You Could Look It Up

Cryptograms are messages in substitution code. Break the code to read the message. THE SMART CAT might become FVO QWGDF JGF if **F** is substituted for **T**, **V** for **H**, **O** for **E**, and so on.

PJD, "BUJ NXNSJ KFIJ YLI XIIXBCNSJ NLRJS
DPWGILVJ" CWG "BUJ BUJIVLGPWCVXKD LY
EXQQC" CIJ BUJ BXBSJD LY CKBFCS NLLHD.

Answers on page 394.

Codeword

The letters of the alphabet are hidden in code: Each is represented by a random number from 1 through 26. With the letters already given, complete the crossword puzzle with English words and break the code. Once you have completed the grid, unscramble the letters found in the gray cells to reveal the name of a hockey team.

23		24		23				18		26		5
2	12	14	23	2	15		26	9	2	14	13	15
14		9		15		5		10		8		10
1	15	9	3	2	9	15		1	9	14	25	9
1		25		15		10		6		26		7
15	10	9	13		13	4	10	14	17			
17		13		12		6		26		10		25
		16	25	19	15	13		25	24	15	12	
15		13		22		9		20		2		15
4	25	1	10	22		15	12	11	14	13	4	13
6		25		11		17		2		14		15
15	11	2	17	15	17		21	15	12	12	15	11
9		4		13			13			18		16

A B C D E F G H I J K L M N O P Q R S T U V W X Y Z

1	2	3	4	5	6	7	8	9	10	11	12	13
P						Y						

14	15	16	17	18	19	20	21	22	23	24	25	26
									Q			

Answers on page 394.

Chain Sudoku

Use deductive logic to complete the grid so that each row, each column, and each connected set of circles contains the numbers 1 through 6 in some order. The solution is unique.

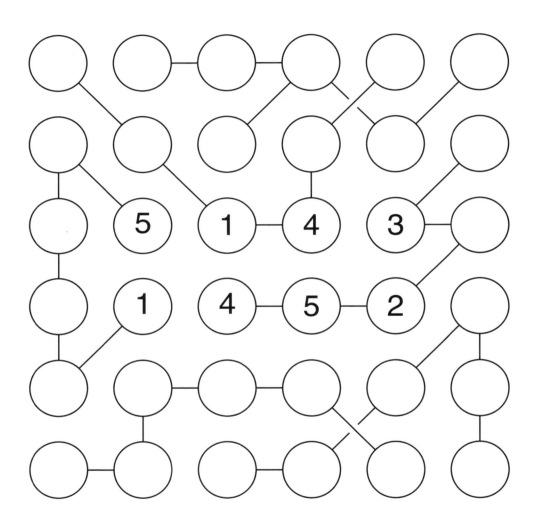

Answer on page 394.

LogiNumber

Determine the values of the variables below using 2 rules: Each variable is no greater than the numbers of variables in the puzzle; none of the variables are equal to each other. Use the grid to help keep track of possible solutions.

$$B - F = 4 - G$$
$$G + E + B = 14$$
$$G + E = C$$
$$F + D = H$$

	1	2	3	4	5	6	7	8
A								
B								
C								
D								
E								
F								
G								
H								

Answer on page 394.

Code-duku

Solve this puzzle just as you would a sudoku. Use deductive logic to complete the grid so that each row, column, and 3-by-3 box contains the letters from the word PONYTAILS.

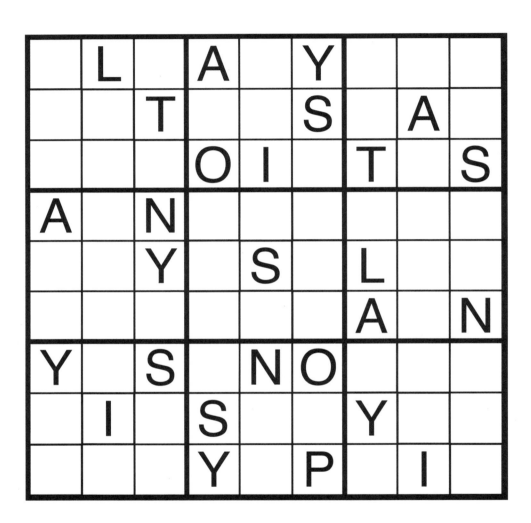

Answer on page 394.

Crypto-Logic

Each of the numbers in the sequence below represents a letter. Use the mathematical clues to determine which number stands for which letter and reveal the encrypted word.

Hint: Remember that a / indicates divided by, and that all sums in parentheses must be done first.

4 2 3 1 4 6 9 4 2 6

Clues:

The number of non-repeated values is equal to the value representing T.

The value representing T squared is found immediately preceding a value that is R multiplied by 4.

(R squared)+R=N

(N squared)-((R squared)-R)=I

(I squared)-10=$\frac{2}{3}$U

(U / 3)+N=S

S+1=G

Crypto-Logic

Each of the numbers in the sequence below represents a letter. Use the mathematical clues to determine which number stands for which letter and reveal the encrypted word.

Hint: Remember that a / indicates divided by, and that all sums in parentheses must be done first.

6 4 1 3

Clues:

2=F

4F=U

U/2=A

A-E=C

F/2=C

2E=P

Answers on page 394.

Cryptoku

Answer the clues below to fill in the grid and discover the 9 different letters used in each 3-by-3 box. Just like a standard crossword, answers read across and down; numbers in parenthesis indicate how many letters are in the solution. And, like a code-doku, each letter appears only once in each 3-by-3 box. When complete, the shaded squares will reveal a mystery word.

ACROSS

1. Personal pronoun (2)
2. Personal pronoun (fem.) (3)
3. Attempt (3)
4. Personal pronoun (masc.) (2)
5. "To be," resent tense (2)
6. Personal pronoun (masc.) (2)

DOWN

7. Wail (3)
8. Seventh music note (2)
9. Personal pronoun (2)
10. Group (3)
11. Second music note (2)
12. Pronoun (neutral) (2)

1	E	7		8 T			S	
I	R	S		M	Y		H	
	S			R			T	9
Y		I	T			2 S		E
	H			I		3	R	
10 S			Y	4	E	C		12
	I		11		S		Y	
T		M	E		H	R	5	S
	Y			M		6	E	

Answer on page 394.

Pray, But Keep Your Eyes Open

Cryptograms are messages in substitution code. Break the code to read the message. THE SMART CAT might become FVO QWGDF JGF if **F** is substituted for **T**, **V** for **H**, **O** for **E**, and so on.

DJOW QJO LTIITYWHCTOI NHLO QY HMCTNH QJOP

JHK QJO ATAUO HWK DO JHK QJO UHWK. QJOP

IHTK, "UOQ XI VCHP." DO NUYIOK YXC OPOI. DJOW

DO YVOWOK QJOL DO JHK QJO ATAUO HWK QJOP

JHK QJO UHWK.

                           –ATIJYV KOILYWK QXQX

Mastermind

The goal of this puzzle is to replace the question marks with a correct sequence of numbers. The numbers you need for the answer are contained in the rows above the question marks. Follow these 2 guides: A black dot indicates that a number needed for the solution is in that row and in the correct position; a white dot means that a number needed for the solution is in that row but in the wrong position. Numbers do not appear more than once in the solution, and the solution never begins with 0.

3	0	1	8	5	○ ○ ○
9	7	2	4	3	● ●
8	3	5	2	0	● ○
1	0	9	4	6	● ●
5	6	7	9	4	○ ○ ○
?	?	?	?	?	

Answers on page 394.

Crazy Calculator

The digits on this calculator don't seem to be working properly. It seems like some wires are crossed, causing 2 problems. If one segment of a pair is supposed to illuminate, its opposite piece will instead; if both segments of a pair are supposed to be illuminated, neither will. Can you identify the faulty pairs and solve the multiplication problem?

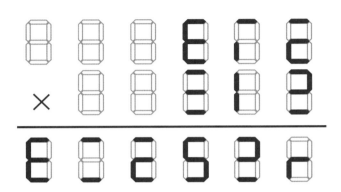

No Extra Charge for Groaners

Cryptograms are messages in substitution code. Break the code to read the message. THE SMART CAT might become FVO QWGDF JGF if **F** is substituted for **T**, **V** for **H**, **O** for **E**, and so on.

WENDVQBT: **LOMV'D VON AQZZNFNTPN SNVLNNT YMDONA RBVMVBND MTA RNM DBER?**

MTDLNF: **MTKBTN PMT YMDO RBVMVBND.**

Answers on page 395.

Acrostic Anagram

Unscramble the words below, then transfer the corresponding letters to the grid. A black square indicates the end of a word. When you're finished, you'll be rewarded with a quote by Voltaire.

A. A M A T A G E M A L S
   50 75 30 45 60 19 1 62 25 65 52

B. E N O N F S I N M E C T
   49 43 12 72 11 54 7 78 48 69 56 42

C. D O N N G H I U
   22 55 18 44 17 58 3 66

D. E H R E W N V E
   21 26 70 59 10 15 2 36

E. H E U R C I M B
   61 9 27 73 41 47 39 24

F. B D U Y A I L
   67 51 71 14 64 20 28

G. A E T H H T O C O
   8 40 74 6 76 33 29 4 53

H. V A N I C L I I
   38 77 34 68 31 16 5 63

I. Y O A I H D L
   57 23 32 37 13 35 46

1 A	2 D	3 C		4 G	5 H	6 G	7 B		8 G	9 E	10 D		11 B	12 B	13 I	14 F	15 D	16 H	17 C
18 C	19 A	20 F		21 D	22 C	23 I	24 E		25 A	26 D	27 E	28 F		29 G	30 A	31 H	32 I		33 G
34 H	35 I	36 D	37 I		38 H	39 E	40 G	41 E	42 B		43 B	44 C	45 A	46 I		47 E	48 B	49 B	50 A	51 F
52 A	53 G		54 B	55 C	56 B	57 I	58 C	59 D	60 A		61 E	62 A	63 H		64 F	65 A		66 C	67 F
68 H	69 B	70 D	71 F		72 B	73 E	74 G	75 A		76 G	77 H	78 B						

Answers on page 395.

LogiNumber

Determine the values of the letters below using 2 rules: Each letter is no greater than the number of letters in the puzzle; none of the letters are equal to each other. Use the grid to help keep track of possible solutions.

$$C + D = A$$
$$D + A = B$$

	1	2	3	4
A				
B				
C				
D				

Christmas Dinner Fit for a King

Cryptograms are messages in substitution code. Break the code to read the fun fact. THE SMART CAT might become FVO QWGDF JGF if **F** is substituted for **T**, **V** for **H**, **O** for **E**, and so on.

ZW ISF PFHL 1213, MZWV UXSW XG FWVEHWY
XLYFLFY HQXKI ISLFF ISXKBHWY RHCXWB
(RSZRMFWB), H ISXKBHWY BHEIFY FFEB, GXKL
SKWYLFY SXVB, XWF SKWYLFY CXKWYB XG
HEDXWYB, HWY IOFWIP-GXKL RHBMB XG OZWF
GXL SZB RSLZBIDHB GFHBI.

Answers on page 395.

Code-duku

Solve this puzzle just as you would a sudoku. Use deductive logic to complete the grid so that each row, column, and 3-by-3 box contains the letters from the word PITCHFORK.

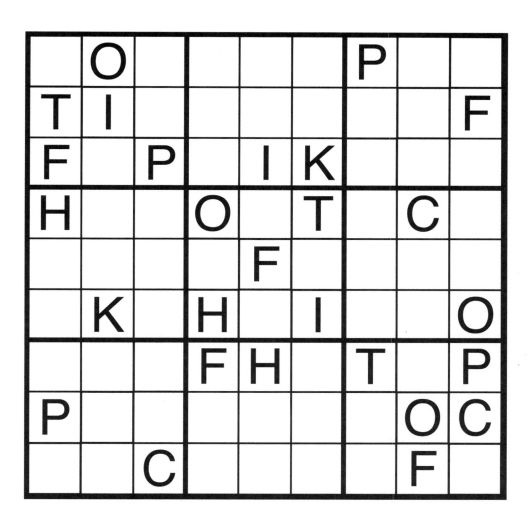

Answer on page 395.

Cryptoku

Answer the clues below to fill in the grid and discover the 9 different letters used in each 3-by-3 box. Just like a standard crossword, answers read across and down; numbers in parenthesis indicate how many letters are in the solution. And, like a code-doku, each letter appears only once in each 3-by-3 box. When complete, the shaded squares will reveal something you might drink.

ACROSS

1. Monkey (3)
2. Gratuity (3)
3. Safety ____ (3)
4. ____, the lion (3)
5. Short sleep (3)

DOWN

6. For shame (3)
7. To be ill (3)
8. Negative (2)
9. African carnivore (4)
10. Santa's helper (3)

Answer on page 395.

Royal Fellows

The letters in the word MAJESTY can be found in boxes 2, 4, 6, 11, 16, 21, 24, but not necessarily in that order. Similarly, the letters in the other medieval titles listed can be found in the boxes indicated. Your task is to insert all the letters into the grid. If you do this correctly, the name of 1 more title will be revealed in the shaded squares.

Hint: Compare DUKE and KING to get the value of K, then KING to GENTLEFOLK to get the value of I.

BARON 3, 5, 11, 19, 20

CROWN PRINCE 2, 3, 5, 8, 10, 14, 18, 20

CZAR 5, 11, 15, 18

DUKE 2, 9, 12, 13

EMPEROR 2, 5, 10, 16, 20

GENTLEFOLK 1, 2, 3, 4, 13, 17, 20, 22

KING 1, 3, 8, 13

KNIGHT 1, 3, 4, 8, 13, 25

MAJESTY 2, 4, 6, 11, 16, 21, 24

MARQUIS 5, 8, 11, 12, 16, 23, 24

NOBLEMAN 2, 3, 11, 16, 19, 20, 22

PHARAOH 5, 10, 11, 20, 25

REX 2, 5, 26

ROYALTY 4, 5, 6, 11, 20, 22

VISCOUNT 3, 4, 7, 8, 12, 18, 20, 24

1	2	3	4	5	6	7	8	9	10	11	12	13

14	15	16	17	18	19	20	21	22	23	24	25	26

Answer on page 395.

Code and Ciphers

Every word listed is contained within the group of letters. Words can be found in a straight line horizontally, vertically, or diagonally. They may be read either forward or backward.

ALGORITHM

BLOCK

CAESAR SHIFT

CODE

CIPHERTEXT

CRYPTANALYST

CRYPTOGRAM

DECRYPTION

ENCRYPTION

HIDDEN

KEY

PLAINTEXT

STREAM

SUBSTITUTION

TRANSPOSITION

VIGENÈRE

```
S  U  B  S  T  I  T  U  T  I  O  N  F  P  N
G  I  C  R  Y  P  T  A  N  A  L  Y  S  T  O
C  N  I  R  U  Y  O  J  N  K  C  Q  Q  N  I
A  O  P  Z  E  B  Q  E  F  S  C  V  Q  Z  T
E  I  H  K  D  L  C  Z  T  M  N  O  P  W  P
S  T  E  M  Q  R  B  R  H  M  U  L  L  U  Y
A  I  R  N  G  V  E  T  A  P  A  X  H  B  R
R  S  T  H  C  A  I  R  H  I  D  D  E  N  C
S  O  E  X  M  R  G  G  N  L  J  R  N  L  E
H  P  X  Q  O  O  Y  T  E  B  U  U  S  Z  D
I  S  T  G  T  F  E  P  S  N  P  Q  M  C  C
F  N  L  P  H  X  Q  N  T  L  È  M  K  O  P
T  A  Y  Q  T  B  N  Q  E  I  T  R  D  X  G
J  R  M  L  A  J  C  Z  U  S  O  E  E  Z  G
C  T  A  Z  U  M  X  D  Q  P  M  N  B  E  L
```

Answers on page 395.

Find the Codebreakers

ACROSS

1. WWII cipher machine
7. Early computer that weighed 30 tons
12. Lament
13. Orange Crush competitor
14. Dwarf tree sheltering a secret group?
15. Midterms and finals
16. Slaughter of baseball
17. Shasta and Hood, e.g.
19. Prefix meaning "self"
20. "Spring forward" letters
21. "Yeah, right!"
22. "Green Gables" girl
23. People held in custody
25. Jot down reminders
28. Astronaut Shepard
29. Blog feed letters
30. Cavs, on a scoreboard
33. RR stop
34. Escort to a seat, slangily
35. Dry as a desert
36. Lays into
38. Secret group in a condition that's far from secure?
40. In a huff
41. International finance coalition
42. Sassafras quartet
43. Ones having a bite

DOWN

1. Drew back, as the tide
2. Bright aquarium fish
3. "___ making this up!"
4. Former CIA director Porter ___
5. Billy goat's bleat
6. Disney cartoonists
7. Immature newts
8. Scot's "no"
9. Secret group in a nutty condition?
10. Get in sync
11. Social classes
18. "Wow, amazing—congrats!"
21. Farm biddy
22. The A of Q&A: Abbr.
23. Lion's retreat
24. What -y becomes, in plurals
25. Five iron
26. Church platforms
27. Secret group found in a midwestern state?
30. Desire strongly
31. One with a long sentence
32. Blissful settings
34. Sporty trucks, for short
35. At ___ time (prearranged)
37. Chowed down
39. Secret codebreaking agency hidden in four words in this puzzle

184

Answers on page 395.

Before Man

The letters in the word JOURNEY can be found in boxes 6, 7, 8, 15, 21, 22, and 24 but not necessarily in that order. Similarly, the letters in the other words listed can be found in the boxes indicated. Your task is to insert all the letters into the grid. If you do this correctly, the name of 1 more phrase will be revealed in the shaded squares.

Hint: Compare ASSEMBLY and BEST to get the value of T, then BEST to STRAIGHT to get the value of S.

ASSEMBLY 1, 2, 3, 5, 6, 15, 23

BEST 3, 4, 6, 23

CAVALRY 1, 2, 12, 15, 16, 22

FELLOW 1, 6, 13, 19, 24

FIRE 6, 9, 19, 22

JAZZ 2, 18, 21

JOURNEY 6, 7, 8, 15, 21, 22, 24

MARRIED 2, 5, 6, 9, 10, 22

QUARRY 2, 8, 11, 15, 22

RIGHTHAND 2, 4, 7, 9, 10, 17, 22, 25

STRAIGHT 2, 3, 4, 9, 17, 22, 25

TAX 2, 4, 20

UPPERCLASS 1, 2, 3, 6, 8, 12, 22, 26

WORKING 7, 9, 13, 14, 22, 24, 25

1	2	3	4	5	6	7	8	9	10	11	12	13

14	15	16	17	18	19	20	21	22	23	24	25	26

Answer on page 396.

Toppers

The letters in the word BOWLER can be found in boxes 6, 7, 9, 11, 15, and 19, but not necessarily in that order. Similarly, the letters in the other hats listed can be found in the boxes indicated. Your task is to insert all the letters into the grid. If you do this correctly, the shaded boxes will spell out the theme of this puzzle.

Hint: Compare STETSON and STOVEPIPE to get the value of N, then STETSON to DERBY to get the value of E.

Unused letter: Q

BALMORAL 2, 6, 7, 8, 15, 19

BILLYCOCK 6, 12, 15, 17, 19, 24, 25

BOWLER 6, 7, 9, 11, 15, 19

COXCOMB 6, 8, 12, 16, 19

DERBY 7, 9, 17, 19, 22

FEDORA 2, 5, 6, 7, 9, 22

FEZ 5, 9, 14

HELMET 1, 3, 8, 9, 15

HOMBURG 1, 6, 7, 8, 18, 19, 20

JOCKEY CAP 2, 6, 9, 12, 13, 17, 21, 25

PORKPIE 6, 7, 9, 13, 24, 25

STETSON 3, 4, 6, 9, 10

STOVEPIPE 3, 4, 6, 9, 13, 23, 24

YARMULKE 2, 7, 8, 9, 15, 17, 20, 25

1	2	3	4	5	6	7	8	9	10	11	12	13

14	15	16	17	18	19	20	21	22	23	24	25	26
												Q

Answer on page 396.

Codeword

The letters of the alphabet are hidden in code: Each is represented by a random number from 1 through 26. With the letters already given, complete the crossword puzzle with English words and break the code.

	18		26		24		4		10		19	
18	13	24	20	12	15		7	14	7	17	16	23
	20		15		10		5		20		21	
16	19	15	18		7	24	24	16	8	7	23	25
			25		22		18		9		25	
3	20	13	5	25	15	24		25	5	6	5	7
	13		16		19		19		23		14	
18	9	16	23	15		21	15	5	8	9	15	19
	15		23		25		12		18			
12	7	11	7	10	5	15	24		25	15	18	25
	11		5		10		1		16		2	
3	7	24	24	15	19		13	5	12	23	5	12
	10		15		15		25		2		19	

A B C D E F G H I J K L M N O P Q R S T U V W X Y Z

1	2	3	4	5	6	7	8	9	10	11	12	13
Y							G		L			

14	15	16	17	18	19	20	21	22	23	24	25	26
		O				U						

Answers on page 396.

Flowers

The letters in AZALEA can be found in boxes 8, 13, 14, and 22 but not necessarily in that order. Similarly, the letters in all the other types of flowers can be found in the boxes indicated. Your task is to insert all the letters of the alphabet into the boxes. If you do this correctly, the shaded cells will reveal the name of other types of flowers.

Hint: Compare PEONY and TULIP to get the value of P, then TULIP and MYRTLE for the value of T.

AZALEA: 8, 13, 14, 22

BUTTERCUP: 2, 3, 11, 13, 15, 19, 21

CHRYSANTHEMUM: 2, 3, 4, 11, 12, 13, 14, 17, 19, 20, 24

DAFFODIL: 1, 5, 6, 14, 22, 25

FOXGLOVE: 1, 9, 13, 22, 23, 25, 26

GLOXINIA: 1, 5, 9, 14, 17, 22, 23

HONEYSUCKLE: 1, 3, 4, 12, 13, 16, 17, 19, 20, 22

JASMINE: 5, 7, 12, 13, 14, 17, 24

JONQUIL: 1, 5, 7, 17, 18, 19, 22

MYRTLE: 2, 11, 13, 20, 22, 24

PEONY: 1, 13, 17, 20, 21

SMILAX: 5, 9, 12, 14, 22, 24

TULIP: 5, 11, 19, 21, 22

WISTERIA: 2, 5, 10, 11, 12, 13, 14

ZINNIA: 5, 8, 14, 17

1	2	3	4	5	6	7	8	9	10	11	12	13

14	15	16	17	18	19	20	21	22	23	24	25	26

Answer on page 396.

Codeword

The letters of the alphabet are hidden in code: Each is represented by a random number from 1 through 26. With the letters already given, complete the crossword puzzle with English words and break the code.

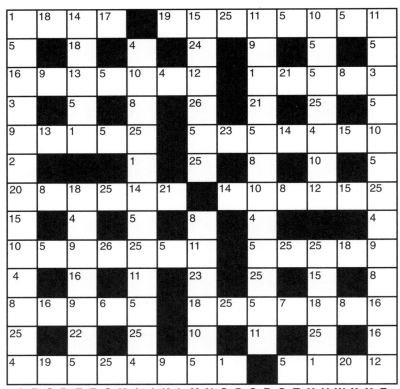

1	2	3	4	5	6	7	8	9	10	11	12	13
										D		

14	15	16	17	18	19	20	21	22	23	24	25	26
				U							N	G

Answers on page 396.

Cryptoku

Answer the clues below to fill in the grid and discover the 6 different letters used in each 3-by-2 box. Just like a standard crossword, answers read across and down; numbers in parenthesis indicate how many letters are in the solution. And, like a code-doku, each letter appears only once in each 3-by-2 box. When complete, the shaded squares will reveal a mystery word.

ACROSS

1. Period (3)
2. Chain pull (3)
3. Depict (4)

DOWN

4. Armed conflict (3)
5. Fishing device (3)

	T		D		R
				W	
		1		T	
2	O			5	
3		A			T
O	W		R		A

Answer on page 396.

Geometry

The letters in the word PRISM can be found in boxes 1, 4, 10, 12, and 22, but not necessarily in that order. Similarly, the letters in the other geometric terms listed can be found in the boxes indicated. Your task is to insert all the letters into the grid. If you do this correctly, the shaded squares will reveal what all these terms have in common.

Hint: Compare OVAL and CIRCLE to get the value of L, then OVAL to TRAPEZOID to get the value of V.

Unused letters: F and J

CIRCLE: 5, 9, 12, 20, 22

CONE: 5, 15, 20, 21

CUBE: 5, 13, 14, 20

DISK: 1, 11, 12, 18

HEXAGON: 2, 3, 5, 7, 15, 17, 21

OVAL: 3, 6, 9, 15

PRISM: 1, 4, 10, 12, 22

PYRAMID: 3, 4, 10, 12, 18, 22, 23

RHOMBUS: 1, 2, 10, 13, 14, 15, 22

SPHERE: 1, 2, 4, 5, 22

SQUARE: 1, 3, 5, 13, 19, 22

TRAPEZOID: 3, 4, 5, 8, 12, 15, 16, 18, 22

TRIANGLE: 3, 5, 9, 12, 16, 17, 21, 22

WHEEL: 2, 5, 9, 24

1	2	3	4	5	6	7	8	9	10	11	12	13

14	15	16	17	18	19	20	21	22	23	24	25	26
											F	J

Answer on page 396.

Slingin' the Slang

Cryptograms are messages in substitution code. Break the code to read the message. THE SMART CAT might become FVO QWGDF JGF if **F** is substituted for **T**, **V** for **H**, **O** for **E**, and so on.

MI YTR LSKSNOEK FSNKH SO JKPIC, LSNIGNRPH MJ
PI "PNXPIJPJ FRHHMIC LPXR," P NPLLSSI GSIR MJ P
"YRIIRJJRR YSSYTQMLX," PIH LTRFMIC YSGPLLS MJ
"FRJY WMNCMIMP LSKRJKPF."

Loopy Laws

Cryptograms are messages in substitution code. Break the code to read the message. THE SMART CAT might become FVO QWGDF JGF if **F** is substituted for **T**, **V** for **H**, **O** for **E**, and so on.

FDDAOUJSI KA OJDG WQJKG JS "EAP DFS ILK
FOOLWKLU VAO KGFK," JK'W JXXLIFX KA VFXX
FWXLLR JS F DGLLWL VFDKAOE JS WAPKG UFHAKF.

Decipher This!

ACROSS

1. Plant supports
6. Jackrabbits
11. Spooky
12. "___ Mio" (popular opera aria)
13. PNRFNE FUVSG (ROT-13 can help you decode it. Stumped? Ask Wikipedia about ROT-13.)
15. Far from fresh
16. Physicians, for short
19. Bert and Ernie's street
23. In the style of
24. Online chuckle
25. More chuckles
26. Bawl out
28. The "m" in E = mc squared
29. "Flowers in the ___" (V. C. Andrews best seller)
31. PELCGBTENCU (likewise!)
37. Birds flying in V's
38. Western, in slang
39. Inspector Appleby's creator Michael
40. Knot again

DOWN

1. "Hold on a ___!"
2. Brewed beverage
3. Before, to a poet
4. Uses an atomizer
5. Blacken, as a steak
6. Low-cost lodging
7. Embers, eventually
8. King, in France
9. Santa's helper
10. Harden, as concrete
14. Italian rice dish
16. It breaks at dawn
17. Bullring cheer
18. Coolidge, to friends
20. Cry of insight
21. Advanced degs.
22. Serpentine curve
24. Former's opposite
27. Run out, as a subscription
28. Jazz legend Carmen
30. Dr. Frankenstein's helper
31. Special effects used in "Avatar," e.g.
32. Stimpy's canine pal
33. Longing for Japanese money?
34. Big inits. in long distance
35. Noted architect I.M. ___
36. Charlemagne's realm: Abbr.

Answers on page 396.

Codeword

The letters of the alphabet are hidden in code: Each is represented by a random number from 1 through 26. With the letters already given, complete the crossword puzzle with English words and break the code.

A B C D E F G H I J K L M N O P Q R S T U V W X Y Z

1	2	3	4	5	6	7	8	9	10	11	12	13
B						H	R					

14	15	16	17	18	19	20	21	22	23	24	25	26
	U										S	

Answers on page 396.

What's On?

The letters in the word FRASIER can be found in boxes 4, 6, 7, 11, 18, and 24, but not necessarily in that order. Similarly, the letters in the other names listed can be found in the boxes indicated. Your task is to insert all the letters into the grid. If you do this correctly, the name of 1 [more thing] will be revealed in the shaded squares.

Hint: Compare FRASIER and PARIS to get the value of P, then PARIS to MAVERICK to get the value of S.

Unused letter: Q

BECKER 6, 15, 18, 19, 25

COLUMBO 5, 14, 15, 16, 23, 25

FRASIER 4, 6, 7, 11, 18, 24

GIDGET 1, 6, 8, 11, 12

HAZEL 4, 6, 10 17, 23

KOJAK 4, 14, 19, 20

MANNIX 3, 4, 5, 9, 11

MATLOCK 1, 4, 5, 14, 15, 19, 23

MAUDE 4, 5, 6, 12, 16

MAVERICK 2, 4, 5, 6, 11, 15, 18, 19

NEWHART 1, 3, 4, 6, 17, 18, 21

PARIS 4, 7, 11, 13, 18

PHYLLIS 7, 11, 13, 17, 22, 23

ROSEANNE 3, 4, 6, 7, 14, 18

SEINFELD 3, 6, 7, 11, 12, 23, 24

1	2	3	4	5	6	7	8	9	10	11	12	13
14	15	16	17	18	19	20	21	22	23	24	25	26
												Q

Answer on page 396.

Women

The letters in ACTRESS can be found in boxes 3, 5, 6, 9, 18, and 19 but not necessarily in that order. Similarly, the letters in all the other types of women names can be found in the boxes indicated. Your task is to insert all the letters of the alphabet into the boxes. If you do this correctly, the shaded cells will reveal the name of another type of women.

Hint: Compare MAJORETTE and DAME to get the value of D, then GRANNY to LADY to get the value of L.

ACTRESS: 3, 5, 6, 9, 18, 19

BARONESS: 3, 5, 6, 13, 17, 19, 22

CHICK: 2, 18, 20, 21

CZARINA: 2, 3, 6, 13, 18, 26

DAME: 6, 8, 12, 19

GRANNY: 1, 3, 6, 13, 24

HOUSEWIFE: 2, 5, 10, 11, 14, 19, 20, 22

LADY: 4, 6, 8, 24

MAJORETTE: 3, 6, 9, 12, 15, 19, 22

PRINCESS: 2, 3, 5, 13, 18, 19, 23

QUEEN: 10, 13, 16, 19

VIRAGO: 1, 2, 3, 6, 22, 25

VIXEN: 2, 7, 13, 19, 25

WOMAN: 6, 11, 12, 13, 22

1	2	3	4	5	6	7	8	9	10	11	12	13

14	15	16	17	18	19	20	21	22	23	24	25	26

Answer on page 397.

An Ancient True Crime

Cryptograms are messages in substitution code. Break the code to read the message. THE SMART CAT might become FVO QWGDF JGF if **F** is substituted for **T**, **V** for **H**, **O** for **E**, and so on.

UYBBLN UDKGYLK CYLC YG 1573, ZPKGLC DO OSL
NODAL. D SLKEYO, SL RDN DWWPNLC HM ZLYGU D
RLKLRHBM—NILWYMYWDBBV, HM AYBBYGU DGC
LDOYGU MHPK WSYBCKLG. SL BYQLC YG MKDGWL.

Lewis Hutchinson

Cryptograms are messages in substitution code. Break the code to read the message. THE SMART CAT might become FVO QWGDF JGF if **F** is substituted for **T**, **V** for **H**, **O** for **E**, and so on.

OGAN PAHHVL TKN BFLE AE NDFOHKEQ BRO CFSVQ
OF MKCKADK, TGVLV GV NVO RI KE VNOKOV
DKHHVQ VQAEBRLZG DKNOHV. OLKSVHVLN TGF
KIILFKDGVQ OGV DKNOHV OFF DHFNVHX OVEQVQ
OF QANKIIVKL. GV LVIFLOVQHX OFNNVQ GAN
SADOACN AEOF K NAEPGFHV. GV TKN DKHHVQ
OGV CKQ CKNOVL FL OGV CKQ QFDOFL FW
VQAEBRLZG. GV VSVEORKHHX NGFO K NFHQAVL
TGF GKQ BVVE NVEO OF DKIORLV GAC. GV OGVE
OLAVQ OF WHVV OGV KLVK, BRO TKN DKRZGO,
OLAVQ, KEQ GKEZVQ.

Answers on page 397.

Interception

You've intercepted a message that is meant to reveal a location for an upcoming meeting between two criminal masterminds. The only problem is, the message shows many place names. Can you figure out the right location?

ABUJA
BUDAPEST
ACCRA
DHAKA
JAKARTA
TRIPOLI
SEOUL
ASTANA
ATHENS

Everybody and His Brother

Cryptograms are messages in substitution code. Break the code to read the message. THE SMART CAT might become FVO QWGDF JGF if **F** is substituted for **T**, **V** for **H**, **O** for **E**, and so on.

PZLJH ZDHFILJADKH VKK AVPWKM LDK BPEJNI
MKLKZLFOK FY LDK 1962 *"EJOFK IDKHVJZR DJVEKI
PYM LDK MKPMVW YKZRVPZK"*. FY 1970, VKK
AVPWKM P DJVEKI PCPFY—IDKHVJZR'I UHJLDKH
EWZHJBL, FY LDK EJOFK *"LDK AHFOPLK VFBK JB
IDKHVJZR DJVEKI"*. DK DPM PVIJ AVPWKM IFH
DKYHW UPIRKHOFVVK FY PY KPHVFKH BFVE
PMPALKM BHJE *"LDK DJNYM JB LDK UPIRKHOFVVKI"*.

Answers on page 397.

Where It's At

The letters in BAILIWICK can be found in boxes 3, 5, 8, 14, 20, 21, and 24, but not necessarily in that order. Similarly, the letters in all these words can be found in the boxes indicated. Your task is to insert all the letters of the alphabet into the boxes. If you do this correctly, the shaded cells will reveal another term.

Hint: Compare ENVIRONS and REGION to get the value of G, then REGION to PRECINCT to get the value of O.

Unused letters: X

BAILIWICK: 3, 5, 8, 14, 20, 21, 24

BOROUGH: 6, 9, 12, 14, 16, 25

DISTRICT: 1, 3, 4, 5, 12, 23

DOMAIN: 5, 6, 7, 8, 11, 23

ENVIRONS: 1, 2, 5, 6, 7, 12, 15

FIELD: 2, 5, 17, 20, 23

JURISDICTION: 1, 3, 4, 5, 6, 7, 9, 12, 22, 23

PRECINCT: 2, 3, 4, 5, 7, 12, 18

QUARTER: 2, 4, 8, 9, 12, 13

REGION: 2, 5, 6, 7, 12, 25

TERRITORY: 2, 4, 5, 6, 10, 12

TOWNSHIP: 1, 4, 5, 6, 7, 16, 18, 21

WARD: 8, 12, 21, 23

ZONE: 2, 6, 7, 19

1	2	3	4	5	6	7	8	9	10	11	12	13

14	15	16	17	18	19	20	21	22	23	24	25	26
												X

Answer on page 397.

Add-a-Letter

This puzzle is an anagram with a twist: Each word or phrase below is missing the same letter. Discover the missing letter, then unscramble. All the "before" AND "after" words can be found in the grid. They may be read either forward or backward.

BUFFS ON	IN HOPE	PET ME
CERTAIN TO	LED UP	PI CAKE
CLIP TIE	LET TIE	PIE DOER
COBRA	LOVE FOG	PIED TEE
DENIES	MEAN IRE	RAN HAT
DO BOLO	MEETER	RUE FIT
EAT IF	MOO BOB	SEA GILA
EEL CUD	MUM AIM	SEEN IT
ELF OR	NO DUPE	SIR LEI
FIEF AD	OUTED	TIE RUM
GO YEN	PAD OAR	UTTERED
HA GONE	PEA ELM	YEA NIT
HEN CAGE	PEN LICE	
IF ABLE	PERT CEDE	

```
S E I N E D J T B Y X I N E O H P A C E O V K P A
X W M Q W M I P D A F F I X E D F W N P Q U I N W
D A F E I F B M E R Z V K D E T P R E C X E T B O
E O M A E O K E R N O G A X E H T R N R D H U E Z
Z S M U X T M X E E X A K C I P O E Y O R F N X D
G U R C R E E E T T E L P M A X E Y E A F H M P F
M R A I R E R R T Y U A O E I T C R X S O E I E I
K R A T X C D N U O P X E D X E I A O P C N X D X
N B X D Q I Z W S I B I E I D D N N W M X C T I A
K E F O A L L Z X L Y E S D Y U E D T A B A U T T
A M Y B B N W E O Y X S E H O L P O E E S G R E E
F R L O V E F O G P Q J E A G C L Z X R N E E W O
U M B L G P D N L P A R A D O X E E T U U Q C F C
E U M O Y Q E I E G N A H C X E X V I T F T P P X
L M E F C G C O T N I A T R E C A O L X F Z X A L
F I D U Y I E K A C I P G M Z S E L E I B F T E U
O X Z X T G B M Q F R Y U Y I E I G I F O I I S T
R A O D A P E L L P S R E R M P T X E G X T N E B
E M T E P L Z E R E E A L H O O T O F E A A E X D
K T R U B E X A M I N E R E O H E F I O T E E E N
U J D A X O N E T I I O A B B N L E X L O D S D O
R E F U R H Q P T Q A L G N O I T C A R T X E N D
L I B S A P M E A N I R E A B C X O B M O O B I U
M M X T V E P E R T C E D E H D X E L P U D F A P
C L I P T I E Y D A N X I E T Y C U E D U C L E E
```

Answers on page 397.

Codeword

The letters of the alphabet are hidden in code: Each is represented by random numbers from 1 through 26. With the letters already given, complete the crossword puzzle with English words and break the code.

1	2	3	4	5	6	7	8	9	10	11	12	13

14	15	16	17	18	19	20	21	22	23	24	25	26
			D					E	Y			

Answers on page 397.

An Alphabetical Phrase

Cryptograms are messages in substitution code. Break the code to read the message. THE SMART CAT might become FVO QWGDF JGF if **F** is substituted for **T**, **V** for **H**, **O** for **E**, and so on.

B EBANIBZ RK B KJAMJAFJ MPBM RAFXOHJK BXX XJMMJIK CL MPJ BXEPBDJM. ZCKM EJCEXJ PBQJ PJBIH MPJ KJAMJAFJ, "MPJ GORFV DICSA LCU TOZEK CQJI MPJ XBYW HCN."

A Mysterious Event

Cryptograms are messages in substitution code. Break the code to read the message. THE SMART CAT might become FVO QWGDF JGF if **F** is substituted for **T**, **V** for **H**, **O** for **E**, and so on.

SCI YITO 1911 DKVLGVIJ T KLSTPGI RTQI LA TOS SCIAS—SCI HLKT GDQT WTQ QSLGIK AOLH SCI GLUVOI PY TK IHMGLYII. CI WTQ RTUBCS SWL YITOQ GTSIO TKJ SCI MTDKSDKB WTQ OISUOKIJ SL DSQ CLHI.

A Surprising Viewpoint

Cryptograms are messages in substitution code. Break the code to read the message. THE SMART CAT might become FVO QWGDF JGF if **F** is substituted for **T**, **V** for **H**, **O** for **E**, and so on. Bonus: Who is the speaker, and which story is the source of the quote?

"R FCAKRHJI MPBM B ZBA'K DIBRA CIRNRABXXW RK
XRVJ B XRMMXJ JZEMW BMMRF, BAH WCO PBQJ MC
KMCFV RM SRMP KOFP LOIARMOIJ BK WCO FPCCKJ.
B LCCX MBVJK RA BXX MPJ XOZDJI CL JQJIW KCIM
MPBM PJ FCZJK BFICKK, KC MPBM MPJ VACSXJHNJ
SPRFP ZRNPM DJ OKJLOX MC PRZ NJMK FICSHJH COM,
CI BM DJKM RK TOZDXJH OE SRMP B XCM CL CMPJI
MPRANK KC MPBM PJ PBK B HRLLRFOXMW RA XBWRAN
PRK PBAHK OECA RM. ACS MPJ KVRXLOX SCIVZBA RK
QJIW FBIJLOX RAHJJH BK MC SPBM PJ MBVJK RAMC
PRK DIBRA-BMMRF. PJ SRXX PBQJ ACMPRAN DOM MPJ
MCCXK SPRFP ZBW PJXE PRZ RA HCRAN PRK SCIV, DOM
CL MPJKJ PJ PBK B XBINJ BKKCIMZJAM, BAH BXX RA
MPJ ZCKM EJILJFM CIHJI. RM RK B ZRKMBVJ MC MPRAV
MPBM MPBM XRMMXJ ICCZ PBK JXBKMRF SBXXK BAH
FBA HRKMJAH MC BAW JUMJAM. HJEJAH OECA RM
MPJIJ FCZJK B MRZJ SPJA LCI JQJIW BHHRMRCA CL
VACSXJHNJ WCO LCINJM KCZJMPRAN MPBM WCO VAJS
DJLCIJ. RM RK CL MPJ PRNPJKM RZECIMBAFJ, MPJIJLCIJ,
ACM MC PBQJ OKJXJKK LBFMK JXDCSRAN COM MPJ
OKJLOX CAJK."

Answer on page 398.

Perfection

Cryptograms are messages in substitution code. Break the code to read the message. THE SMART CAT might become FVO QWGDF JGF if **F** is substituted for **T**, **V** for **H**, **O** for **E**, and so on.

B CBE EBCZV DFMZHS NLWYYBLV TBM FEZ FG OSZ
AZNZEVBLX DZTZA OSWZRZM FG SWM BNZ. WE 1913,
SZ MOFAZ B GBCFQM MOLWEN FG HLZPWFQM HZBLAM
GLFC B MZBAZV JFU TSWAZ OSZX TZLZ WE OLBEMWO.
BVVWEN WEMQAO OF WEDQLX, SZ LZHABPZV OSZ
HZBLAM TWOS MQNBL PQJZM JZGFLZ MZBAWEN OSZ
JFU BEV AZBRWEN OSZ OSZGO OF JZ VWMPFRZLZV.

Han van Meegeren

Cryptograms are messages in substitution code. Break the code to read the message. THE SMART CAT might become FVO QWGDF JGF if **F** is substituted for **T**, **V** for **H**, **O** for **E**, and so on.

PBCO MQPZB KWCIPRN DRAWI WO WI WNPCOP JT
JNCACIWG UJNF, AWCICIA OJHR OQZZROO. BJURSRN,
BCO UJNF UWO OJHRPCHRO ZNCPCLQRM WO
MRNCSWPCSR WIM QIJNCACIWG. BR RSRIPQWGGX
PQNIRM PJ TJNARNCRO, CIZGQMCIA JT MQPZB KWCIPRN
EJBWIIRO SRNHRRN. MQNCIA UJNGM UWN CC, JIR JT
PBR TJNARN'O KWCIPCIAO RIMRM QK CI PBR BWIMO JT
IWYC BRNHWI AJNCIA. SWI HRRARNRI UWO WNNROPRM
WTPRN PBR UWN TJN ZJGGWDJNWPCJI UCPB PBR
RIRHX—QIPCG BR RVKGWCIRM PBWP BR BWMI'P OJGM
W NRWG SRNHRRN, DQP W TJNARNX. BR UWO ACSRI
W GROORN ORIPRIZR TJN TNWQM, PBJQAB BR MCRM
DRTJNR BR ORNSRM PCHR CI KNCOJI.

Answers on page 398.

Code-doku

Solve this puzzle just as you would a sudoku. Use deductive logic to complete the grid so that each row, column, and 3-by-3 box contains the letters from the words WRY NAVELS. When you have completed the puzzle, read the shaded squares from left to right and top to bottom to reveal a hidden message regarding something to do in New York City.

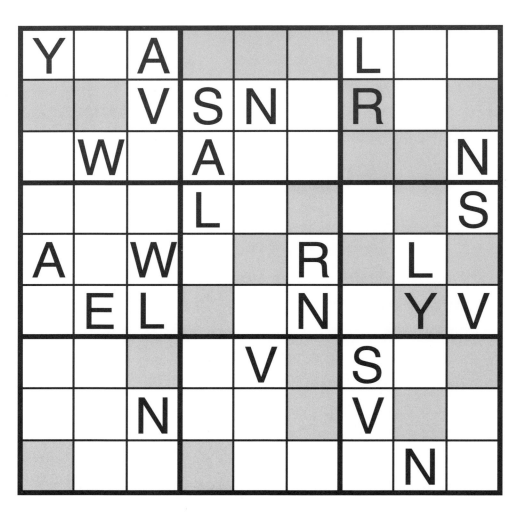

Hidden Message: _____

Answer on page 398.

Code-doku

Solve this puzzle just as you would a sudoku. Use deductive logic to complete the grid so that each row, column, and 3-by-3 box contains the letters from the words GIN RUM TEA. When you have completed the puzzle, read the shaded squares from left to right and top to bottom to form a refreshing beverage.

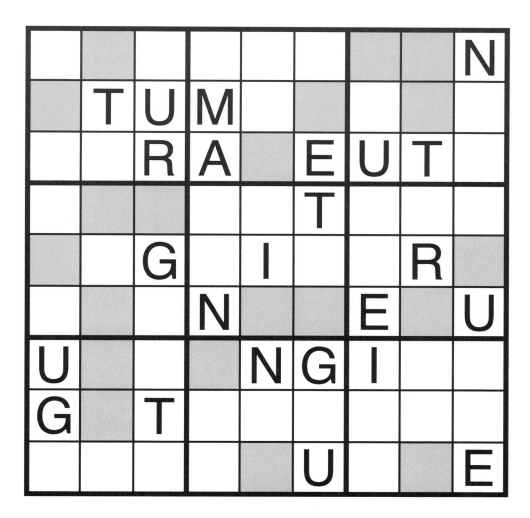

Hidden Message: _____

Answer on page 398.

Add-a-Letter

This puzzle is an anagram with a twist: Each word or phrase below is missing the same letter. Discover the missing letter, then unscramble. All the "before" AND "after" words can be found in the grid. They may be read either forward or backward.

APPENDER	IRON US
CAR ROD	MORE APT
CAREERS	OLD PIN
CARPET	PA COPRA
CART RACE	RENT ALL
CITE SCAM	SALT GRIT
COSMIC PAL	SOD INSET
CREATE	SOLO HIPPY
DIP LOSS	TAMEST MICA
EMIT SONG	TEAR WEED
ENTREAT	TIN DRAWING
EWES LOOM	TINY SECT
FOUL SIR	TRIM UP
IN MECCA	TUT FURL
INTO AIRS	YOU TRAIT

```
A T D U E C S S M O R E A P T T U T F U R L O D
R I I P K D S S V L O F W H O L E S O M E Y I Z
P X I N T O A I R S L N A A P P E N D E R A D F
O P R I L L T O W O O N S T A R L I G H T C S U
C Z M P T T H W U R D N E H E R P P A T D I V M
A E I G E P I R E W E S L O O M R D Z Q R M O E
P D R F A N I N R S L I P S H O D L Q P A T X F
P I R T H S T I Y P P I H O L O S O M C H S D S
T O E K H A T R R S S C H E M A T I C I C E Q O
E M Q N L I R H E E E H L X C E S T Q T R M T M
T U H L N G E O P A T C S M Q X C N N E O A E E
T S H G T Z G W U H T P T I L E I H H H I T S T
L R E S W C O S M I C P A L L C T T A T R F N H
U N I N I U I H I L Y A A H X P A S U N O R I I
F D I U O R R T R U J R O W C E M R W Y I L D N
H C H H M H U E T S H V Y R W T E O R S U C O G
T A C I P P S O T T V O T T P T H V C O J G S Q
U C R S C L H I N C U E E L H P T X P C D B O W
R C A T H M O E D T A C A R T R A C E T A E R C
T E E O E J P D R R K R E L T E M I T S O N G A
Y M S R A T P A W V H A A U T H O R I T Y T L R
B N E I T J I E R I T N Y H P O S O L I H P A P
U I R A E T E S R E E R A C C I T E S C A M A E
L J R N R D T I N D R A W I N G F O U L S I R T
```

Answers on page 399.

Add-a-Letter

This puzzle is an anagram with a twist: Each word or phrase below is missing the same letter. Discover the missing letter, then unscramble. All the "before" AND "after" words can be found in the grid. They may be read either forward or backward.

ACUTE DIN	LATRINE
ALTAR PRY	LET MAIM
ANT TAXI	MICE CONS
BAN BECK	MILE TREK
BAY NUT	NIXES NAP
CAB COT	OH NIL TZAR
CERTAIN DO	OUR DOT
CORN VINES	PALE CUP
CRIB TO	PERT TYPO
DARN PANGS	PIN PAT
DIM FIRE	POT PIES
FENCER	RAILING
ISSUER	SIP INTO
KEEP CROWD	SIR POPE
LASH TIP	SPORTIER

R Z I M F B L A S H T I P N O I T I S O P T N B Q M
E S P V C P G J X D D S M I L E T R E K D O A S V C
C C C L E T M A I M E T P R O T O T Y P E D I O S R
N S A I A X V X U N O I T A X A T C E X W R W S O Y
E H E L M L W R I L G D I R V T Z T P C P U N O R E
F O S Q U O X V A N C L B P T A A A O O A O D P K K
P R P Z T P N U N O F A Z H I L N N P Q C T R G L B
R I O Y N R O O J T K N F B O S V E Y E U A S A M Z
E Z R L O E O P C T I I T M I E C P C O T U E H T K
L O T C I Q C I I E X G M O R L J I J L E P R W O I
A N R H T T P R R A A I N S J B M Z A H D G I C C L
T T A L A U P P O E T R I P A T L E G B I K O N B O
I A Y F C N A O S F T O T N N L A T R I N E U O A M
O L A E U Y R P T S N S B I T B W G Z Y D V S W C E
N D L E D Y O U K S A E O H N I L T Z A R Y K O M T
O A K U E R N L N S C P J P G N I L I A R X J O X E
P E J I T Y X A J K P S J O E S G N A P N R A D R R
Y Z N I A U P O L A C E R T A I N D O L Y D Q P S E
T Q E B W D D A H C D O H N U H N H P E W X F E B I
T R U G R I T L I X M H P I P T N A Y O U B I C A F
R R N A M I E S I O P R O P Y M N O R N I P C K I I
E H G F P R O B O T I C G I O S X C E D T I F E S D
P O I S P B A C K B O N E S E S P B O O Q N X R S O
N R O C C A B O T I V X P X M E I G P I A P Q P U M
E H F V K U F V C R B Q I L E X D T D J V A H Y E D
E T A N I D R O O C F N B K D U D T E Y O T M E R S

Answers on page 399.

Festive Fare

The letters in CAKE can be found in boxes 11, 14, 20, and 21, but not necessarily in that order. Similarly, the letters in all the other words can be found in the boxes indicated. Your task is to insert all the letters of the alphabet into the boxes. If you do this correctly, the shaded cells will reveal another Christmas food item.

CAKE: 11, 14, 20, 21

CHORIZO: 1, 3, 6, 12, 14, 19

CRANBERRY SAUCE: 8, 9, 11, 14, 18, 19, 21, 22, 26

CUSTARD: 2, 8, 11, 14, 17, 18, 19

GATEAUX: 11, 16, 17, 18, 21, 24

HAM: 1, 11, 25

JELLY: 5, 21, 22, 23

MINCE PIES: 8, 9, 12, 14, 15, 21, 25

PLUM PUDDING: 2, 5, 9, 12, 15, 18, 24, 25

SQUASH: 1, 8, 11, 13, 18

STRAWBERRIES: 8, 10, 11, 12, 17, 19, 21, 26

STUFFING: 7, 8, 9, 12, 17, 18, 24

VEGETABLES: 4, 5, 8, 11, 17, 21, 24, 26

ZUCCHINI: 1, 6, 9, 12, 14, 18

1	2	3	4	5	6	7	8	9	10	11	12	13
14	15	16	17	18	19	20	21	22	23	24	25	26

Answer on page 399.

Cryptoku

Answer the clues below to fill in the grid and discover the 9 different letters used in each 3-by-3 box. Just like a standard crossword, answers read across and down; numbers in parenthesis indicate how many letters are in the solution. And, like a code-doku, each letter appears only once in each 3-by-3 box. When complete, the shaded squares will reveal a mystery word.

DOWN

1. First digit (3)
2. Have (3)
3. Two thousand pounds (3)
4. Geologic age (3)
5. In no way (3)

G		¹	Y					L
	L			T			Y	
	T					V	⁵	O
I	²		L		N			
				⁴				
	E		I		Y			
³		I				O		
	E		Y				V	
N			G					E

Answer on page 399.

Endearment

The letters in ANGEL can be found in boxes 1, 4, 8, 9, and 21 but not necessarily in that order. Similarly, the letters in all the other terms of endearment listed below can be found in the boxes indicated. Your task is to insert all the letters of the alphabet into the boxes. If you do this correctly, the shaded cells will reveal another loving nickname.

Hint: Compare SWEETIE and SWEETHEART to get the value of I, then DEAR to DARLING for the value of E.

Unused letters: J, Q, and Z

ANGEL: 1, 4, 8, 9, 21

BABYDOLL: 1, 2, 8, 11, 15, 18

BUTTERCUP: 4, 5, 10, 13, 14, 18, 22

DARLING: 1, 5, 8, 9, 11, 20, 21

DEAR: 4, 5, 8, 11

DUMPLING: 1, 9, 11, 12, 14, 20, 21, 22

FOXY LADY: 1, 2, 6, 8, 11, 15, 19

HONEYBUNCH: 2, 4, 10, 14, 15, 17, 18, 21

LAMBKIN: 1, 8, 12, 16, 18, 20, 21

LOVE OF MY LIFE: 1, 2, 3, 4, 12, 15, 19, 20

SNOOKUMS: 2, 7, 12, 14, 16, 21

SUGAR: 5, 7, 8, 9, 14

SWEETHEART: 4, 5, 7, 8, 13, 17, 23

SWEETIE: 4, 7, 13, 20, 23

TREASURE: 4, 5, 7, 8, 13, 14

1	2	3	4	5	6	7	8	9	10	11	12	13

14	15	16	17	18	19	20	21	22	23	24	25	26
										J	Q	Z

Answer on page 399.

Composers Letterbox

The letters in BAX can be found in boxes 15, 18, and 19, but not necessarily in that order. Similarly, the names of all the other composers can be found in the boxes indicated. Your task is to insert all the letters of the alphabet into the boxes. If you do this correctly, the shaded cells will reveal the name of another composer.

Unused letter: Q

BAX: 15, 18, 19

BEETHOVEN: 1, 2, 5, 6, 14, 18, 23

FRANCK: 6, 11, 17, 19, 20, 22

GRIEG: 12, 21, 22, 23

JANACEK: 6, 9, 17, 19, 20, 23

LISZT: 3, 4, 5, 16, 21

LULLY: 3, 8, 13

MOZART: 2, 5, 16, 19, 22, 24

PUCCINI: 6, 8, 10, 20, 21

VERDI: 7, 14, 21, 22, 23

WEBER: 18, 22, 23, 25

1	2	3	4	5	6	7	8	9	10	11	12	13

14	15	16	17	18	19	20	21	22	23	24	25	26
												Q

Answer on page 399.

Add-a-Letter

This puzzle is an anagram with a twist: Each word or phrase below is missing the same letter. Discover the missing letter, then unscramble. All the "before" AND "after" words can be found in the grid. They may be read either forward or backward.

ALIBI DUTY

ARTY TIE

BAN BAD DO

BOP ELM

CAPE AN APE

CAR CHEAT

CHOSE ART

GERMANE TAN

GET AUDIT

GIVES AGES

GOTH MAIL

HARK TUBE HOG

HAUNTED DOG

IF ZEE

IMP SEE

LYE GAL

NEWEST

NICE FEAT

OUT HIM

PEP SKI

SCAM ANTE

SEND ASK

SIDE NET

STEEP CUE

TARDY ME

THE IMAGE

THE ONUS

TINTED

VICE DUET

WE KNOT

```
Z R B V S N I C E F E A T E D Y Y E W L C E O W J
H A R K T U B E H O G R X T E O R S Y A H E H F F
D U R A B I L I T Y E S E U R D E Y G G O Z N C G
O R C H E S T R A J H H V C Y D L Y V E S F E A D
T T C A P E A N A P E U I E T A L M Q Y E I W R A
E H B E G G T E N E D I S S R B A E Y L A D E C R
R E G V G Q L K Y O L H S R A N G L P B R U S H K
T O T U X A C U I M P S E E M A Q B M R T G T E N
I N K R O W T E N J H S R P X B G O X T E S Q A E
A U I Q N N T I A W I H G T S V U R H Y O M V T S
R S W Q W F D N M D Q X G N E Z J P A U X I I J S
Y J Q B H R I A E R X J A E I E O P T T M V C S K
Y M E E H I G N E M E C N M Q D W H N R I X E G E
L L E L R E T C A R A H C E N E E X W E H T D O X
S M G R L Z Z I R A D R T G K R L B I D T E U D U
S C T I A E G J K F L N C N N D C T U Y U U E D R
B E A R E P P I K S E G O A Q E Y A G C O Y T E E
K R G M M T P K N D P T O R S T D R P Q P H H T D
S B O A A U A E I T W E J R R N W E S T E R N N U
A K X A S N I R A Z E C P A I I E E Q M E B T U C
D G V G D E T R D R B R E A K T H R O U G H F A T
N Y Z B S B V E O Y A L F F S Y H M L E P O B H I
E G O T H M A I L H M N X A E G A M I E H T P Y V
S C G T U E K N G U T E C N C A L I B I D U T Y E
G E T A U D I T D Q W Z X E G E R M A N E T A N S
```

Answers on page 399.

The letters in CYRPUS can be found in boxes 2, 7, 8, 17, 20, and 21, but not necessarily in that order. Similarly, the letters in all these words can be found in the boxes indicated. Your task is to insert all the letters of the alphabet into the boxes. If you do this correctly, the shaded cells will reveal what there "no man's lands" have in common.

Hint: Compare JAVA and MAJORCA to get the value of V, then JAVA to NAXOS to get the value of J.

Unused letter: Q
CYPRUS 2, 7, 8, 17, 20, 21
FALKLANDS 2, 3, 4, 5, 6, 16, 25
HOKKAIDO 1, 4, 6, 10, 19, 25
ICELAND 1, 3, 4, 5, 6, 9, 21
JAVA 4, 13, 18
LUZON 3, 5, 7, 10, 14
MADAGASCAR 2, 4, 6, 15, 17, 21, 23
MAJORCA 4, 10, 13, 15, 17, 21
MANHATTAN 4, 5, 12, 15, 19
NAXOS 2, 4, 5, 10, 24
SICILY 1, 2, 3, 8, 21
TAIWAN 1, 4, 5, 12, 22
VANCOUVER 4, 5, 7, 9, 10, 17, 18, 21
ZANZIBAR 1, 4, 5, 11, 14, 17

1	2	3	4	5	6	7	8	9	10	11	12	13

14	15	16	17	18	19	20	21	22	23	24	25	26
												Q

Answer on page 399.

Cryptoku

Answer the clues below to fill in the grid and discover the 9 different letters used in each 3-by-3 box. Just like a standard crossword, answers read across and down; numbers in parenthesis indicate how many letters are in the solution. And, like a code-doku, each letter appears only once in each 3-by-3 box. When complete, the shaded squares will reveal a mystery word.

ACROSS

1. Gained (3)
2. Man's name: abbr. (3)
3. Either/_____ (2)
4. Week (abbr.) (2)
5. Not either (3)

DOWN

6. Us (2)
7. Negative (2)
8. Gained (3)
9. Off/_____ (2)
10. Chief officer: abbr. (2)

K		¹		N				C
	N		E				W	
		H			B	R		K
H			N		C	E		R
⁶O			²B			C		
E		⁷N	H	³R		⁴		B
				⁸W	K			
	W		R	⁹	¹⁰		B	
C				K	⁵			W

Answer on page 399.

Cryptoku

Answer the clues below to fill in the grid and discover the 9 different letters used in each 3-by-3 box. Just like a standard crossword, answers read across and down; numbers in parenthesis indicate how many letters are in the solution. And, like a code-doku, each letter appears only once in each 3-by-3 box. When complete, the shaded squares will reveal a mystery word.

ACROSS

1. Pronoun: masc. (3)
2. Creative expression (3)

DOWN

3. Small floor covering (3)
4. Group of stores (5)

³	R		G		I		H	
		⁴	S					O
T						M		R
	M				H			
			S			H		
		T					M	
	A	¹				T		G
I			H		S	²		

Answer on page 400.

Separated Cities

The letters in ANN ARBOR can be found in boxes 2, 3, 4, 5, and 13, but not necessarily in that order. Similarly, the letters in all the other words can be found in the boxes indicated. Your task is to insert all the letters of the alphabet into the boxes. If you do this correctly, the shaded cells will reveal another location.

Hint: Compare BAR HARBOR and DES MOINES to get the value of O, then BAR HARBOR to ABU DHABI to get the value of R.

Unused letters: Q, X, and Z

ABU DHABI: 1, 3, 4, 9, 18, 19

ANN ARBOR: 2, 3, 4, 5, 13

BAR HARBOR: 2, 3, 4, 13, 18

DES MOINES: 5, 6, 9, 12, 13, 15, 19

HAI PHONG: 4, 5, 7, 9, 13, 18, 21

KEY WEST: 6, 10, 12, 14, 16, 23

LAS VEGAS: 4, 6, 8, 12, 17, 21

LOS ANGELES: 4, 5, 6, 8, 12, 13, 21

NEW BEDFORD: 2, 3, 5, 11, 12, 13, 19, 23

SAN JUAN: 1, 4, 5, 6, 22

SAO PAULO: 1, 4, 6, 7, 8, 13

SUN CITY: 1, 5, 6, 9, 10, 14, 20

TEL AVIV: 4, 8, 9, 10, 12, 17

1	2	3	4	5	6	7	8	9	10	11	12	13

14	15	16	17	18	19	20	21	22	23	24	25	26
										Q	X	Z

Answer on page 400.

Add-a-Letter

This puzzle is an anagram with a twist: Each word or phrase below is missing the same letter. Discover the missing letter, then unscramble. All the "before" AND "after" words can be found in the grid. They may be read either forward or backward.

ALE GANG	GLIB DIN
ARM BELL	HAIRY TOT
AS ACTION	ICE DEAN
AT IBEX	LAB VEAL
BITES DIRT	MAIN CLIP
BITTER	MARLIN TAR
COINED AT	MOTEL AD
COT CON	NEUTRAL SPAR
DATING ME	NITRIC TONS
DID SNEER	NO STRICT CON
DOG NERD	OBTAIN CLIP
DOTES	PIE TRAVELS
FORMAL	POOR LEG
GILLS SEE	QUILT PEN
GIN LED	TAIL RINDS

```
S U P E R L A T I V E D I S T R I B U T E H G G A
H R M A G N I T U D E V S U M G E L P U T N I U Q
H E T A L U D O M N Q H B K N Q X V A L U A B L E
T A I L R I N D S Q Y C Z O C S Y K E L H Z N U F
S U P E R N A T U R A L I I L L E B M R A I L O N
E S L E V A R T E I P T A I C B W A G T S M R C O
D Q N A N I E A E E C B N B B E M W N T G M O L S
U Q N O B W N U T U D T U E V U D F I C U I O N T
C T Q U C A G D R N R I N R A E I E T L N P O D R
A Y T I R O H T U A I A D K B B A L A E L T E D I
T E Y Q L C S M M L B L E S Y W P L D N C D E U C
I I T O L N A U O A G L R C N B W A R I N L N S T
O J R N O I R S X C T E S A N E T A R U N O L T C
N P X C N A B N Y R C R I B M E E T O I I G A U O
H O L C L P K G I H F B D L K N I R G T N M M N N
G E L R O O P D O D F M E B O N G D C G O U R O X
I I E C F U S U O B B U P I W A Z U U N I N O C E
P S S E L E L I U G T I T R X X R V H A T I F O B
U H T O T Y R I A H N A L S E T O D K G C C E C I
V K E I O N O C T O C E I G S T X M E E A I Z U T
R M B A U X I T E I H K R N E U T R A L S P A R A
G I L L S S E E L V K I I D C Q B I G A A A B K V
D A L E T O M B E G A U G N A L F W B O Y L R Y Y
B P R V E G U L A I R T S U D N I J M O H S D N F
H B B E D P C A U S A T I O N N E P T L I U Q N G
```

Answers on page 400.

Add-a-Letter

This puzzle is an anagram with a twist: Each word or phrase below is missing the same letter. Discover the missing letter, then unscramble. All the "before" AND "after" words can be found in the grid. They may be read either forward or backward.

ANTLION	LIP ART
BELL CUP	MUM MIX
BLUE LIPS	OMIT NUN
BRIDGE	OWL RECTOR
CHIC ELM	PINE ROOT
COG END	PLUM TIN
DUNCE BAN	RUTTY RIB
FILM AIR	SPY SPIED
FIT MORON	SURGED ON
GEM SIGNS	TEAL RIM
GETS INVITE	TEPID ONION
IF FENCE	THEE QUARK
INCH ME	TINY LOT
LENT LYRICS	TUNE INLET
LEST SINS	VETO CAD

```
C Q Y F W I M E N I E F F A C Z B I R Y T T U R L
C S T R I B U T A R Y V E T O C A D T G F E N F S
H S I A F D N Y S J S W A T E R C O L O R H Z P I
I E L I F U I V D M G O O O K D O D P A R T I A L
C L A L E N T W H C P S E T C R I A M L I F Z K P
E N N I N C A U U I U N F T E P I D O N I O N G L
L I O M C E L L N O E M G N Z T E C N A D N U B A
M A T A E B P I R L S C I R Y L T N E L F O R V U
V T M F R A O E G L A P U C L L E B V M O I V Z S
W S G I B N G E N I P I U O M I T N U N R T T U I
Q T D L A N M E S E R I R M A K V M Q T M A I D B
U G E T A S O P Y R E B A E X K I O E M A R N L L
E U E D I S E I Q H T G R T T X R N K C T E Y A E
R D D G L P R N L G I E E I A A I A A O I P L N N
O P N S S Y D E R T V L A M G H M D U V O O O O I
T S M Y I S S J J L N B L L C A V Y Q Q N D T I A
C P D L I P A R T I I A J A R O D D H C E D F T T
E I X R C I N J E E S B M L C I N E T G T E R A N
R L I V H E Q N S U T G X A S E M L R Z P C H N U
L E M K E D U M P T E Z T P G M Q U A W S A L T O
W U M X M T Q W Z E G E O O D R S C E H O G F Z M
O L U H I X R I A N Q Z C P W F I T M O R O N V B
R B M G C R Y S T A L L I N E L E S T S I N S Q L
L X J J A N J G B N N E T A G I T S E V N I J L O
H R T V L I I N I T M U L P M E S S A G I N G F R
```

Answers on page 400.

Not a Hack

Every word listed is contained within the group of letters. Words can be found in a straight line horizontally, vertically, or diagonally. They may be read either forward or backward. Leftover letters reveal a fact about Gene Hackman.

ABSOLUTE POWER

ANOTHER WOMAN

ANTZ

BEHIND ENEMY LINES

BITE THE BULLET

THE CHAMBER

CLASS ACTION

THE CONVERSATION

CRIMSON TIDE

ENEMY OF THE STATE

EUREKA

EXTREME MEASURES

THE FIRM

GET SHORTY

HEIST

HOOSIERS

LEX LUTHOR

THE MEXICAN

MISUNDERSTOOD

NO WAY OUT

POWER

PRIME CUT

REDS

RIOT

TARGET

TWILIGHT

UNFORGIVEN

WYATT EARP

Leftover Letters: _____

```
H M I S U N D E R S T O O D E W O
N S A N N Y T R O H S T E G O S R
C E A R F F T O E A E A R B H I E
W N S R O O H M C N R R L I E U W
Y I A S R J E I R O U G M T R N O
A L M Y G X C I I T S E R E W O P
T Y P O I P O E M H A T K T R W E
T M Y C V T N M S E E A E H E A T
E E A D E H V R O R M N P E B Y U
A N O Y N G E I N W E T R B M O L
R E D S L I R F T O M Z I U A U O
P D E I S L S E I M E N M L H T S
T N H O E I A H D A R F E L C R B
E I O N C W T T E N T H C E E C A
O H E I S T I N L E X L U T H O R
N E N E M Y O F T H E S T A T E E
C B T I O N N O I T C A S S A L C
```

Answers on page 400.

Where the Heart Is

The letters in CAPE COT COTTAGE can be found in boxes 1, 3, 4, 5, 11, 13, 15, and 22, but not necessarily in that order. Similarly, the letters in all these words can be found in the boxes indicated. Your task is to insert all the letters of the alphabet into the boxes. If you do this correctly, the shaded cells will reveal another word.

Hint: Compare PUP TENT and HUNTING LODGE to get the value of P, then PUP TENT to WHITE HOUSE to get the value of N.

Unused letters: J, X, and Z
CAPE COD COTTAGE 1, 3, 4, 5, 11, 13, 15, 22
COUNTRY VILLA 1, 3, 7, 8, 9, 10, 11, 13, 14, 20, 21
CRASH PAD 1, 4, 6, 10, 13, 15, 16
DUDE RANCH 1, 4, 5, 9, 10, 13, 14, 16
GRASS SHACK 1, 6, 10, 13, 16, 19, 22
HOLIDAY INN 1, 3, 4, 7, 8, 14, 16, 20
HUNTING LODGE 3, 4, 5, 7, 9, 11, 14, 16, 20, 22
LOG CABIN 1, 2, 3, 7, 13, 14, 20, 22
MOTOR HOME 3, 5, 10, 11, 16, 17
PUP TENT 5, 9, 11, 14, 15
QUONSET HUT 3, 5, 6, 9, 11, 14, 16, 23
SKI CHALET 1, 5, 6, 7, 11, 13, 16, 19, 20
TRUCK FARM 1, 9, 10, 11, 12, 13, 17, 19
WHITE HOUSE 3, 4, 5, 6, 7, 9, 11, 16, 18

1	2	3	4	5	6	7	8	9	10	11	12	13

14	15	16	17	18	19	20	21	22	23	24	25	26
										J	X	Z

Answer on page 400.

Codeword

The letters of the alphabet are hidden in code: Each is represented by a random number from 1 through 26. With the letters already given, complete the crossword puzzle with English words and break the code.

	20		5		13		15		11		2	
2	4	7	4	25	5		7	1	15	13	21	13
	1		25		8		9		25		26	
7	10	10	9		12	1	21	12	16	9	16	6
			5		19		25		12		12	
15	25	3	15	23	16	15		1	16	18	16	26
	21		17		12		13		10		15	
15	5	17	16	1		22	15	12	21	10	25	4
	17		5		13		1		5			
18	1	15	9	9	16	17	16		23	16	3	5
	10		16		14		15		4		21	
3	21	1	4	15	21		19	21	5	17	25	4
	5		26		4		5		5		24	

A B C D E F G H I J K L M N O P Q R S T U V W X Y Z

1	2	3	4	5	6	7	8	9	10	11	12	13
								F				

14	15	16	17	18	19	20	21	22	23	24	25	26
			T	G								

Answers on page 400.

Forever Jung

Every word listed is contained within the group of letters. Words can be found in a straight line horizontally, vertically, or diagonally. They may be read either forward or backward.

ARCHITECT	EXTRAVERSION	ISTJ
ATTITUDE	FEELING	ISTP
AUXILIARY	FIELDMARSHAL	JUDGMENT
CHAMPION	FUNCTION	LIFESTYLE
COMPOSER	HEALER	MASTERMIND
COUNSELOR	INFERIOR	PERCEPTION
CRAFTER	INFJ	PERFORMER
DOMINANT	INFP	PROMOTER
ENFJ	INSPECTOR	PROTECTOR
ENFP	INTJ	PROVIDER
ENTJ	INTP	SENSING
ENTP	INTROVERSION	SUPERVISOR
ESFJ	INTUITION	TEACHER
ESFP	INVENTOR	TERTIARY
ESTJ	ISFJ	THINKING
ESTP	ISFP	

```
I F I W E P R C T E A M A I G I C I A N I S H O U
L D C A F U H S E P T S E I N F E R I O R E T H E
S I T S U A A T R I J F N E O T O N C O R R E S P
O N I D M I N G T T O T T H E T R S T I M U L U S
T O J P A A P P I E A R S I N N P O C R A F T E R
C R I F P R E A A L I T Y E B U T T V A S W E R A
E O R E S F C N R E D I V O R P N O T E M A P E G
N X M I C I N H Y I A N N S W E I M U T R T G T S
B E T P N C O I I N I T E N T E D W I T N S N O H
T J H R O O E S U T L A H S R A M D L E I F I M B
S F T M A S I I T U E T E S F N O R R R E A L O L
I S R T A V E T Y T P C P G O O H G R E Z N E R N
E E M E R S E R C V Z T T B B I P J T S L P E P S
C B L K H O T R G N I K N I H T C E S F P A F H U
O J D Q P C T E S E U Z A T T I T U D E N G E N P
U A T P I N A C R I S F A J T U P J F O I I W H E
N U A N E Z O E E M O E V G D T I S T P Y S U O R
S X Z R E R J I T T I N N O O N X S W I U X T R V
E I M C P M F J T R O N K S M I Y F F I N A Z J I
L L M X Y W G O P P B R D X I I N S P E C T O R S
O I O K J O K D R X E B P H N N Q J X Q D J J K O
R A V F B F E B U M T C W M A F G Q F I K P G N R
R R H U U S I N F J E U R W N B L I F E S T Y L E
L Y O J T Q Y D K G O R Z E T Q C A C F S E N T J
W W T F E B S O J R V P T L P F P V F Z K F H F D
```

Answers on page 400.

Codeword

The letters of the alphabet are hidden in code: Each is represented by a random number from 1 through 26. With the letters already given, complete the crossword puzzle with English words and break the code.

24	26	7	2	20	8			4		20	22	16
	15			1		13	3	20	4	22		26
12	3	17	3	24	12	10		24		22		8
	12			8		24		9	16	1	24	1
22	20	21	9	3	15	20	6			22		6
	4			6		11		20		4		1
22	3	19	20	4	3		3	12	20	22	3	19
23		3		22		11		7			24	
21		18			16	20	6	21	5	5	20	16
3	14	20	24	4		1		20			22	
24		21		20		22	21	13	22	3	4	22
9		24	1	22	25	4		24			1	
16	1	4		5			18	3	24	26	6	10

A B C D E F G H I J K L M N O P Q R S T U V W X Y Z

1	2	3	4	5	6	7	8	9	10	11	12	13
				K	N			C				

14	15	16	17	18	19	20	21	22	23	24	25	26
X												

Answers on page 401.

Code-doku

Solve this puzzle just as you would a sudoku. Use deductive logic to complete the grid so that each row, column, and 3-by-3 box contains the letters from the word KEYBOARDS.

Answer on page 401.

Word Columns

Find the hidden quote from Laura Knightlinger by using the letters directly below each of the blank squares. Each letter is used only once. A black square or the end of the line indicates the end of a word.

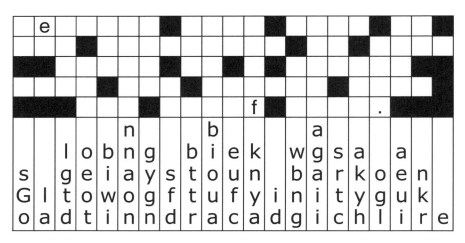

Word Columns

Find the hidden quote from Robert A. Heinlein by using the letters directly below each of the blank squares. Each letter is used once. A black square indicates the end of a word.

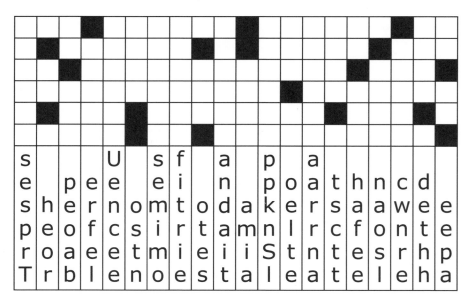

Answers on page 401.

Acrostic

Solve the clues below, and then place the letters in their corresponding spots in the grid to reveal a historic quote. The letter in the upper-right corner of each grid square refers to the clue the letter comes from. A black square indicates the end of a word.

A. Author of quote: 2 wds.

43 2 50 5 46 42 14 41 22 7 24

B. Surprise football tactic

54 23 31 57 71

C. Resided

12 1 55 11 15

D. 31st U.S. President (1929–33)

65 27 48 21 3 19

E. Candid and straight to the point

28 72 56 64 67 69 34 36 16 29

F. "King _____" (1933)

33 68 35 25

G. Unfair circumstances

20 73 17 59 60 9 37 53 26 44

H. Metropolis of northern India

47 6 40 45 61

J. Corpulent

51 52 10 63 38 8

I. Sister's son

4 39 18 30 66 49

K. State of agreement

13 32 70 62 58

1 C	2 A	3 D	4 I	■	5 A	6 H	7 A	■	8 J	9 G	10 J	11 C	12 C	■	13 K	14 A
15 C	16 E	17 G	■	18 I	19 D	20 G	21 D	22 A	23 B	24 A	25 F	26 G	■	27 D	28 E	■
29 E	30 I	31 B	32 K	33 F	34 E	35 F	36 E	■	37 G	38 J	39 I	■	40 H	41 A	42 A	43 A
44 G	45 H	46 A	47 H	48 D	49 I	■	50 A	51 J	■	52 J	53 G	54 B	55 C	56 E	57 B	58 K
59 G	60 G	61 H	62 K	63 J	■	64 E	65 D	66 I	■	67 E	68 F	69 E	70 K	71 B	72 E	73 G

Answers on page 401.

Code-doku

Solve this puzzle just as you would a sudoku. Use deductive logic to complete the grid so that each row, column, and 3-by-3 box contains the letters from the word GYMNASTIC.

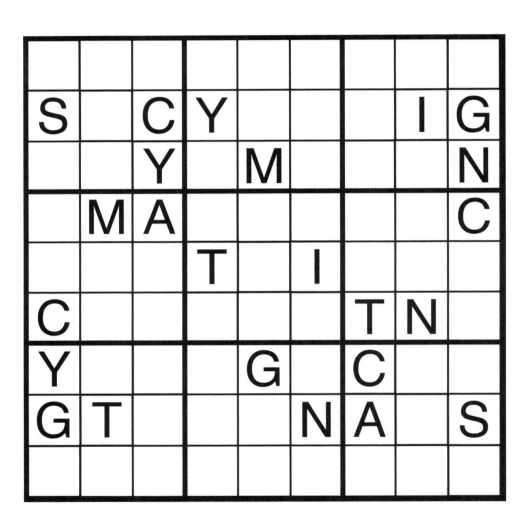

Answer on page 401.

Mastermind

The goal of this puzzle is to replace the question marks with a correct sequence of numbers. The numbers you need for the answer are contained in the rows above the question marks. Follow these 2 guides: A black dot indicates that a number needed for the solution is in that row and in the correct position; a white dot means that a number needed for the solution is in that row but in the wrong position. Numbers do not appear more than once in the solution, and the solution never begins with 0.

```
2  5  4  6  3    ● ● ● ○
3  8  7  1  2    ○ ○ ○
1  4  5  9  0    ○ ○
9  8  7  6  5    ●
─────────────
?  ?  ?  ?  ?
```

Cipher Trivia

Cryptograms are messages in substitution code. Break the code to read the message. THE SMART CAT might become FVO QWGDF JGF if **F** is substituted for **T**, **V** for **H**, **O** for **E**, and so on.

AMXL FSSO GMTLIVW, FSXL WIRHIV ERH VIGIMZIV

YWI XLI WEQI FSSO EW XLI OIC XS XLI GMTLIV.

XLI FMFPI ERH TEVXMGYPEV IHMXMSRW SJ XLI

HMGXMSREVC EVI WSQIXMQIW YWIH FIGEYWI XLIC

LEZI QERC ASVHW EZEMPEFPI. SXLIV TISTPI QMKLX

YWI E QSVI SFWGYVI FSSO JSV ER IBXVE PECIV SJ

WIGYVMXC.

Answers on page 401.

Codeword

The letters of the alphabet are hidden in code: Each is represented by a random number from 1 through 26. With the letters already given, complete the crossword puzzle with English words and break the code.

14	21	22	8	19		18	10	15	20	25	15	24
10		7		10		9		22		19		7
8	22	7	25	23	6	17		2	8	25	23	11
25		6		7		3		6		15		11
18	7	11	8	22		11	19	11	8	22	6	23
10				14		12				15		
24	6	22	14	16	24		1	11	5	11	6	24
		12				24		9				25
2	11	15	5	11	11	12		21	22	15	11	24
25		25		4		11		25		25		15
15	18	13	10	11		11	19	2	8	22	14	11
11		10		12		26		25		8		8
24	5	11	11	15	25	11		15	11	22	19	24

A B C D E F G H I J K L M N O P Q R S T U V W X Y Z

1	2	3	4	5	6	7	8	9	10	11	12	13
							R					

14	15	16	17	18	19	20	21	22	23	24	25	26
T								A		I		

Answers on page 401.

Code-doku

Solve this puzzle just as you would a sudoku. Use deductive logic to complete the grid so that each row, column, and 3-by-3 box contains the letters from the words TENDS GOAL.

Answer on page 401.

They Are the Champions

Solve the clues below, and then place the letters in their corresponding spots in the grid to reveal a song lyric from Queen. The letter in the upper-right corner of each grid square refers to the clue the letter comes from. A black square indicates the end of a word.

A. "_____ Rhapsody"

__ __ __ __ __ __ __ __
78 50 34 30 10 58 37 60

B. 1985 Queen hit single: 2 wds.

__ __ __ __ __ __ __ __ __
2 82 39 26 47 61 13 66 19

C. Eases discomfort

__ __ __ __ __ __ __
36 9 18 32 62 23 84

D. "_____ of Magic": 2 wds.

__ __ __ __ __
15 67 74 24 7

E. Queen B-side, "_____ My Heart"

__ __ __ __ __ __
22 17 69 3 14 75

F. Bowie collaboration, "Under _____"

__ __ __ __ __ __ __ __
11 80 68 21 64 70 54 44

G. Goes hungry

__ __ __ __ __ __ __
55 72 79 28 4 76 45

H. Queen bassist John

__ __ __ __ __ __
41 63 56 49 5 51

I. "_____ Crazy": 2 wds.

__ __ __ __ __ __ __ __ __
20 33 81 48 25 8 59 12 42

J. Inspiration for "Crazy Little Thing Called Love"

__ __ __ __ __
83 73 52 6 71

K. Concert equipment

__ __ __ __ __ __ __ __
46 65 27 40 29 53 43 85

L. Try

__ __ __ __ __ __ __
77 1 57 35 38 31 16

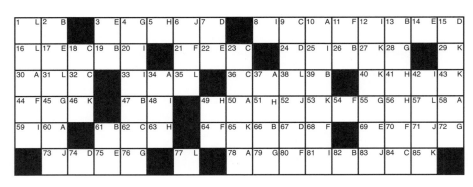

Answers on page 402.

LogiNumber

Determine the values of the letters below using 2 rules: Each letter is no greater than the number of letters in the puzzle; none of the letters are equal to each other. Use the grid to help keep track of possible solutions.

$A + D = 6$

$B + F + A = 8$

$F + A = D$

$B + C = D$

	1	2	3	4	5	6
A						
B						
C						
D						
E						
F						

LogiNumber

Determine the values of the letters below using 2 rules: Each letter is no greater than the number of letters in the puzzle; none of the letters are equal to each other. Use the grid to help keep track of possible solutions.

$E + D = B + A$

$D + B = C$

$F + A = 11$

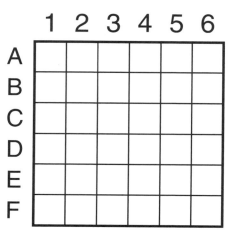

Answers on page 402.

Cryptoku

Answer the clues below to fill in the grid and discover the 9 different letters used in each 3-by-3 box. Just like a standard crossword, answers read across and down; numbers in parenthesis indicate how many letters are in the solution. And, like a code-doku, each letter appears only once in each 3-by-3 box. When complete, the shaded squares will reveal a mystery word.

ACROSS

1. Total (3)
2. Geologic age (3)
3. Group (3)
4. Knock (3)
5. Asphalt (3)

DOWN

6. Dine (3)
7. _____ capita (3)
8. To place (3)
9. First person pronoun (2)
10. Father (2)

¹S		M	O		P	E		A
²	R			U		⁸	M	
		P			E			⁶S
	S		R	⁹	A		O	
M	U		³	E		⁴R		⁷P
⁵	A		¹⁰		U		S	
		O		T				R
	M		U		O		E	
A		T		S		O		M

Answer on page 402.

Code-doku

Solve this puzzle just as you would a sudoku. Use deductive logic to complete the grid so that each row, column, and 3-by-3 box contains the letters from the word LACEWORKS.

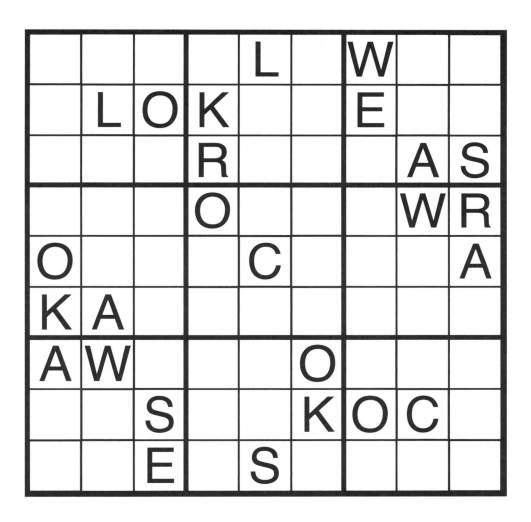

Answer on page 402.

Acrostic

Solve the clues below and then place the letters in their corresponding spots in the grid to reveal an artistic quote. The letter in the upper-right corner of each grid square refers to the clue the letter comes from.

A. Author of quote: 2 wds.

— — — — — — — — — — —
26 63 30 9 27 54 68 44 55 3 18

B. 124th Japanese Emperor

— — — — — — — —
66 81 48 47 11 25 36 51

C. Bivouac

— — — — — — — —
50 59 32 58 60 31 29 12

D. Averted

— — — — — — — — —
39 19 67 76 70 78 61 40 53

E. Deserving of time or effort

— — — — — — — — — —
45 15 6 64 56 71 37 74 34 5

F. Elijah and Ezekiel

— — — — — — — —
13 41 28 21 22 77 79 42

G. Paired with maid or pot

— — — — — — —
 8 46 20 4 62 23 24

I. Much warmer

— — — — — —
72 43 82 10 49 52

H. Famous physicist

— — — — — — — —
57 1 2 80 16 38 7 75

J. Cyclone

— — — — — — —
65 35 33 14 73 17 69

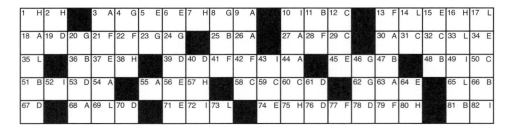

Answers on page 402.

Codeword

The letters of the alphabet are hidden in code: Each is represented by a random number from 1 through 26. With the letters already given, complete the crossword puzzle with English words and break the code. Once you have completed the grid, unscramble the letters found in the gray cells to reveal the name of a hockey penalty.

3	14	18	14	24	24	14	26		17	23	14	11
	17		23		4		13		22		19	
10	22	24	8	4	1		23	13	3	2	4	1
	23		5		8	24	16		3		1	
6	4	12	4		21		1	4	8	20	4	1
	15				15				15			
1	3	22	9	9	1		13	15	21	23	4	1
			23				8				13	
1	7	22	4	13	23		23		21	8	1	3
	22		25		4	23	18		24		3	
24	4	6	8	17	4		4	25	8	23	4	1
	4		15		24		15		23		24	
1	15	13	21		1	4	3	3	23	8	15	21

A B C D E F G H I J K L M N O P Q R S T U V W X Y Z

1	2	3	4	5	6	7	8	9	10	11	12	13
		T		C					J			

14	15	16	17	18	19	20	21	22	23	24	25	26
O												

Answers on page 402.

Codeword

The letters of the alphabet are hidden in code: Each is represented by a random number from 1 through 26. With the letters already given, complete the crossword puzzle with English words and break the code.

ABCDEFGHIJKLMNOPQRSTUVWXYZ

1	2	3	4	5	6	7	8	9	10	11	12	13
					A							

14	15	16	17	18	19	20	21	22	23	24	25	26
	P							O			L	

Answers on page 402.

Code-doku

Solve this puzzle just as you would a sudoku. Use deductive logic to complete the grid so that each row, column, and 3-by-3 box contains the letters from the word OUTFIELDS.

	F	O	D			U		
E				U	L		S	
								E
	L	E	O					
			F	L	U			
				I	F	D		
O								
	D		E	I				O
		T			D	I	F	

Answer on page 402.

Dial Tone

Decipher the encoded word in the quip below using the numbers and letters on the phone pad. Remember that each number can stand for 3 or 4 possible letters.

Essential items for your purse include a makeup bag, cell phone, and 2-6-6-2!

Wisdom of the Moors

Cryptograms are messages in substitution code. Break the code to read the message. THE SMART CAT might become FVO QWGDF JGF if **F** is substituted for **T**, **V** for **H**, **O** for **E**, and so on.

PGPDB UPPJOP QA L ILYPOOP QZ JKP PBPA VX QJA CVJKPD.

— CVDVTTLZ WDVGPDU

Answers on pages 402-403.

Codeword

The letters of the alphabet are hidden in code: Each is represented by a random number from 1 through 26. With the letters already given, complete the crossword puzzle with English words and break the code.

20	13	14	9	25	26			18		3	24	11
	20			14		14	2	6	9	13		21
11	21	14	20	12	13	15		14		21		24
	24			10		16		26	14	12	16	4
17	1	13	9	5	13	13	22			17		4
	13			24		20		9		7		13
24	20	4	13	9	20		21	24	20	13	14	9
20		6		13		15		11			1	
22		7			15	4	9	17	20	11	13	9
13	21	25	17	3		17		9			9	
8		21		13		14	12	17	21	26	4	13
13		13	23	13	12	4		6			13	
22	6	22		19			13	15	12	6	22	17

A B C D E F G H I J K L M N O P Q R S T U V W X Y Z

1	2	3	4	5	6	7	8	9	10	11	12	13
V	Z							R				

14	15	16	17	18	19	20	21	22	23	24	25	26
A												

Answers on page 403.

Cryptoku

Answer the clues below to fill in the grid and discover the 6 different letters used in each 3-by-2 box. Just like a standard crossword, answers read across and down; numbers in parenthesis indicate how many letters are in the solution. And, like a code-doku, each letter appears only once in each 3-by-2 box. When complete, the shaded squares will reveal a mystery word.

ACROSS

1. United States: abbr. (3)
2. Very dry (4)

DOWN

3. Advertisements: abbr. (3)
4. Not happy (3)

	R	¹		A	
		S			
S				D	
	³A			I	⁴
I			¹		
¹		²			D

Answer on page 403.

Word Columns

Find the hidden humorous anecdote by using the letters directly below each of the blank squares. Each letter is used only once. A black square indicates the end of a word.

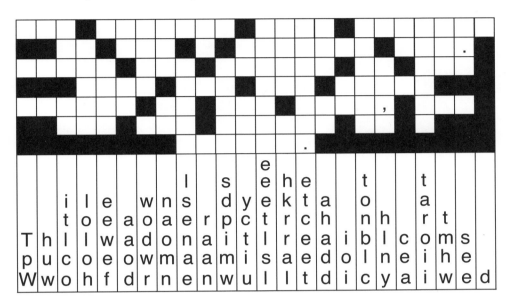

Crypto-Logic

Each of the numbers in the sequence below represents a letter. Use the mathematical clues to determine which number stands for which letter and reveal the encrypted word.

5 6 9 7 8 3 2 1 4

Clues:

N is sensory

G is reflection

C is time

S is the muses

L is a crowd

I sounds like a victory in the past

T is mortal errors

A is almost heavy except for "U + U"

O is the first three combined

Answers on page 403.

Code-doku

Solve this puzzle just as you would a sudoku. Use deductive logic to complete the grid so that each row, column, and 3-by-3 box contains the letters from the word PROCLAIMS. When you have completed the puzzle, read the shaded squares to reveal a hidden message regarding exploration.

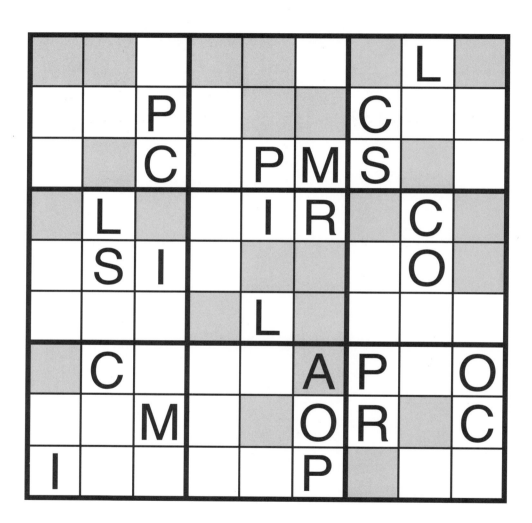

Hidden Message: _____

Answer on page 403.

Codeword

The letters of the alphabet are hidden in code: Each is represented by a random number from 1 through 26. With the letters already given, complete the crossword puzzle with English words and break the code.

25	14	22	8	18	11	16	■	19	13	13	10	14
19	■	12	■	3	■	2	■	10	■	22	■	19
1	14	18	25	25	17	18	16	25	■	24	22	26
22	■	■	■	14	■	■	■	18	■	17	■	22
9	18	20	14	22	■	1	22	14	22	16	19	11
■	■	19	■	13	■	17	■	■	■	19	■	25
21	19	26	■	25	19	5	10	18	■	11	22	26
22	■	6	■	■	■	10	■	5	■	18	■	■
13	19	14	16	22	4	18	■	10	1	16	18	25
15	■	17	■	10	■	■	■	22	■	■	■	19
18	26	18	■	7	17	4	2	25	4	19	12	7
25	■	7	■	25	■	22	■	19	■	12	■	18
16	17	23	18	16	■	1	22	14	25	7	18	14

A B C D E F G H I J K L M N O P Q R S T U V W X Y Z

1	2	3	4	5	6	7	8	9	10	11	12	13
				Q	N				U			

14	15	16	17	18	19	20	21	22	23	24	25	26
				E							T	

Answers on page 403.

Code-doku

Solve this puzzle just as you would a sudoku. Use deductive logic to complete the grid so that each row, column, and 3-by-3 box contains the letters from the word FAVORITES.

	R	O	S					V
	V							O
A	T					F		
	E		I	R				
		A		T		R		
			E	A				I
	R						E	T
O						I		
T				R	S	F		

Answer on page 403.

LogiNumber

Determine the values of the variables below using 2 rules: Each variable is no greater than the numbers of variables in the puzzle; none of the variables are equal to each other. Use the grid to help keep track of possible solutions.

$A + F = 5$

$B + E = 8$

$B > E$

$F + E = D + B$

	1	2	3	4	5	6
A						
B						
C						
D						
E						
F						

LogiNumber

Determine the values of the variables below using 2 rules: Each variable is no greater than the numbers of variables in the puzzle; none of the variables are equal to each other. Use the grid to help keep track of possible solutions.

$B + A = E$

$E + 1 = C$

$A > D$

	1	2	3	4	5
A					
B					
C					
D					
E					

Answers on page 403.

Sequence

What comes next?

A, BC, EFG, JKLM,

STUVW, QRSTU, OPQRS, RSTUV, PQRST

Sequence

What comes next in this sequence?

1/2 1/3 2/3 1/5 3/4 1/7 4/5 1/9 5/6 ___

Answers on page 403.

Magazine Rack

Can you make sense of these titles? Below are 6 jumbled phrases or words. Each is an anagram (rearrangement) of a word or phrase that fits the story. Can you decipher all 6?

"Huddle up here, folks," said the journalism instructor to his small group of students at the large downtown newsstand. "These are magazines some of you could be working at someday. And since you deal with language, we're going to have a little fun and mix up the letters a tad. Take this one, for example," he said, picking up a copy of **YELTSIN**. "Would you want to work for a publication that appears to be named for the first president of the Russian federation?"

"Appearances are deceiving," piped up a female student at his side. "That magazine actually deals with fashion, beauty, and celebrities."

"Very good," said the instructor. "How about this one, called **QUERIES**? An appropriate title for all you question-askers."

"Yeah, but that's an old-timey man's magazine," said a young man in the group. "These days it's outpaced by Maxim and Blender and all the other 'lad mags.'"

"Aha. How about **ORAL GUM** then, or **TEN-FOUR**? Anyone here want to work for them?"

Another girl chimed in. "**ORAL GUM** would be fun if you had a passion for fashion," she said. "And **TEN-FOUR** is strictly for business types, not CBers on the road."

"Right you are," said the instructor. "Here's one called **RATIFY IVAN**. What's it about?"

"Well," said a student, "it's pretty famous for a 1991 cover of Demi Moore naked and pregnant. And it's known for top photographers and good articles."

"You folks are on target today," the instructor beamed. "Here's your last choice, a magazine I'm calling **ORLON SNIGLET**. Want to work for it?"

"Sure! That magazine rocks!" said a girl whose sweatshirt read "I'm with the band."

Answers on page 403.

Codeword

The letters of the alphabet are hidden in code: Each is represented by a random number from 1 through 26. With the letters already given, complete the crossword puzzle with English words and break the code.

	18		24		16		17		19		9	
15	17	8	13	7	19		9	19	16	14	16	21
	15		7		24		10		29		19	
16	15	15	10		16	26	7	19	21	13	23	7
			7		21		14		7		7	
20	17	13	5	5	7	21		23	4	23	5	7
	21				22		23				5	
5	11	13	19	24		1	11	23	25	10	16	21
	26		13		15		12		21			
15	16	19	10	6	7	11	19		16	21	4	2
	6		3		19		7		12		11	
10	7	3	17	13	21		19	11	12	17	19	21
	24		7		10		11		4		24	

A B C D E F G H I J K L M N O P Q R S T U V W X Y Z

1	2	3	4	5	6	7	8	9	10	11	12	13
			Y									

14	15	16	17	18	19	20	21	22	23	24	25	26
					R					D		

Answers on page 404.

Code-doku

Solve this puzzle just as you would a sudoku. Use deductive logic to complete the grid so that each row, column, and 3-by-3 box contains the letters from the words OLD MAKEUP.

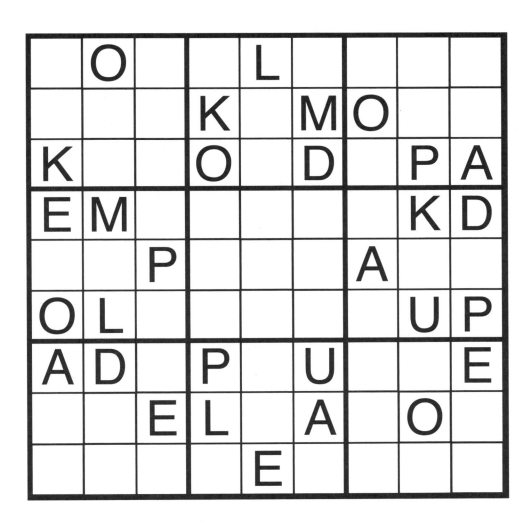

Answer on page 404.

Tourist Attractions

Oops! A new worker at the USA visitors center removed 3-letter words from 12 major tourist attractions. Each missing word was rounded up and put into the box below. Can you put each word into an empty space to name the real attractions?

ACE BET CAT COT ELL HIT IRE LIB OLD RAN TOW USE

1. __ __ __ S Y R O S S H O U S E (Philadelphia)
2. A L __ __ __ R A Z I S L A N D (San Francisco)
3. E M P __ __ __ S T A T E B U I L D I N G (New York City)
4. E P __ __ __ C E N T E R (Orlando)
5. F __ __ __ K L I N I N S T I T U T E (Philadelphia)
6. G E T T Y M __ __ __ U M (Los Angeles)
7. G __ __ __ E N G A T E B R I D G E (San Francisco)
8. L I B E R T Y B __ __ __ (Philadelphia)
9. W I L L I S __ __ __ E R (Chicago)
10. S P __ __ __ N E E D L E (Seattle)
11. S T A T U E O F __ __ __ E R T Y (New York City)
12. W __ __ __ E H O U S E (Washington, D.C.)

Bungle Gym

If he builds it, they will come… mainly to laugh! Can you decipher the anagrams below without breaking anything?

We wanted to build a jungle gym for our 5-year-old and his playmates, so we called a carpenter. We wanted it made of wood and plastic, so we should have had a clue when he asked for his **BROW CLOTH**. Things went downhill after that. He didn't know how to use the **CRUCIAL WARS**, and we got a little worried when he shouted, "**I SAW CHAN**!" This was followed by "I need my **WEB ATLAS**." Later he went back to his truck for some **LOGIC SPRINKLE**. As you can see, the result was less than ideal. "You're outta here!" shouted my husband, brandishing his **CAR BROW**.

Answers on page 404.

Music

The letters in the word UKULELE can be found in boxes 12, 16, 19, and 22, but not necessarily in that order. Similarly, the letters in the other musical instruments listed can be found in the boxes indicated. Your task is to insert all the letters into the grid. If you do this correctly, the names of 2 more instruments will be revealed in the shaded squares.

Hint: Compare BANJO and BASSOON to get the values of J and S. Then compare BASSOON and DOUBLE BASS to get the value of N.

BANJO: 5, 6, 7, 8, 21

BASSOON: 5, 6, 7, 20, 21

DOUBLE BASS: 5, 7, 14, 16, 19, 20, 21, 22

FLUTE: 10, 13, 16, 19, 22

OCARINA: 4, 5, 6, 7, 15, 23

ORGAN: 1, 5, 6, 7, 15

PICCOLO: 3, 4, 7, 19, 23

SAXOPHONE: 2, 3, 5, 6, 7, 11, 20, 22

TIN WHISTLE: 2, 4, 6, 9, 10, 19, 20, 22

TRUMPET: 3, 10, 15, 16, 17, 22

UKULELE: 12, 16, 19, 22

VIOLA: 4, 5, 7, 19, 24

XYLOPHONE: 2, 3, 6, 7, 11, 19, 22, 25

ZITHER: 2, 4, 10, 15, 18, 22

1	2	3	4	5	6	7	8	9	10	11	12	13

14	15	16	17	18	19	20	21	22	23	24	25	26
												Q

Answer on page 404.

Girls' Names

The letters in the name ZOE can be found in boxes 4, 17, and 19, but not necessarily in that order. The same is true for the other names listed below. Using the names and the box numbers that follow each name as your guide, insert all the letters of the alphabet into the boxes. If you do this correctly, the shaded cells will reveal another name.

Hint: Look for words that share a single letter. For example, KATE shares only an A with LAURA and only an E with QUEENIE. By comparing the number lists following the names, you can deduce the box numbers of the shared letters.

BETH: 5, 7, 17, 25

BRENDA: 5, 15, 17, 18, 20, 23

CILLA: 21, 22, 23, 24

DAVINA: 15, 16, 20, 21, 23

FRANCES: 6, 10, 17, 18, 20, 22, 23

GLADYS: 6, 12, 14, 15, 23, 24

JOSIE: 1, 6, 17, 19, 21

KATE: 3, 17, 23, 25

LAURA: 13, 18, 23, 24

MARY: 14, 18, 23, 26

MAXINE: 2, 17, 20, 21, 23, 26

PATSY: 6, 11, 14, 23, 25

QUEENIE: 8, 13, 17, 20, 21

WANDA: 9, 15, 20, 23

ZOE: 4, 17, 19

1	2	3	4	5	6	7	8	9	10	11	12	13

14	15	16	17	18	19	20	21	22	23	24	25	26

Answer on page 404.

Codeword

The letters of the alphabet are hidden in code: Each is represented by a random number from 1 through 26. With the letters already given, complete the crossword puzzle with English words and break the code.

	26		4		1		24		16		7	
7	17	2	23	16	11		17	12	17	2	10	7
	16		20		16		11		12		22	
14	23	3	25		10	17	2	4	17	2	14	9
			19		17		7		11		21	
24	17	13	17	19	16	9		7	19	22	8	7
	6				7		21				22	
7	8	11	14	17		4	22	11	3	23	2	4
	11		5		18		7		23			
11	2	10	22	15	20	17	7		10	22	17	7
	4		14		2		22		5		9	
16	17	14	21	23	2		2	22	17	14	17	7
	4		7		9		1		16		7	

A B C D E F G H I J K L M N O P Q R S T U V W X Y Z

1	2	3	4	5	6	7	8	9	10	11	12	13
	N					S				A		

14	15	16	17	18	19	20	21	22	23	24	25	26
			E									

Answers on page 404.

Code-doku

Solve this puzzle just as you would a sudoku. Use deductive logic to complete the grid so that each row, column, and 3-by-3 box contains the letters from the word EDUCATION.

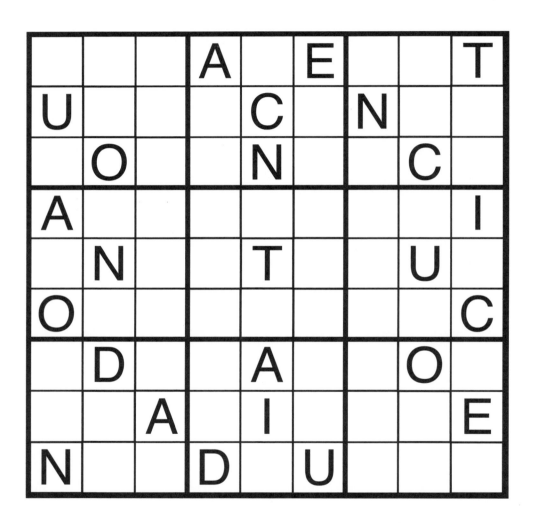

Answer on page 404.

4-Letter Anagrams

Fill in the blanks in each sentence below with words that are anagrams (rearrangements) of one another.

1. We could smell the foul _____ as soon as we opened the barn _____.
2. When the chef tried to carry a stack of _____, one _____ off and made a terrible clang.
3. The _____ of the litter waited for his _____ at the food dish.
4. The actor portrayed his _____ so well that he had the _____ attention of the audience.
5. When Sally's boyfriend gave her a _____, she had a happy _____ on her face.
6. The street _____ cast strange shadows through the leaves of the _____ tree.
7. The _____ letter was _____ an insurance company.
8. As the woman tried to keep _____ with her friend, the wind blew her _____ around her.

Queen Ana Gram

Queen Ana Gram of the tiny nation of Laity was know from coast to coast (about a mile) as the nation's queen of anagrams, which are words or phrases formed by rearranging the letters of another word or phrase. Queen Ana Gram was undefeated in anagram competitions until one fateful day when a stranger came to her palace with this challenge: "Give me a word that is an anagram of itself." According to the law of the land of Laity, anyone who defeats the queen in anagrams will take over the throne. The citizens of Laity are ready to boot the queen out and put the crown on the stranger. Can you help her by finding the anagram? Bonus: Laity is an anagram of what real country?

Answers on page 404.

Letterbox Big Screen

The letters in Marx can be found in boxes 1, 2, 11, and 20, but not necessarily in that order. The same is true for the other actors' names listed below. Using the names and the box numbers that follow them to guide you, insert all the letters of the alphabet into the boxes. If you do this correctly, the shaded cells will reveal 2 more film stars.

BULLOCK: 6, 7, 15, 19, 21, 26

CLIFT: 7, 8, 13, 16, 19

DE NIRO: 3, 6, 8, 9, 20, 24

GIBSON: 3, 4, 6, 8, 15, 18

JACKSON: 3, 4, 5, 6, 11, 19, 26

KIDMAN: 1, 3, 8, 11, 24, 26

MARX: 1, 2, 11, 20

McQUEEN: 1, 3, 9, 19, 21, 25

PACINO: 3, 6, 8, 11, 17, 19

SCHWARZENEGGER: 3, 4, 9, 11, 12, 18, 19, 20, 22, 23

SMITH: 1, 4, 8, 16, 23

VALENTINO: 3, 6, 7, 8, 9, 10, 11, 16

WAYNE: 3, 9, 11, 12, 14

1	2	3	4	5	6	7	8	9	10	11	12	13

14	15	16	17	18	19	20	21	22	23	24	25	26

Answer on page 404.

Cryptoku

Answer the clues below to fill in the grid and discover the 9 different letters used in each 3-by-3 box. Just like a standard crossword, answers read across and down; numbers in parenthesis indicate how many letters are in the solution. And, like a code-doku, each letter appears only once in each 3-by-3 box. When complete, the shaded squares will reveal a mystery word.

ACROSS

1. Crazy (3)
2. Decay (3)
3. Land amphibian (4)
4. Part of a circle (3)
5. Small bed (3)

DOWN

6. Take a break (4)
7. Railed vehicle (4)
8. Group of same items (3)
9. Famous Chinese Leader (3)
10. Grassy earth (3)

T			M					A
	O		S				C	
	1	A	2			7 T	8	
3		A		M				
				6				10
4		T		E				
	T	A			E	9		
	D	5		T		A		
R		M					T	

Answer on page 405.

Codeword

The letters of the alphabet are hidden in code: Each is represented by a random number from 1 through 26. With the letters already given, complete the crossword puzzle with English words and break the code.

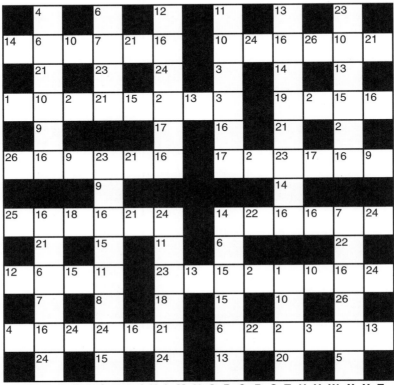

1	2	3	4	5	6	7	8	9	10	11	12	13
								M				

14	15	16	17	18	19	20	21	22	23	24	25	26
		E					L	A				F

Answers on page 405.

Chain Sudoku

Use deductive logic to complete the grid so that each row, each column, and each connected set of circles contains the numbers 1 through 7 in some order. The solution is unique.

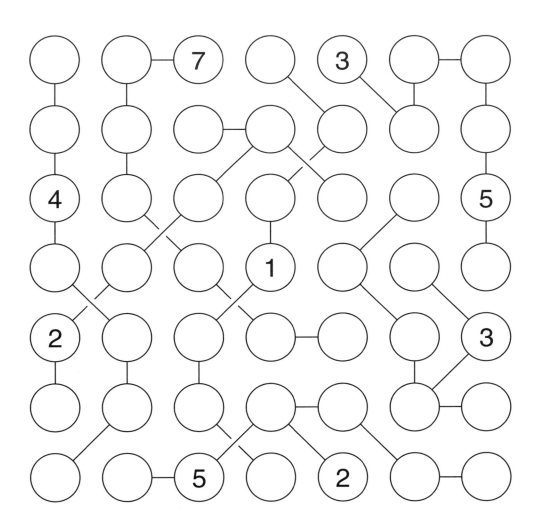

Answer on page 405.

One Out of Three Ain't Bad

Cryptograms are messages in substitution code. Break the code to read the message. THE SMART CAT might become FVO QWGDF JGF if **F** is substituted for **T**, **V** for **H**, **O** for **E**, and so on.

BNMMTOB X KTM MKGNN MTLNY HFM HD MNO XM

QXM TY IHOYTRNGNR XO NWINPPNOM XANGXBN.

BNHGBN YIKXPPNG XOR HMKNG OXMFGXPTYMY

KXAN HQYNGANR MKXM PTHOY XOR IKNNMXKY

XGN XPYH YFIINYYDFP HOPV XQHFM X MKTGR HD

MKN MTLN TO IXSMFGTOB MKNTG SGNV.

Word Columns

Find the hidden quote from Casey Stengel by using the letters directly below each of the blank squares. Each letter is used once. A black square indicates the end of a word.

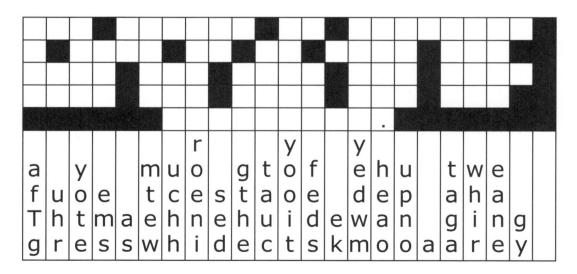

Answers on page 405.

Codeword

The letters of the alphabet are hidden in code: Each is represented by a random number from 1 through 26. With the letters already given, complete the crossword puzzle with English words and break the code.

9		1		24		10		10		26
7	18	13	16		14	7	19	24	9	2	1	24
	2		20			9		22		10		12
12	1	7	6	9	19	23	24		22	2	12	13
	12				11		4		24		7
9	24	4	9	15	1	23		24	4	9	8	12
		21		24		17		25			
2	19	7	22	17		17	9	5	9	15	9	24
	1		9		24		17				17
26	9	20	19		6	8	1	1	3	1	19	24
	24		20		9		19		1		7
14	7	21	22	1	6	6	1		19	20	18	2
	18		15		1		23		7		24

A B C D E F G H I J K L M N O P Q R S T U V W X Y Z

1	2	3	4	5	6	7	8	9	10	11	12	13
E			H				W				L	

14	15	16	17	18	19	20	21	22	23	24	25	26
					R							

Answers on page 405.

Add-a-Letter

This puzzle is an anagram with a twist: Each word or phrase below is missing the same letter. Discover the missing letter, then unscramble. All the "before" AND "after" words can be found in the grid. They may be read either forward or backward.

ACE LOP	HASSLE IT
AD NUANCE	HEN CARS
AIR FACET	HOARY PIG
ALIAS TO	IN GUILD
ALSO HI	LOAN YE
ARCS AS	OX HOSE
ART NORMS	RAG EAR
AVAIL ALE	SAIL SKI
CAR LIE	SEA TOSS
CUE SEA	STATION
CURBS RISE	SWAY US
EELS TOO	THIN TRUMP
ERR AIR	TOUGHER HARK
FOUR IS	WRY ERE
GAS INK	ZONER

```
I E C N A U N D A G B A E L A L I A V A V M C U V
U Q L D S Y A W B U S Y T Z G E U K A A E J O C W
E C N A D N U B A U S O T S E B S A I R O X B P T
B A R N S T O R M J V P Y L K A Y E E A H F C T S
Z Q Z E S T A B L I S H O R I A E Y U O J C G I N
N O H V A A R C S A S A O L E N R P S C P N R E X
B O N N F E G W R A N N B A E W J E I N G U I L D
C T I M N B S N L Y I O H E R C E R T V O T R S R
W S S O A C A I E B A R B H G Y A R T F B K A S P
T L Z R A V A L A T J T F U G A P A B R S M E A U
Z E Q R A S M R O N T R A A I U R I P U O P G H M
Q E A U T C R G S N K Q Y B C L O R G S L A A V S
I B A O G I N H A O E E H O C E D R A V E V R T E
S H C Z E I O E S Q Z Y P L C M T I H B T A L O A
V D O R K E C W H S F J A I T A L W N T E I S U T
W A T S B A A O O A S N R S Q S R P T G K L A G O
Y B A O L Y A Q B E F U G H K C M L H E T A V H S
Q B X I U A M R P M E V O I U B R A I Y N B E E S
S U B S C R I B E R Z C I R X A H C N E O L E R R
Q E P S G C G A S I N K B Z B S G E T H I E H H B
R K E N A S M P H F O S Y U R I T B R K T M D A G
T X O T T H U M B P R I N T D L F O U K A V X R T
T A E X D F N D A I B E P U E I V F M X T E V K K
G B R A N C H E S X B E C A U S E E P U S X Q T K
B C G G Z C Z E J B V F I X I K Y R L N D J S Z U
```

Answers on page 405.

Code-doku

Solve this puzzle just as you would a sudoku. Use deductive logic to complete the grid so that each row, column, and 3-by-3 box contains the letters from the words CANDY TIME.

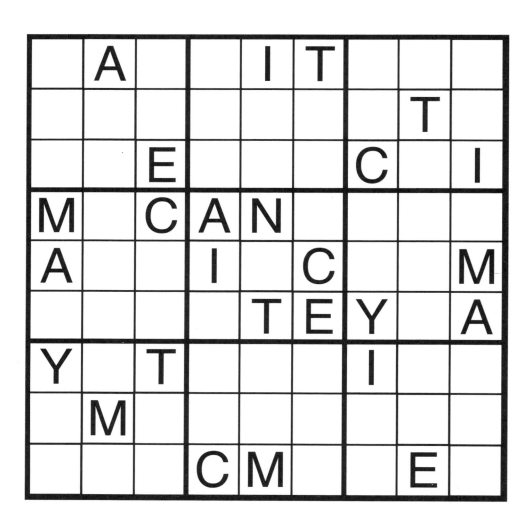

Answer on page 405.

What's Next?

Which figure completes this sequence?

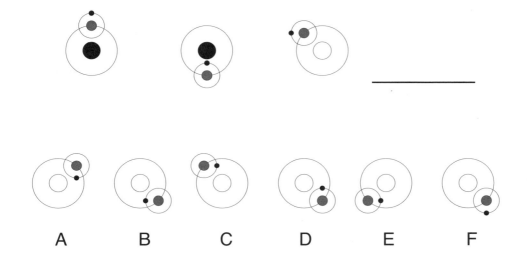

A   B   C   D   E   F

Sleigh Bells

Determine the next letter in this progression.

D, D, P, V, C, ___ D, B

Answers on page 406.

Add-a-Letter

This puzzle is an anagram with a twist: Each word or phrase below is missing the same letter. Discover the missing letter, then unscramble. All the "before" AND "after" words can be found in the grid. They may be read either forward or backward.

AFTER ALL

ARTY YEN

ASK SEEN

AVOIDS

FLOUNDER

FROG LINE

GAVEL THEN

GILL END

LARK BUS

LAY LEE

MITTEN IRE

NERD ILK

NOSH PIT

NOT EMEND

PAIN OWNED

PAN PEERS

RESTORING

ROAD HARE

SAT LACK

SAY HIGH

SEE LIGHTS

SELL AS

SETS THOU

SIGN PAN

SOP COKE

THIN GEEK

WHY AORTA

WOK ODOR

WONT NOD

WORD DELI

```
B J I F W Y S I G N P A N W O N D E R F U L W W I
T O W N S H I P A H I S T H G I L E E S F X B I C
W L L A R E T F A R I F W L C T I F R O G L I N E
E O D G N Y E F N U R G N I L L E W D K O Y A T Q
R W R W S L Z V L E D O H C N A G N I R O T S E R
I E E O A Y L D L O Y K W W P D F U Q Q O G A R W
N E T R L V H A N D W Y R H A E O R N S D B T T E
E K I L L Z E T Y O B E T O E Y N W E E E V L I N
T N R D E Z N L M C S W R R W A S D P T E P A M T
T I W W S O Y S E S O H O I A D D S O A A S C E R
I G G I W Z S E D N R W P R N X O R T W N W K S Y
M H N D I E Q F X C G E P I D G B O Z J M E W S W
W T O E L B S D X O H T E O T D M P W I W E I E A
R I S W A L L E Y E D I H P K E E G N I H T N L Y
E G A H Q J I R E E L A C D N E L L I G D G G T J
D L A R K B U S L R P C K I G A S Q I N O B S H C
N E R D I L K K S A Y H I G H P W E H W X P G A
U S V B A C N J B D C H N P W P E M D I N M A I T
O E O U T I D R I I B H D F O A E V E S T W N E W
L T Z L R I P I T O O J N A K T S O P C O K E W A
F S B W O Q M L S V P A I N O W N E D N W E A Q L
U T G A A E E L Y A L X E N D R C S G C N U T I K
S H W R Y J R P Q N V S E V O R E P A P S W E N S
N O R K H P M A P T S O T H R O W A W A Y H R V F
W U G S W O H S O U T H W E S T G A V E L T H E N
```

Answers on page 406.

Codeword

The letters of the alphabet are hidden in code: Each is represented by a random number from 1 through 26. With the letters already given, complete the crossword puzzle with English words and break the code.

1	2	3	4	5	6	7	8	9	10	11	12	13
	P										A	

14	15	16	17	18	19	20	21	22	23	24	25	26
O	L						S					

Answers on page 406.

Code-doku

Solve this puzzle just as you would a sudoku. Use deductive logic to complete the grid so that each row, column, and 3-by-3 box contains the letters from the word QUICKSAND.

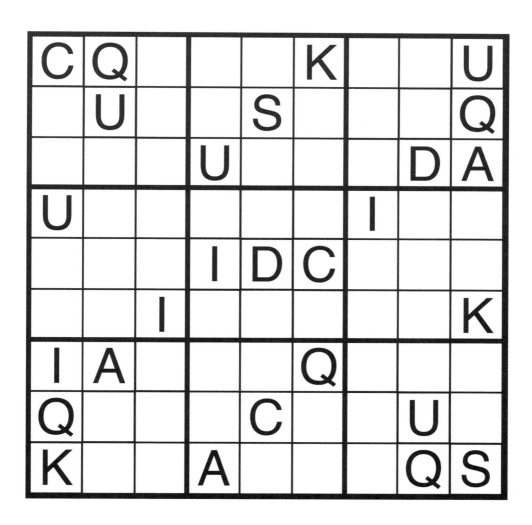

Answer on page 406.

Fashionable Anagrams

Fill in the blanks in the sentence below with 8-letter words that are anagrams (rearrangements of the same letters) of one another.

The clothing _____ was _____ to the fact that his work wasn't good enough, so he decided to _____ the entire fall collection.

Backyard Barbecue

Throw some shrimp (and some anagrams!) on the barbie! Below are 10 jumbled phrases indicated by capital letters. Each is an anagram (rearrangement) of a word or phrase that fits the story. Can you decipher all 10?

The kids were playing on the **WET SIGNS**, Uncle Frank and Jack from next door were playing a game of **HOSS HEROES**, and it was time to grill. The **THICK TRIO** was lighted, and the **TOAST PIE** had been dusted off. Kristen, their teenager, was stretched out on the **EAGLE CUSHION** and talking on her **CLONE HELP** as usual. The **RUM LABEL** offered some shade, and it was time for the announcement: "**NO HBO CONCERT**!" This was followed by **PRESCRIBE MAD HUB** and a genial reminder: **TO CHOKE SKIS**!

Answers on page 406.

Chain Sudoku

Use deductive logic to complete the grid so that each row, each column, and each connected set of circles contains the numbers 1 through 7 in some order. The solution is unique.

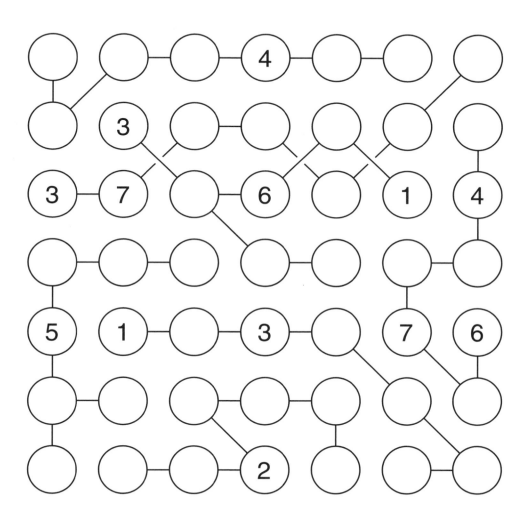

Answer on page 406.

Interception

You've intercepted two messages. One has the date of a meeting. The other must be the location—but the intercepted list has 13 place names on it. Can you decipher where the meeting is?

THAILAND

ECUADOR

ITALY

YORK, ENGLAND

FAROE ISLANDS

U.S. VIRGIN ISLANDS

TIPPERARY, IRELAND

NIGERIA

NAMIBIA

BIG LAKE

GHANA

OTTAWA

EL SALVADOR

Addagram

This puzzle functions exactly like an anagram with an added step: In addition to being scrambled, each word below is missing the same letter. Discover the missing letter, then unscramble the words. When you do, you'll reveal a weather phenomenon, a state of delirium, a synonym for "refuge," and a word describing a central support.

PHOTON

HASTIER

MAULS

STAMINA

Answers on pages 406-407.

Codeword

The letters of the alphabet are hidden in code: Each is represented by a random number from 1 through 26. With the letters already given, complete the crossword puzzle with English words and break the code.

	21		14		17		8		3			
26	23	12	20		3	7	20	20	18	17	20	
	21		5		3		7		20		23	
21	23	19	17	6	22	5	20		7	25	5	1
		13		20		24				5		
23	14	5	25	19	3		3	22	10	10	17	16
	20		18					20		19		
20	5	23	3	20	5		3	2	23	26	26	9
	6				22		11		18			
18	2	22	13		15	25	22	11	22	20	18	3
	20		23		17		23		5		2	
13	23	21	3	20	24	3		20	4	20	19	
	20		3		2		3		9			

A B C D E F G H I J K L M N O P Q R T S V U W X Y Z

1	2	3	4	5	6	7	8	9	10	11	12	13
												D

14	15	16	17	18	19	20	21	22	23	24	25	26
						E	M		A			

Answers on page 407.

Code-doku

Solve this puzzle just as you would a sudoku. Use deductive logic to complete the grid so that each row, column, and 3-by-3 box contains the letters from the word WORKPLACE.

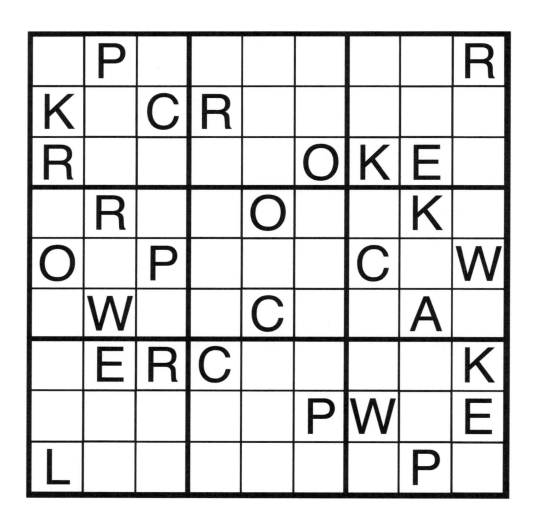

Answer on page 407.

Baseball Teams Letterbox

The letters in BRAVES can be found in boxes 1, 4, 6, 10, 12, and 21 but not necessarily in that order. Similarly, the letters in all the other baseball teams can be found in the boxes indicated. Your task is to insert all the letters of the alphabet into the boxes. If you do this correctly, the shaded cells will reveal another baseball team.

Hint: Compare BRAVES and BREWERS to find the value of W, then BRAVES to PADRES to find the value of A.

Unused letters: F, Q, and Z

ASTROS: 1, 6, 10, 22, 23

BLUE JAYS: 1, 4, 5, 6, 7, 9, 12, 18

BRAVES: 1, 4, 6, 10, 12, 21

BREWERS: 4, 6, 10, 12, 17

CARDINALS: 1, 2, 5, 6, 10, 13, 16, 20

CUBS: 6, 9, 12, 20

MARLINS: 1, 2, 5, 6, 10, 14, 16

PADRES: 1, 4, 6, 10, 11, 13

RED SOX: 4, 6,10, 13, 15, 23

TIGERS: 3, 4, 6, 10, 16, 22

WHITE SOX: 4, 6, 15, 16, 17, 19, 22, 23

YANKEES: 1, 2, 4, 6, 7, 8

1	2	3	4	5	6	7	8	9	10	11	12	13

14	15	16	17	18	19	20	21	22	23	24	25	26
										F	Q	Z

Answer on page 407.

Chain Sudoku

Use deductive logic to complete the grid so that each row, each column, and each connected set of circles contains the numbers 1 through 6 in some order. The solution is unique.

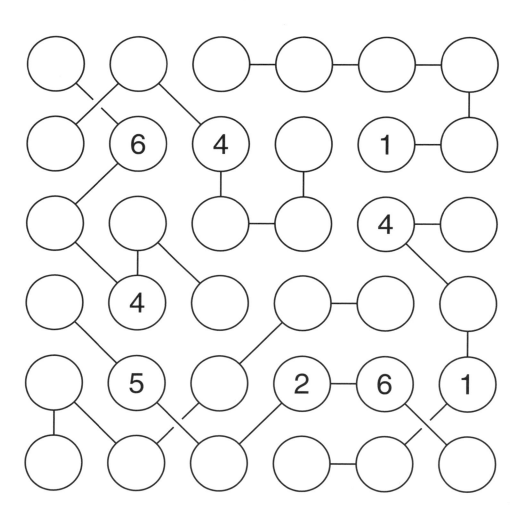

Answer on page 407.

Codeword

The letters of the alphabet are hidden in code: Each is represented by a random number from 1 through 26. With the letters already given, complete the crossword puzzle with English words and break the code.

26	22	21	17	16		3	22	5	22	13	17	22
1		4		22		25			20		2	
12		19		7		21		17	25	18	22	15
22	24	1	8	26	22	17	8		7		26	
13		13		1		24		17	8	26	8	17
22	17	17	8	26	23	8	8		23			2
6		21		6				17		10		22
19			18		21	24	25	7	23	25	7	26
22	13	9	25	13		22		1		25		5
	1		24		12	19	24	17	19	13	22	24
22	14	14	1	11		6		17		2		8
	17		21			2		8		8		21
1	21	17	2	10	19	21		13	22	26	5	21

A B C D E F G H I J K L M N O P Q R S T U V W X Y Z

1	2	3	4	5	6	7	8	9	10	11	12	13
I												

14	15	16	17	18	19	20	21	22	23	24	25	26
F			T	P								

Answers on page 407.

Cryptogram

Cryptograms are messages in substitution code. Break the code to read the humorous quote and its source. THE SMART CAT might become FVO QWGDF JGF if **F** is substituted for **T**, **V** for **H**, **O** for **E**, and so on.

"CVV UAIGDL TVCLDJO CJD MBVBFZRCV. SUDL GFAQ
DFZVBOU CFH TJAXCFBSL."

—ZAJHBD UAQD

LogiNumber

Determine the values of the variables below using 2 rules: Each variable is no greater than the numbers of variables in the puzzle; none of the variables are equal to each other. Use the grid to keep track of possible solutions.

$2C = D$

$C - 1 = B$

	1	2	3	4
A				
B				
C				
D				

Answers on page 407.

LogiNumber

Determine the values of the variables below using 2 rules: Each variable is no greater than the numbers of variables in the puzzle; none of the variables are equal to each other. Use the grid to keep track of possible solutions.

$$BC = 2D$$

$$C + D = 6$$

	1	2	3	4
A				
B				
C				
D				

Baseball Quirks

Cryptograms are messages in substitution code. Break the code to read the message. THE SMART CAT might become FVO QWGDF JGF if **F** is substituted for **T**, **V** for **H**, **O** for **E**, and so on.

"DEF 'RARVXOD' EPR SXASTX CPAU FAG'OX

JETCHPV EMAGJ MEDXMETT. DEF 'MOEKXD' EPR JYXF

EDC, 'UYEJ OXDXOKEJHAP?' DEF 'OXRD' EPR JYXF

JYHPC AN LAWWGPHDW. DEF 'SEROXD' EPR JYXF

TAAC EOAGPR NAO E SOHXDJ."

-JAWWF TEDAORE

Answers on page 407.

291

Boys' Names

The letters in the name BILL can be found in boxes 2, 8, and 18, but not necessarily in that order. The same is true for the other boys' names listed below. Using the names and the box numbers that follow them to guide you, insert all the letters of the alphabet into the boxes. If you do this correctly, the shaded cells will reveal 2 more names.

Hint: Look for words that share a single letter. For example, PAUL shares only a P with STEPHEN and only an A with MAX. By comparing the number lists following those 2 names, you can deduce the box numbers of those shared letters.

BARRY: 6, 7, 18, 24

BILL: 2, 8, 18

CARL: 4, 6, 7, 8

DAVID: 2, 6, 16, 26

FRED: 7, 9, 12, 16

GREGORY: 7, 9, 22, 24, 25

JOHN: 3, 5, 22, 23

JIM: 2, 3, 14

MARK: 6, 7, 14, 19

MAX: 6, 14, 15

PAUL: 1, 6, 8, 11

QUENTIN: 2, 9, 11, 17, 21, 23

ROWAN: 6, 7, 13, 22, 23

STEPHEN: 1, 5, 9, 10, 21, 23

ZAK: 6, 19, 20

1	2	3	4	5	6	7	8	9	10	11	12	13

14	15	16	17	18	19	20	21	22	23	24	25	26

Answer on page 407.

World Cities Letterbox

The letters in LONDON can be found in boxes 3, 10, 16, and 26, but not necessarily in that order. The same is true for the other cities listed below. Insert all the letters of the alphabet into the boxes. If you do this correctly, the shaded cells will reveal another world city.

Hint: Look for words that share a single letter. For example, ROME shares an O with SOFIA and an E with QUEBEC. By comparing the number lists following these 3 words, you can deduce the values of the 2 shared letters.

BRUSSELS: 7, 9, 18, 19, 21, 26

COPENHAGEN: 1, 3, 4, 5, 6, 16, 18, 24

HELSINKI: 1, 8, 9, 13, 16, 18, 26

JAKARTA: 2, 6, 7, 13, 20

LONDON: 3, 10, 16, 26

MEXICO CITY: 3, 4, 8, 15, 18, 20, 22, 23

QUEBEC: 4, 14, 18, 19, 21

QUEZON CITY: 3, 4, 8, 14, 15, 16, 17, 18, 19, 20

REYKJAVIK: 2, 6, 7, 8, 11, 13, 15, 18

ROME: 3, 7, 18, 23

SANTIAGO: 3, 6, 8, 9, 16, 20, 24

SOFIA: 3, 6, 8, 9, 12

VILNIUS: 8, 9, 11, 16, 19, 26

WARSAW: 6, 7, 9, 25

1	2	3	4	5	6	7	8	9	10	11	12	13

14	15	16	17	18	19	20	21	22	23	24	25	26

Answer on page 407.

Codeword

The letters of the alphabet are hidden in code: Each is represented by a random number from 1 through 26. With the letters already given, complete the crossword puzzle with English words and break the code. Once you have completed the grid, unscramble the letters found in the gray cells to reveal a hockey player.

A B C D E F G H I J K L M N O P Q R S T U V W X Y Z

1	2	3	4	5	6	7	8	9	10	11	12	13
				Z						L		

14	15	16	17	18	19	20	21	22	23	24	25	26
					E				N	G		

Answers on page 408.

Code-doku

Solve this puzzle just as you would a sudoku. Use deductive logic to complete the grid so that each row, column, and 3-by-3 box contains the letters from the word MAYFLOWER.

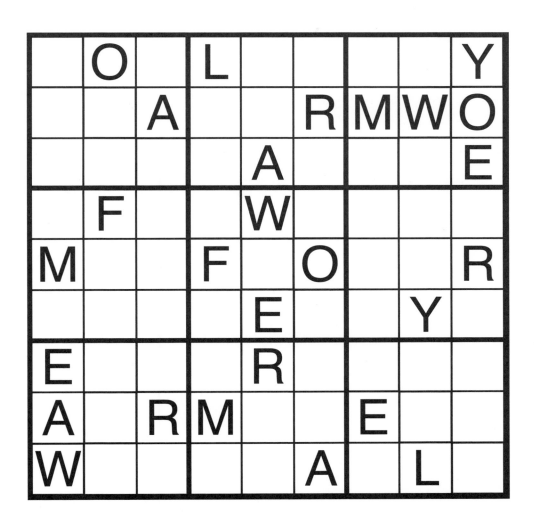

Answer on page 408.

What Comes Next?

Which figure completes this sequence?

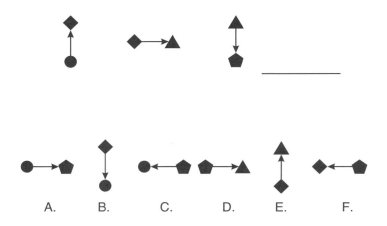

Visual Sequence

Which of the lettered figures continues this sequence?

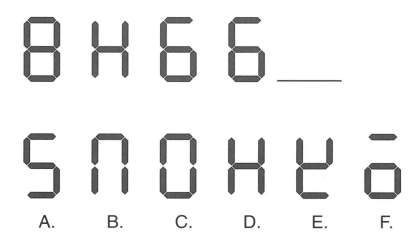

Answers on page 408.

Living Large Anagram

Below are 10 jumbled phrases indicated by capital letters. Each is an anagram (rearrangement) of a word or phrase that fits the story. Can you decipher all 10?

At the Museum of Unambiguously Large Things, a 7-foot docent addressed the group of tourists.

"We like to think big," he said. "Our favorite biblical person is **HOT GAIL**. Over there you'll see our **THE PLANE** statue, representing our favorite animal. Our favorite geographical unit is **CNN TONITE**."

"What's your favorite vehicle?" a tourist asked.

"The **OSTRICH MELT**, of course," the docent grinned.

"How about your favorite tourist attraction?" ventured another sightseer.

"The **LEO MUSIC**, naturally! Now please follow me as I point out some other big things. Here, for instance, is a model of our favorite ocean-going vessel, the **SUSIE CHIRP**. And in this display you see our most revered athletes, **NO EMOLLIENT FLAB**. Although we surely give props to the **MEOW RUSTLERS** as well! Over here you can see a satellite view of that glorious hole in the ground, the **NANCY DRAGON**. And finally," he said, concluding the tour, "on that wall you see the **END BATTALION**, a large number that gets larger every second. I must admit that it is not one of our favorite things...but it is, as they say, totally ginormous!"

Answers on page 408.

Codeword

The letters of the alphabet are hidden in code: Each is represented by random numbers from 1 through 26. With the letters already given, complete the crossword puzzle with English words and break the code.

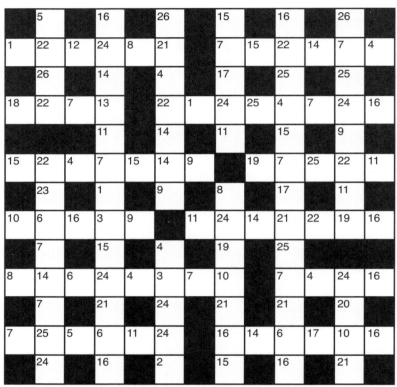

A B C D E F G H I J K L M N O P Q R S T U V W X Y Z

1	2	3	4	5	6	7	8	9	10	11	12	13
			C								Z	

14	15	16	17	18	19	20	21	22	23	24	25	26
										E		

Answers on page 408.

Codeword

The letters of the alphabet are hidden in code: Each is represented by a random number from 1 through 26. With the letters already given, complete the crossword puzzle with English words and break the code.

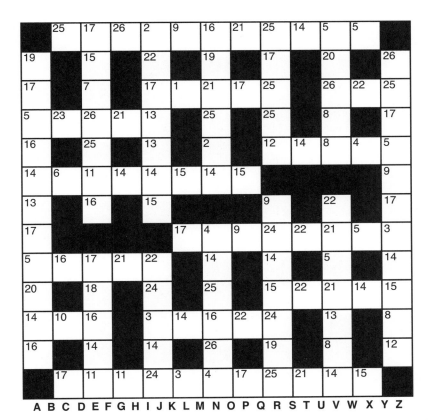

1	2	3	4	5	6	7	8	9	10	11	12	13
								H				B

14	15	16	17	18	19	20	21	22	23	24	25	26
								R				

Answers on page 408.

Chain Sudoku

Use deductive logic to complete the grid so that each row, each column, and each connected set of circles contains the numbers 1 through 7 in some order. The solution is unique.

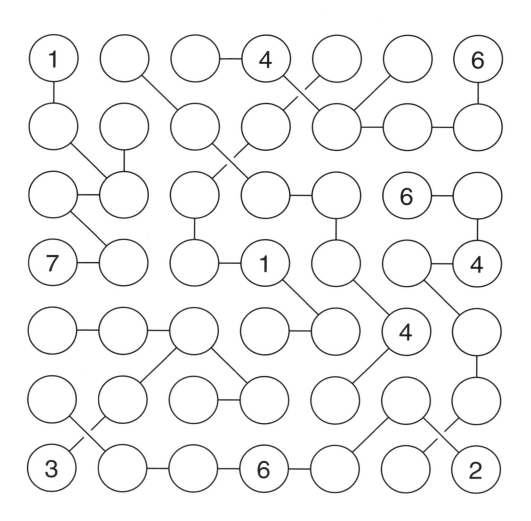

Answer on page 408.

Code-doku

Solve this puzzle just as you would a sudoku. Use deductive logic to complete the grid so that each row, column, and 3-by-3 box contains the letters from the word CHEMISTRY.

				S	M			
						Y		H
S	C			R			I	
	H	T				E		
			M					
		M				C	H	
	S			E			M	T
I		Y						
			T		I			

Answer on page 408.

On That Note

Every word listed is contained within the group of letters. Words can be found in a straight line horizontally, vertically, or diagonally. They may be read either forward or backward.

ALCAHUETE	GARKLEIN	RAVANAHATHA
ARPEGGIONE	GOBLET DRUM	RHAITA
BALABAN	GUSLI	SABAR
BANJO CELLO	HARMONICO	SARANGI
BASS DRUM	HIRA-DAIKO	SEA ORGAN
BAZOOKA	HUQIN	SHINOBUE
BONGO DRUMS	ISHAKWE	SODINA
CAJON	KAKKO	SUBIDOR
CHANDE	KEN BAU	SWORDBLADE
CITTERN	KHOL	TAN-TAN
COR ANGLAIS	KOTO	TENORA
CRWTH	LAUNEDDAS	TRIANGLE
DAHU	LYRE	TUBAX
DAP	MANDOLA	UKULELE
DHIMAYA	MELODICA	VIOLA
DIZI	NAGAK	WHIP
DRUM KIT	OCARINA	YANGQIN
DVOJNICE	PALENDAG	ZURNA
FIDDLE	PICCO PIPE	
FLUTINA	PSALTERY	

```
D  D  V  O  J  N  I  C  E  P  A  T  R  I  A  N  G  L  E  B  X  J  C
P  Y  P  C  B  I  J  R  T  D  I  L  E  N  O  I  G  G  E  P  R  A  K
G  O  A  I  N  E  T  L  V  F  A  H  O  F  F  L  Z  S  A  B  A  R  A
S  L  S  N  Z  I  O  K  I  H  S  X  W  D  C  J  D  F  I  R  Z  N  R
H  L  E  O  G  E  G  D  B  R  O  O  B  W  N  R  N  D  H  N  Q  V  O
I  E  R  M  M  Q  D  N  S  A  D  D  E  N  U  A  L  E  K  B  P  M  N
N  C  H  R  Z  L  I  W  A  G  I  M  V  M  N  V  M  U  D  O  O  C  E
O  O  R  A  E  O  N  N  T  R  N  U  K  A  S  A  K  M  E  N  C  C  T
B  J  O  H  V  K  R  Y  I  E  A  I  R  C  A  N  R  U  Z  G  A  M  F
U  N  D  F  E  I  E  J  A  U  T  S  S  I  C  A  Q  R  R  O  R  H  F
E  A  I  O  L  A  T  M  H  T  J  M  W  D  S  H  S  D  B  D  I  X  C
O  B  B  S  E  D  T  N  R  B  A  Z  O  O  K  A  P  S  B  R  N  P  M
K  M  U  R  L  A  I  O  I  T  N  Q  R  L  F  T  N  S  U  U  A  A  U
E  G  S  E  U  R  C  S  T  Q  I  K  D  E  G  H  P  A  C  M  V  L  R
N  J  I  Z  K  I  B  I  H  O  U  N  B  M  L  A  P  B  B  S  I  E  D
B  E  T  E  U  H  A  C  L  A  K  H  L  Y  Y  Z  N  J  E  A  O  N  T
A  I  N  I  E  L  K  R  A  G  K  J  A  W  R  U  A  A  M  F  L  D  E
U  Z  O  K  K  A  K  T  U  C  M  W  D  M  E  E  O  Y  T  I  A  A  L
Y  I  M  A  N  I  T  U  L  F  A  Z  E  W  K  R  T  H  A  N  T  G  B
S  D  U  G  V  W  I  B  W  Q  Y  J  I  H  G  J  T  L  V  M  A  F  O
C  O  R  A  N  G  L  A  I  S  Z  B  O  A  D  W  Q  N  A  S  I  T  G
U  B  Q  N  O  V  D  X  K  T  X  L  N  N  R  A  W  E  K  S  N  H  X
U  H  A  D  P  I  C  C  O  P  I  E  C  Y  J  P  Z  Z  W  P  A  D
```

Answers on page 409.

LogiNumber

Determine the values of the letters below using 2 rules: Each letter is no greater than the number of letters in the puzzle; none of the letters are equal to each other. Use the grid to help keep track of possible solutions.

$$F + E = H + C$$
$$F + 1 = A$$
$$A + G + E = 15$$
$$C + 1 = F$$
$$2D = A + 11$$

	1	2	3	4	5	6	7	8
A								
B								
C								
D								
E								
F								
G								
H								

LogiNumber

Determine the values of the letters below using 2 rules: Each letter is no greater than the number of letters in the puzzle; none of the letters are equal to each other. Use the grid to help keep track of possible solutions.

$$E + B > A$$
$$H + B < D$$
$$D + G = 9$$
$$E + H = G$$
$$D + 1 = C$$

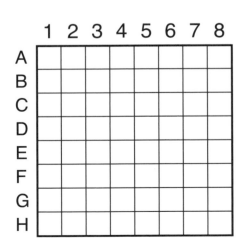

	1	2	3	4	5	6	7	8
A								
B								
C								
D								
E								
F								
G								
H								

Answers on page 409.

Codeword

The letters of the alphabet are hidden in code: Each is represented by a random number from 1 through 26. With the letters already given, complete the crossword puzzle with English words and break the code.

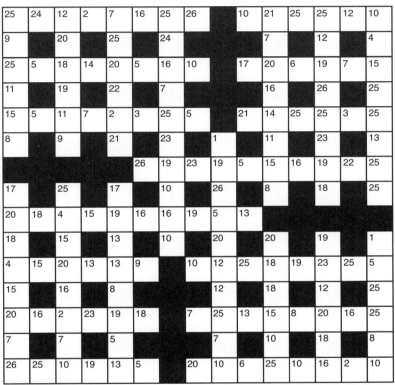

1	2	3	4	5	6	7	8	9	10	11	12	13
	O											

14	15	16	17	18	19	20	21	22	23	24	25	26
		T	C	I	A				M			

Answers on page 409.

Code-doku

Solve this puzzle just as you would a sudoku. Use deductive logic to complete the grid so that each row, column, and 3-by-3 box contains the letters from the word PALMISTRY.

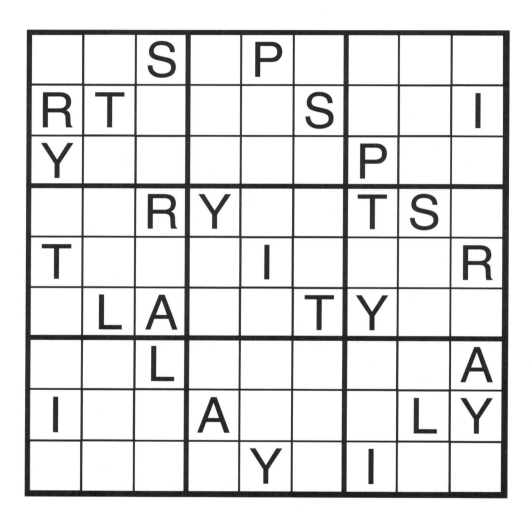

Answer on page 409.

Addagram

This puzzle functions exactly like an anagram with an added step: In addition to being scrambled, each word below is missing the same letter. Discover the missing letter, then unscramble the words. When you do, you'll reveal a wading bird, a precious metal, a word meaning "humor," and a word meaning "residue."

LOAFING

NUPTIAL

DECOY

TANNER

Addagram

This puzzle functions exactly like an anagram with an added step: In addition to being scrambled, each word below is missing the same letter. Discover the missing letter, then unscramble the words. When you do, you'll reveal a referee, a numerical symbol, financial protection, and a word for "income."

PRIME

GRIEF

CRANNIES

VENEER

Answers on page 409.

Honeycomb

Answer each clue with a 6-letter word. Write the words in either a clockwise or counterclockwise direction around the numerals in the grid.

CLOCKWISE

2. Wading birds
4. Good buddy
7. More solid
10. Shims
12. Use a credit card
16. House of worship
17. Having a meal
20. Bonding agent
22. Cylindrical inflorescence
23. Make
24. Colored slightly
26. Sides
28. Figures
30. Food samples
32. More lofty
36. European measures
37. Small river

COUNTERCLOCKWISE

1. Illegal acts
3. Champagne cocktail
5. Desert vision
6. Most achy
8. Male goose
9. Shiny metal
11. Tailored
13. Need for food
14. Call it a career
15. Part of the eye
18. Young cat
19. Likelihood
21. Eateries
25. Chess piece
27. Ribbed
29. Sire
31. Lower in rank
33. Picture borders
34. High regard
35. Closer

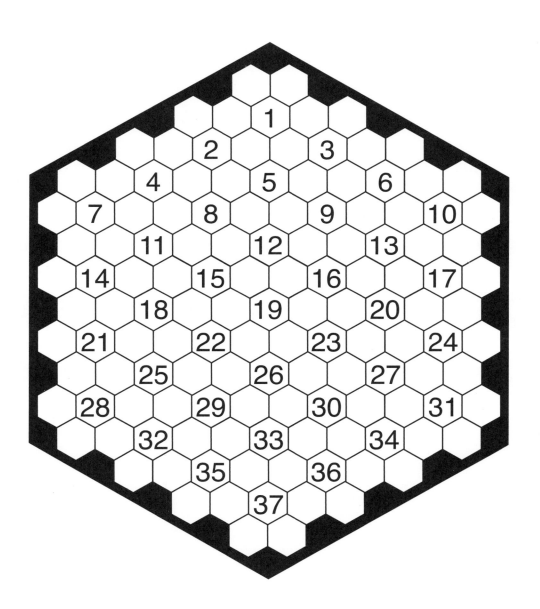

Answers on page 409.

Group Dynamics

Every word listed is contained within the group of letters. Words can be found in a straight line horizontally, vertically, or diagonally. They may be read either forward or backward.

AMBUSH	CHATTERING	GAGGLE	RAFTER
ARMY	CLOUD	GANG	RASP
ARRAY	CLOWDER	GAZE	RICHESSE
BADLING	COHORT	GULP	ROOKERY
BALE	COMPANY	HERD	SCHOOL
BANK	COVERT	HORDE	SCOURGE
BARREL	COVEY	HOST	SCREAM
BASK	CRASH	HOVER	SEDGE
BELLOWING	DECEIT	HURTLE	SHREWDNESS
BESYNESS	DESCENT	INTRUSION	SIEGE
BEVY	DOLE	KINDLE	SLEUTH
BIKE	DOPPING	LEAP	SOUNDER
BIND	DOWN	LEASH	SPRING
BLOAT	DOYLT	MEMORY	TIDING
BOIL	DRAY	MESS	TRIP
BOUQUET	DRIFT	MURDER	UNKINDNESS
BROOD	DROVE	MUSTER	WAKE
BUILDING	FALL	PACK	WATCH
BUNCH	FAMILY	PARCEL	WHISP
CACKLE	FLEET	PARLIAMENT	WING
CARAVAN	FLING	PARTY	WISDOM
CAST	FLUFFLE	PITYING	YOKE
CETE	FLUSH	PLAGUE	
CHARM	FLUTTER	PRIDE	

```
D Y K R A R H R L X X G K D A L T Z Y P F T Z Q O
N M Q U E V O E I K G Q P D E S M Y R Y I R T D T
E R T D O Y L T O F U R Y C O E R C E R S R C P E
D A R Y Z C K F B A I A R H R D A O K O A O T L U
M U S T E R A A U D R A C T E G H H O M V L G A Q
M A G D D R I R E R P Z L L V E C O O E J N N G U
L T R N H E R D A C I S E V O R D R R M I P B U O
C O D B I D S C O V E Y C R H U F T K D G T A E B
H L D G R W G C J A A N P H B A D L I N G E R U H
A E O U U O O N E R E N K U O C C T U L A E R Z Y
T A L L R L O L I N T R U S I O N O H T B L E S W
T P E P L C M D L L T A U A E E L X M S T F L S A
E C A S T A G A Z E F M O R L E G H P P A E B E K
R V K G U F F Y V E B O C L A H H R T S A E R N E
I Y A P G D T G N I D L I U B L T Y U U A N L Y L
N N S T M F H T J S F L U F F L E O O O E R Y S G
G N I W I C V N I S G S O B E L D N I K C L Q E G
I Y I R N W N E O E A I C U N K I N D N E S S B A
Y C D U Q X G M O M K B S S E N D W E R H S H Q G
L R B R F E X A B C A C K L E T J O X U O B A S K
I A N X L E K I B R I C H E S S E W R U B A N K V
M S W C U Y N L D W A T C H T R H T N W I S D O M
A H O E S D K R R P A R T Y I I L D T I E C E D B
F C D T H I I A A M B U S H S E E P I T Y I N G P
S C R E A M Y P Y G N I R P S R G N I P P O D A P
```

Answers on page 409.

Mastermind

The goal of this puzzle is to replace the question marks with a correct sequence of numbers. The numbers you need for the answer are contained in the rows above the question marks. Follow these 2 guides: A black dot indicates that a number needed for the solution is in that row and in the correct position; a white dot means that a number needed for the solution is in that row but in the wrong position. Numbers do not appear more than once in the solution, and the solution never begins with 0.

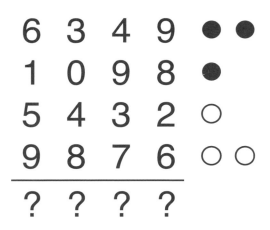

Crypto-Logic

Each of the numbers in the sequence below represents a letter. Use the mathematical clues to determine which number stands for which letter and reveal the encrypted word.
Hint: Remember that a / indicates divided by, and that all sums in parentheses must be done first.

5 7 2 3

Clues:

L = 10	S = 1
L / N = D	D + 2 = O
D − 4 = S	L − O = E

Answers on page 409.

Code-doku

Solve this puzzle just as you would a sudoku. Use deductive logic to complete the grid so that each row, column, and 3-by-3 box contains the letters from the word COMPUTERS.

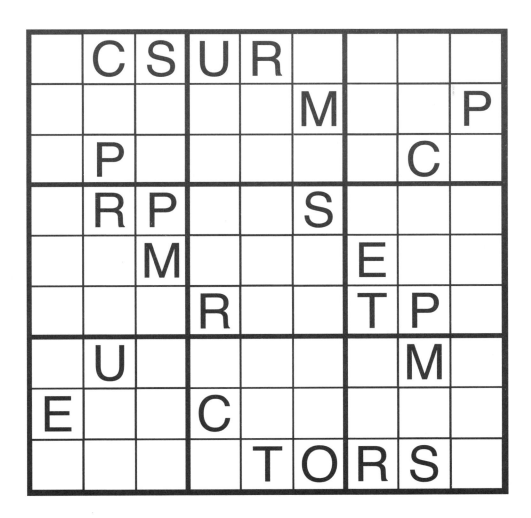

Answer on page 410.

Variety Pack

Every word listed is contained within the group of letters. Words can be found in a straight line horizontally, vertically, or diagonally. They may be read either forward or backward.

ACHIEVE	ECLAT	MASK	SKIFF
ALLOW	EMOTION	MENTAL	SMALLER
ANOTHER	EVER	MISSION	SOIL
ARROW	FAINT	MOSAIC	SPADE
AVENGER	FEATURE	MYSELF	SPOON
BANK	FINAL	NIGHT	START
BEFORE	FLOAT	OATMEAL	STORE
BETWEEN	FORM	ORIENTAL	STUDY
BLOWOUT	FRIEND	PALE	SUPPORT
BOUND	GARDEN	PEACE	TABLE
BROUGHT	GLIMMER	PILE	TEMPT
CADET	GRATEFUL	POKE	THIRD
CASUAL	GUNWALE	PRESENCE	TIMID
CHASM	HATH	PROTECT	TOWEL
CLAD	HERMIT	QUIET	TROUBLE
COLICKY	HOMAGE	REAL	UNCLE
CONSIST	HUNGER	REMADE	USER
COURT	INDICATE	RESULT	VICINITY
CRITICAL	ITSELF	ROBE	WANDER
DATE	KEEP	SAFE	WEAPON
DENTAL	LANGUAGE	SCORN	WHEREIN
DINNER	LECTURE	SENTENCE	WINDFALL
DONATION	LIST	SHELF	WORSHIP
DREARY	LUCKY	SHROUD	ZENITH

```
N T S P E L J C O N S I S T I L X S T S N R V T K
I W H E E L A T N E D T R O U B L E U R F E I X Y
F H R E C F C T T Y W P C D R I H T O O A M Q W D
L E O K F B R N N Y M I P G O I Z C W V I W V R M
E R U T A E F E U E Q H N R J A S M O D N A D E I
H E D O S L D V M J I S F D O H T N L G T N O M S
S I N U D A T H G I N R V I F T U M B N I D N M S
I N E S M P Y G E O H O O N N A E N E L B E A I I
J U Y E O T R T P O Y W O L L A L C G A S R T L O
F S R B P Q A A P Q D N E I R F L L T E L P I G N
F X K M U C E M G H U C L G M W V P M A R T O I W
L V E I I W R H F N T L A A Q A E O R V L O N O A
E T E D F B D I O U S I W R N A T Z R E S U L T N
S T N J A F Y O R L G S N D C I J F D N S O D Q E
Y I A O R E V E M C A T U E O C L N T G B E I I E
M D D D R G M O S A I C G N Z E U W A E R T N L W
Y A L A E L K H L D C L I M S O C H L R E O N C T
T Y R C L U S G A E I H A T B G W N C U H W E P E
I T S O L C A E U T K R I E I O R T E J T E R B B
N H T U A K M R S E H O E E R R H A X T O L M M E
I G A R M Y S O A F Y B P R V Y C O T K N N U L P
C U R T S P K F C A M E A H O E H L M E A E I P M
I O T L A T N E M S U P P O R T A F X A F P S K C
V R K D G R A B J G T I M R E H S L A N G U A G E
G B E R T A B L E C O L I C K Y M A A R K E L Z L
```

Answers on page 410.

Add-a-Letter

This puzzle is an anagram with a twist: Each word or phrase below is missing the same letter. Discover the missing letter, then unscramble. All the "before" AND "after" words can be found in the grid. They may be read either forward or backward.

AEON TILT	IN INGOT
AIR LIME	INSERTED
ALERTERS	LAVA PRO
ALL REAL	OAR CHAP
AM ARRIVE	ONLY GO
ASCOT HIDES IT	QUAINT
CALM TEEN	RECITE
CLOSE TEE	RED FOIL
CRUDE ORE	RUE TIC
DIME ACT	SEA MONKS
EARL SON	SECRETIVE
EEL RADISH	SIC BOORS
FRIES SOON	SUITED
HAM ICON	TALON ARM
ICE BLUR	TRIED IN

```
Y Y B J D P R E S I D E N T D G F R I E S S O O N
P E R S O N A L K S I C B O O R S J L A V A P R O
I M P E R I A L T E L E S C O P E O G O I Q F E I
K D C A L M T E E N E P R I M A V E R A P X P C S
J P D L R F V H Z R D E T A C I T S I H P O S E S
T A L O N A R M U N O A D I M E A C T Q L A C I E
E H M M S B L D M B G R R N D Q T R Y Y J R R P F
D E C D O K E L N O Y L O Q M E X U G Q E S A T O
T E T A E C N P E W L S R F B L L O P T A T A T R
H N T E O T N O R L N O P U Q R N I I S R B L R P
E M I R S R C D M O O N N I L P E V F O I Q L I S
S T P A E O P A I A B R F O Q B E P L O B D R E V
P Z P P U S L P P P E O H I C U E M U D R D E D N
O P O A G Q N C A M E S S H E I A C H B L P A I T
K I T S D E T I U S I R A C I N M N I D L P L N R
E H E C U K U B Q D O M T N I K B A T O P I E E E
S S N O A R C H A P P X I N F S E A H R Q M C A L
M R T T K G D R I I I N P C I P L R O J E I R I R
A E I H V H L O O W G P X F O E Z V O C T A H R E
N D A I B E E N D O C E V I R R A M A E C E H L D
L A L D E E R U T C I P N T U L R L R W D N Y I F
R E E E G K F V D T B T E E C J P X B C W U R M O
P L A S T E R E R T I R T E V I T C E P S E R E I
U V T I U G X B U N S I R B Q H P T E K Z G D C L
T E R T R C V M G Q C Y Q T D L T T L I T N O E A
```

Answers on page 410.

Cryptoku

Answer the clues below to fill in the grid and discover the 9 different letters used in each 3-by-3 box. Just like a standard crossword, answers read across and down; numbers in parenthesis indicate how many letters are in the solution. And, like a code-doku, each letter appears only once in each 3-by-3 box. When complete, the shaded squares will reveal a mystery word.

ACROSS

1. Female chicken (3)
2. Preposition (2)
3. Egyptian symbol (4)
4. Point of an old pen (3)
5. Devour (3)

DOWN

6. Doctor's command, with "say" (2)
7. Transgression (3)
8. Seventh music note (2)
9. First person, to be (2)
10. Article (2)

Answer on page 410.

Codeword

The letters of the alphabet are hidden in code: Each is represented by a random number from 1 through 26. With the letters already given, complete the crossword puzzle with English words and break the code.

	8		19		26		26		10		22		4	
20	9	24	25	7	5		23	5	18	6	17	23	5	12
	25		15		13		20		6		14		4	
4	25	15	8	6	9	9	15		20	24	24	23	6	5
	23		23		5		17		19			14		
10	17	22	17	14	13		14	25	19	9	5	21	5	14
	14		5				13		9		15			
20	13	5	14	12	20	10		7	5	3	5	12	9	15
			12		12		20				16		20	
16	11	17	10	1	5	23	10		10	1	17	23	2	10
	5				18		26		5		2		5	
21	17	9	17	5	6		5	3	26	25	14	5	14	2
	13		12		20		24		2		5		5	
23	11	5	25	10	2	20	2		17	14	10	17	10	2
	2		9		5		10		24		10		10	

A B C D E F G H I J K L M N O P Q R S T U V W X Y Z

1	2	3	4	5	6	7	8	9	10	11	12	13
K	T								S			

14	15	16	17	18	19	20	21	22	23	24	25	26
			I						R			

Answers on page 410.

Add-a-Letter

This puzzle is an anagram with a twist: Each word or phrase below is missing the same letter. Discover the missing letter, then unscramble. All the "before" AND "after" words can be found in the grid. They may be read either forward or backward.

ARGON	MARLIN POT
ARK BODY	MOTORMEN
ASP GAS	NO HURTS
CALM ID	NUMERATION
CAN FIN	PI CLAN
CHOMP IRON	PRIOR SONGS
CIRCLET	ROMPER
CONSUL	RUM COST
CRASH	SLAB LAB
CURB SO	SPUR ME
DUB VALOR	STORY
ILL MONAD	SWAN ERAS
IN LOUT	TIC TURN
IN TONS	TIN CAB
INNER PAL	UNCLE FIN

E N I L O P M A R T C D T V Z D T I N C A B K K X
R E T S Y O L W R O P O X B I A E R Q F A F E K F
D B B A L B A L S Z S F N O X N S R F S S A G Y I
A R M A R L I N P O T B P S I O E P E K C R A S H
A J A S S E N E R A W A R L U M N B G O C C S P D
E A N O C G N C O E Z Q T U O L A O U A F I S U C
F N N K B S E W M M C U S T C L N N I P S R A R L
M Q B B E Y R Y P E O K S S L I S S P S I T P M A
L O R A M C E M E R L U G E N E T O M F N C D E P
Z Z R K P A P K R P C N N T L R P Z U Q U E L D R
Y C Z M E B M I C U O O O Q U E V C U T C L T A E
H D E V R I K A G S I N O H D Z M U I M H E V T N
N B O R O N M N R L S N O X G E O E Y R D E E T N
N O U B R E C O L C A N F I N K U Q D W C H R I I
E R R Y K T I A P T R R P O E C N A N I F L U N L
M U O I G R D S T O R Y H B Y E T M V N C R E C N
R M B A P E A R Z U Y P Z Z Z C A R N D U A Q T O
O C S O M M M E T R O N O M E N I O B N S E L U I
T O C C U L O Z E R S L M J Z E N T C C A U I R T
O S U A A L K H C T Y Y N E G U E L U O R D Q E A
M T R V R L E I C F S K F I N L E P L R E T C K R
E U E O N D M V P E L I C A N F R R O A N Z Q E E
N O G R A V X I A N W Y R A I N D Y P N A I H S M
D U B V A L O R D R E A V N P I C Q I G W C V C U
D T D T I C T U R N D H V I P R O G R E S S I O N

Answers on page 410.

Code-doku

Solve this puzzle just as you would a sudoku. Use deductive logic to complete the grid so that each row, column, and 3-by-3 box contains the letters from the word MACHINERY.

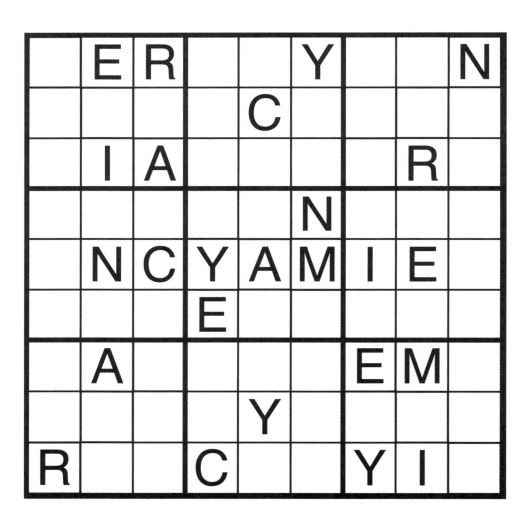

Answer on page 411.

Astrological Discovery

Cryptograms are messages in substitution code. Break the code to read the message. THE SMART CAT might become FVO QWGDF JGF if **F** is substituted for **T**, **V** for **H**, **O** for **E**, and so on.

"EN XSYR'L FW RFVQG LSPW. S'E F XFQRV LSPW. QJPRQGRV XR EFAR EZK."

—GRWWN NJZWPEFW.

Word Columns

Find the hidden humorous statement by using the letters directly below each of the blank squares. Each letter is used only once. A black square indicates the end of a word.

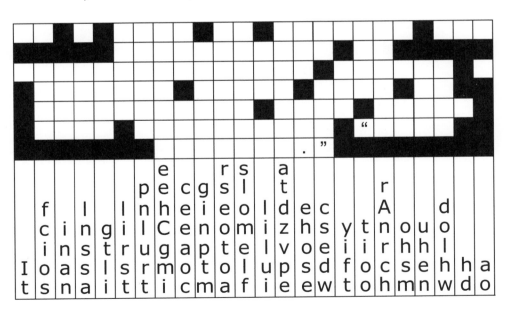

Answers on page 411.

Chain Sudoku

Use deductive logic to complete the grid so that each row, each column, and each connected set of circles contains the numbers 1 through 7 in some order. The solution is unique.

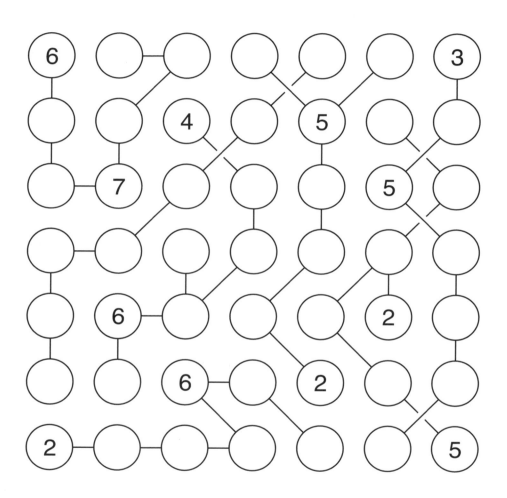

Answer on page 411.

Codeword

The letters of the alphabet are hidden in code: Each is represented by a random number from 1 through 26. With the letters already given, complete the crossword puzzle with English words and break the code.

1	26	15	5	■	10	8	8	3	16	11	23	12
15	■	26	■	21	■	14	■	1	■	19	■	15
13	11	18	16	26	15	8	■	11	4	9	22	8
8	■	1	■	2	■	17	■	21	■	11	■	18
23	26	15	7	8	17	24	26	22	11	22	20	■
7	■	■	■	22	■	7	■	11	■	1	■	5
8	7	25	11	15	8	■	8	17	16	11	22	12
3	■	11	■	17	■	25	■	17	■	■	■	1
■	11	23	23	8	6	8	22	11	7	1	26	15
11	■	12	■	15	■	11	■	7	■	15	■	3
21	22	1	5	7	■	22	8	1	5	5	9	8
11	■	15	■	11	■	8	■	23	■	8	■	8
22	8	21	9	6	11	22	5	■	5	7	8	24

A B C D E F G H I J K L M N O P Q R S T U V W X Y Z

1	2	3	4	5	6	7	8	9	10	11	12	13
		D										

14	15	16	17	18	19	20	21	22	23	24	25	26
					Q							

Answesr on page 411.

Add-a-Letter

This puzzle is an anagram with a twist: Each word or phrase below is missing the same letter. Discover the missing letter, then unscramble. All the "before" AND "after" words can be found in the grid. They may be read either forward or backward.

AID SLICES	GILT WHEY
AIRMAIL	HILT SAP
ALL TOIL	IGNORE
AUTUMN ACRE	ION SPORES
BACTERIA	LAB LOOT
CANINE	LION RAM
CAUSER	METRO RAPS
CUT END	NEE MINI
DEER DEN	NO TIN COIN
DENIM LEI	NO TUNIC
DO RUNE	ONE CRIER
ELF MUD	OUR POND
ENTICE CUT	SALUTE
FIT HAUL	TAN FLUE
GAITER	UNSAID ERR

```
Z M G Z V O I N F O R M A L Z J D R O G E C P R A
J E Y F Q J S E R O P S N O I N O N F I C T I O N
T T E N I N A C H I L T S A P F D F L A T S H I P
Q R H T U M D L T D A F F L U E N T I Q I E O J D
C O W H A F U O Z U K Y P E D N A E F D R C N E X
K R T R F C O F I N A N C E N X P W T D N E F H R
F A L B E L I O F U O X I C O D Y W N I E E F E H
O P I N B S P R T L H D W N P U H U T M N A T T L
R S G A H N I U B B E K O O R M O O I D I I N U R
E F L A E O M A N A A D K H U F N N E T A G N X C
I E L M I N E D R O F L S N O L I R H G C Z O O S
G Q K O A D T Z H D I Q L R E E Z F A M I L I A R
N I R C T T S I A N N S P S S U U M A R N O I L W
N M R D S I C L C I Z U S P D L L N T V L C G E A
V E E L R N L N I E R N F E D E U F E N U R O D R
H F D E M E U L U C C E T F F F I K N I V P G E O
L U I I L C I V A F E U T S A O X F U A Z S S Q R
U N A F I I G N O R E S T C O H R O I E T U L A S
A C S E O N M R F Z Z D T K A R J P X S A R P S U
H T N N T U K Q A O Z U J G N B F M L C S F H T L
T I U I L T N J N Z R A P J V A R A I R M A I L F
I O G M L O E D Q E H C W E N I N I M E F C L T A
F N D D A N O N E C R I E R K G P B W R Q E Y C T
E T A G I R F A L R V P G G T L N E D R E E D W E
F E T T U C C I N E F L Y W E I G H T T Y P E J R
```

Answers on page 411.

Cryptoku

Answer the clues below to fill in the grid and discover the 9 different letters used in each 3-by-3 box. Just like a standard crossword, answers read across and down; numbers in parenthesis indicate how many letters are in the solution. And, like a code-doku, each letter appears only once in each 3-by-3 box. When complete, the shaded squares will reveal a mystery word.

ACROSS

1. Ego (2)
2. Ratio of circumference to diameter (2)
3. Noah's boat (3)
4. Bottomless _____ (3)
5. Impersonal pronoun (2)

DOWN

6. Hat (3)
7. Feline (3)
8. To be free of (3)
9. Auto (3)
10. Hello: abbr. (2)

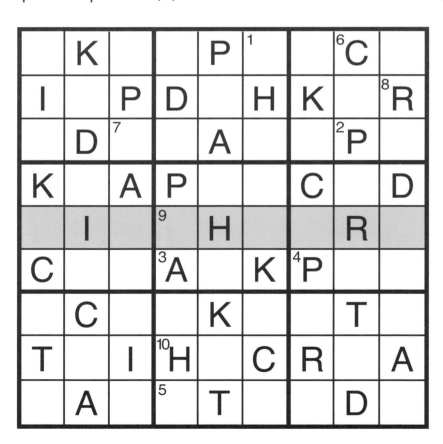

Answer on page 411.

LogiNumber

Determine the values of the letters below using 2 rules: Each letter is no greater than the number of letters in the puzzle; none of the letters are equal to each other. Use the grid to help keep track of possible solutions.

$$2D = F + 9$$

$$B + A = E$$

$$B + C = G$$

$$B + 2 = A$$

```
    1 2 3 4 5 6 7
A
B
C
D
E
F
G
```

LogiNumber

Determine the values of the letters below using 2 rules: Each letter is no greater than the number of letters in the puzzle; none of the letters are equal to each other. Use the grid to help keep track of possible solutions.

$$C + E = 7$$

$$A > G$$

$$F - C = B$$

$$D - E = C - 2$$

$$B + G = D + C$$

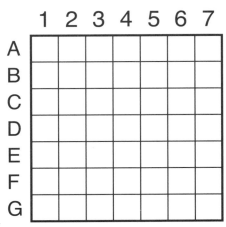

Answers on page 411.

Add-a-Letter

This puzzle is an anagram with a twist: Each word or phrase below is missing the same letter. Discover the missing letter, then unscramble. All the "before" AND "after" words can be found in the grid. They may be read either forward or backward.

ACTION RATS	HIT GNU
AGED SITE	ICY DOTS
AIL LACE	ITS OATS
CAB RAIN	MICE TIP TOO
COOL EL	MOM TUNE
CUE MOM	MUTTON EAR
CURT CRONE	OPEN AXIS
DASTARD	ORE PIE
FED CUT	OUR SPICES
FISH CARE	PERT SEER
GAVE DATA	RACY ODES
GILD WADS	RIP COVE
GO LOB	SECT IT IS
GUILT IS	SIR COGS
HE CLAN	WISH POT

```
U B T S T A R N O I T C A D D T S I U G N I L A C
W E S W A D D L I N G T O W N S H I P D A B E U U
C V T S I T N E I C S H S I T L I U G P L R L J R
B O L O G A D V A N T A G E T P C V F F C Q O V T
B C U T I D M I C E T I P T O O Y M R B E P O M C
G P C A C I P F G A V E D A T A D U A Y H B C O R
B I N D O N F H C I Z A N Z I G O T N H Z C H N O
M R F E D C U T U N L O E Y P V T T C F I S L U N
E R A C H S I F Q N I D Q U R C S O H O C T Y M E
T E C A L L I A E S T A W Y H J S N I T B X G E T
X O K C W R B F N D D I R A H P E E S T Y L L N A
S L U F R A B A N N I C N B D L C A E O S Y O T U
S S K R V C P Y R V F N O G A S T R H U L O R N S
V E F P N X Q P M R E D S Z E C I K H R E C A L G
M D C G E A S O P L C I R N O I T C A S N A R T R
D O S O M C M T T E X O D Z O B I W K P O S G C S
E Y M T N T N E A A R T M Y D Q S G D I L W N O B
S C P E U D R I N T G C N P S R R R Z C O I I N E
I A U N U O A E V T I E U E E T A O H E C S S C N
G R E D R C P R E O O O D S S T O D X S X H S U U
N R E E N O I P Y S R C N S S E I N N E L P O R M
A W P S I R C O G S T P R A I I R T I A D O R R M
T I A L L I A N C E V R D E K T O P I C T T C E O
E A K X V T D Z M N B E E W A X E N E O H S H N C
P B O U E T B S U K X U M P M T P O A R N L S T S
```

Answers on page 412.

Code-doku

Solve this puzzle just as you would a sudoku. Use deductive logic to complete the grid so that each row, column, and 3-by-3 box contains the letters from the word MAGNITUDE.

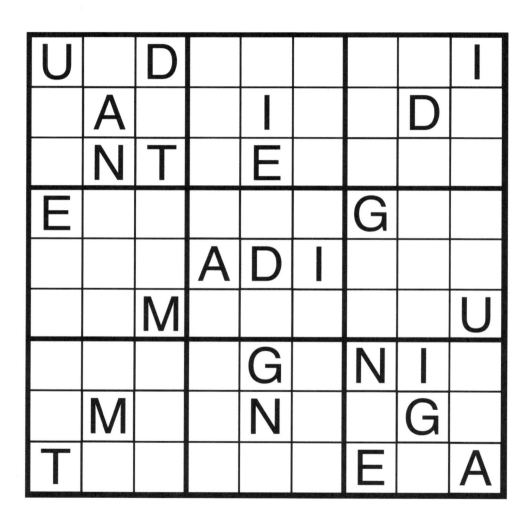

Answer on page 412.

Cryptoku

Answer the clues below to fill in the grid and discover the 9 different letters used in each 3-by-3 box. Just like a standard crossword, answers read across and down; numbers in parenthesis indicate how many letters are in the solution. And, like a code-doku, each letter appears only once in each 3-by-3 box. When complete, the shaded squares will reveal a mystery word.

ACROSS

1. Seventh music note (2)
2. Chemical symbol for copper (2)
3. Personal pronoun (2)
4. Take seated position (3)
5. Preposition (2)
6. Habit (6)
7. Thomas (3)
8. Personal pronoun (2)
9. Preposition (2)
10. French coin (3)
11. Connection (abbr.) (2)

DOWN

12. Preposition (2)
13. Yes! (Sp.) (2)
14. Yes! (Sp.) (2)
15. Conjunction (2)

¹²T	¹³			I				Z
	I	M		¹		²C		
	³	E		O	⁴S			
E	⁵		I	Z	M			S
⁶	U	¹⁴	⁷ O		³	Z		
M		I	E	⁸ S		⁹		O
¹⁰		U	¹⁶	C	T			
	¹¹C	¹⁵S				O		
Z			T		⁶			C

Answer on page 412.

Codeword

The letters of the alphabet are hidden in code: Each is represented by a random number from 1 through 26. With the letters already given, complete the crossword puzzle with English words and break the code.

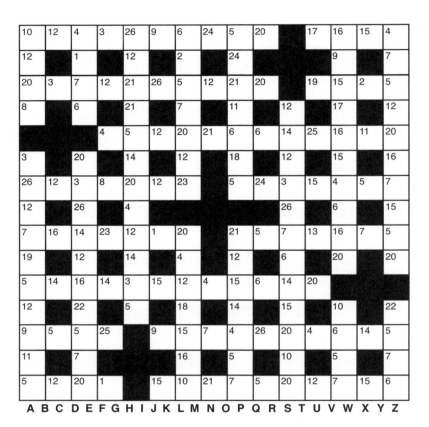

A B C D E F G H I J K L M N O P Q R S T U V W X Y Z

1	2	3	4	5	6	7	8	9	10	11	12	13
Y			E			K					A	

14	15	16	17	18	19	20	21	22	23	24	25	26
						S						

Answers on page 412.

Mastermind

The goal of this puzzle is to replace the question marks with a correct sequence of numbers. The numbers you need for the answer are contained in the rows above the question marks. Follow these 2 guides: A black dot indicates that a number needed for the solution is in that row and in the correct position; a white dot means that a number needed for the solution is in that row but in the wrong position. Numbers do not appear more than once in the solution, and the solution never begins with 0.

9 8 4 1 6 ○ ○ ○
3 5 9 1 2 ● ● ○
8 3 6 1 4 ● ●
7 9 3 0 2 ● ○
―――――――――
? ? ? ? ?

Addagram

This puzzle functions exactly like an anagram with an added step: In addition to being scrambled, each word below is missing the same letter. Discover the missing letter, then unscramble the words. When you do, you'll reveal a small bomb, a seasonal immune system sensitivity, a dwarf, and a something denoted by vertical lines on a map.

ENDEAR

REALLY

TIMED

OUTLINED

Answers on page 412.

Add-a-Letter

This puzzle is an anagram with a twist: Each word or phrase below is missing the same letter. Discover the missing letter, then unscramble. All the "before" AND "after" words can be found in the grid. They may be read either forward or backward.

AGE ERA

ALIEN BITE

ALL BEAU

BOA HEIR

CERISE

CITE CELLO

EATING TIES

ELF TUNE

ENGINE

GRAY IT

I UNTIE IT

ICY AT IT

LION ROUTE

NO CRONIES

ON ICE

OUR SUIT

PER SEER

QUAINT EEL

RESALE

RITUAL

RIVING US

RYE CORE

SALE ERR

SEA ROLL

SOBERER

TEAL OIL

TEE TITAN

TOO APE EAR

WHEAT GLEN

WINE RITE

```
R E R E B O S R M F T K A A V U Q U W B P J N A T
E P F T D U G V I R T U A L C O B S E R V E R X K
N E A E E J J C I T E C E L L O U L T V A L V B X
L R Y N L Q W C O P U U E T I B N E I L A J H P I
Q S Y Y O B U L L O R A E S T K E L P S T T Q A N
P E V E I V A I C Z D U L K V J M A R I G W Z Y T
H E I L N P I T V E L I T A L O V E U N E H P F U
Y R R M T K U C I A J W G V N S V S E V W E V K I
T N T C E R I S E V L E J H U E R L I C Y A T I T
I S U C R E F E S R E E E G R U E T N E S T Y U I
V K O O V I A I R B N N R O V N V N V U G T N V
I W U H I R P E A G G I I T A E H E E E R L I T E
T I S I E J H W L I V X S W T T I L T N V E V I O
C N R S W A S I N I R L X T Q E G F A T I N A E U
A E E A O Z O E R E L B A U L A V T G F V N R I O
O R B B E N J H V A R R E E L A S U I U I F G T T
P I U P R E E V R E V O L U T I O N T L N G N I O
V T L O C N P E D Y R E V O C E R E S N G N Y L R
Y E U C Z E V A P O R A T E C I V R E S F A N K Y
D T E A L O I L O G E Y L A N W P G V N R Z O G E
E O B B B L W Y X O S E I N O R C O N G R X J O C
G N S R D T E E T I T A N B E H A V I O R V M X O
A I E A T I N G T I E S C O N V E R S I O N I Z R
W C Y Y X L E E T N I A U Q C O L L E C T I V E E
V E L A S E R G E G A R E V A M G N E H S K K N G
```

Answers on page 412.

Futoshiki

Place the numbers 1 through 6 in each row and column. Numbers do not repeat in any row or column. Inequality restraints (less-than and greater-than symbols) must be met when placing numbers.

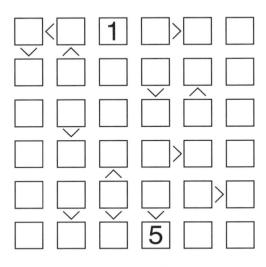

SquarO

Shade in circles around each square as indicated by the numbers. For example, a square with a number 3 in it will have 3 of the 4 connected circles shaded in.

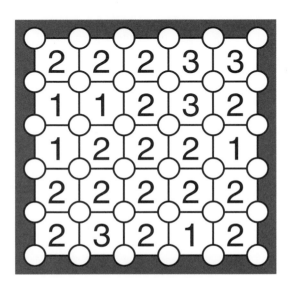

Answers on page 412.

Codeword

The letters of the alphabet are hidden in code: Each is represented by a random number from 1 through 26. With the letters already given, complete the crossword puzzle with English words and break the code.

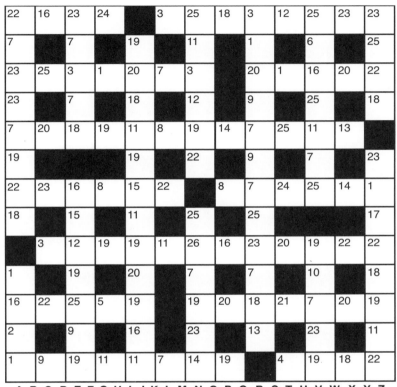

1	2	3	4	5	6	7	8	9	10	11	12	13
	Z											

14	15	16	17	18	19	20	21	22	23	24	25	26
		U					W	L				

Answers on page 413.

Add-a-Letter

This puzzle is an anagram with a twist: Each word or phrase below is missing the same letter. Discover the missing letter, then unscramble. All the "before" AND "after" words can be found in the grid. They may be read either forward or backward.

ABLE INKER	JUST BE
AM HERB	LEAST
ANNOUNCE IT	LOCATIONS
ARISE NUN	NERVY ROOTS
ATE TEA	OPERA TOE
COIL HAT	PIE BLUR
COINER	PLAIN PATIO
DART IS	REUSE
DIE MEN	RIB TOO
DOT IN ION	ROUND COT
FILES SAID	SAFE BOUT
FIT NOUN	SOME PRO
FLU MIRE	SOUL ICON
HEARERS	STYMIES
IVY AT IT	TELEVISE

```
S Y S R E V O R T N O C R H M N R E U S E A B X C
O D B I A R R E K C A B E N I L N G V J A I I D I
U P T Y C O N T I N U A N C E B S U A K R C C J M
L L I R E K N I E L B A E R A C U T O S O F I D E
I A K E X E F H S Y C S R O O E T L Y N G F N O T
C I T O B O R A I E I H R W C T U E O M T M X P S
O N M Z K L T S T B L C A E J C C C L F I I Z E Y
N P N J S E U A R T B O C M R A L U S E F E F R S
N A E E T U R A S U O T E B A O U D E V J S A Z Z
A T T E M E B I D U P P I I S E E R S N R I N T N
P I A C E E C J V J E E V T T S R H P I O N S O O
P O C N L O I G E Y R R I Y U P T Z B E O C O E I
L M S A H E T D Z C A A T J A Z K T N U M N C V T
I T U R C A S T L E T T Y R C J O D N C L O Z M I
C U F U L R A G J M N E I O G O E C C T O T S H D
A O B S A D R Q E E F S T T G M E H O K F A K C N
T B O N S R D R H P E E O A I I U W T R U H Q R O
I E F I S N C K C N P E C C T V Z E F H N L U A C
O F O Z I I C E U N Q O D C A T H O L I C I U E A
N A R E F Q O N D O T I N I O N F C N A T O C S L
T S Z U I C O I N E R Q U L P P R H M Z I C V E B
O H L S E L E C T I V E O A B J I H H T O F A R V
W A T A D S T O O R Y V R E N J E C L M N S M I U
F L U M I R E C O M P O S E R R X K K M T U G W S
U N G S K F I L E S S A I D B L O C A T I O N S I
```

Answers on page 413.

Code-doku

Solve this puzzle just as you would a sudoku. Use deductive logic to complete the grid so that each row, column, and 3-by-3 box contains the letters from the words A VILE SORT. When you have completed the puzzle, read the shaded squares to reveal a hidden message.

	I	O		E			A	
					S	I	T	
	R		A					
E		R	S					A
	L			I				
								V
		S	L	A				E
L	E		O		T			
	A							

Hidden Message: _____

LogiNumber

Determine the values of the variables below using 2 rules: Each letter is no greater than the numbers of letters in the puzzle; none of the letters are equal to each other. Use the grid to help keep track of possible solutions.

$$E + D = C$$
$$C + E = B$$
$$E + B = A$$

	1	2	3	4	5
A					
B					
C					
D					
E					

LogiNumber

Determine the values of the variables below using 2 rules: Each letter is no greater than the numbers of letters in the puzzle; none of the letters are equal to each other. Use the grid to help keep track of possible solutions.

$$B + D = A$$
$$D + E = B$$
$$C + B + E = 10$$

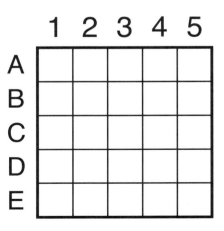

	1	2	3	4	5
A					
B					
C					
D					
E					

Answers on page 413.

Codeword

The letters of the alphabet are hidden in code: Each is represented by a random number from 1 through 26. With the letters already given, complete the crossword puzzle with English words and break the code.

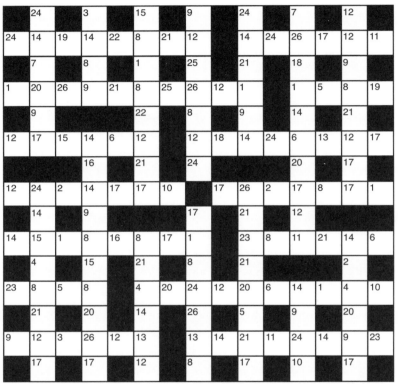

1	2	3	4	5	6	7	8	9	10	11	12	13
										D	E	

14	15	16	17	18	19	20	21	22	23	24	25	26
A			S							M		U

Answers on page 413.

Code-doku

Solve this puzzle just as you would a sudoku. Use deductive logic to complete the grid so that each row, column, and 3-by-3 box contains the letters from the word PREACHING.

	C	A					R	E
P		E	A	C				
		I						
					C	P	G	
	P			R			I	
	G	H	N					
						G		
				I	R	N		P
I	H					E	C	

Answer on page 413.

This puzzle is an anagram with a twist: Each word or phrase below is missing the same letter. Discover the missing letter, then unscramble. All the "before" AND "after" words can be found in the grid. They may be read either forward or backward.

AGREER	**LANCER**
AM ONTO	**MAIN DON**
BE WISE	**MANAGE**
BY LIRE	**NO ICY MUM**
CARTONS	**OH POLE**
COCA PUN	**OPEN HEEL**
CREEPS	**RAVEN POD**
ENTER IN	**REAL TOE**
FORESAW	**RICE ROD**
GURGLES	**RUE AGO**
HE HINGE	**RUIN DIALS**
HI SLICK	**SATIRIC**
HOY SIR	**VICIOUS OR**
ICY SLAM	**YE CLAN**
IN CARE	**YES FIT**

```
K A R X D I B P B B T X G X H N A D W D Z E A L E
D Q Q Y A R P B C D O P N E V A R E O T L A E R S
P N V H V N N R I C A N O S R P P R I G W E A F Y
N A L C E Y O I T U G D S J T U E C G B H N M R K
O M W C N E H S S T R V A F I C I U D N C K O A A
I O I E P S P Y I B E I T V I M R N E M M T M V T
C T H R O F O O T A E C I R W T Y P D A S O Y I N
Y T L T R I L H R T R T R N S A O T N I N A R C A
M O Z A T T E I A H V O I R V X S A H T A Q T I N
U H B I C I E R Y A W R C T U Y G E O R I L C O I
M I T N G I E G S B E I L Z P E C R R W I A S U M
Y O C H T L T D N T G O C C U P A N T O R O L S O
V Z T Y O S A S N I H U N W W P B G E T F G L O D
G E H T S R N E Y D S Y C W K D J O T N M B R Q
N M S M L L G F L M I E W M N T F N W B A D J C Z
E E I P K P A B T E B C H J E C S A E F W L T I F
T U L P U Z M M Y C K S H L A E R W T Q O I E C N
E W K O K I C R O L E M E Z T E I O B U H S N E O
S Z C Q H O E N U M I P W I Q S X F T X L P R N D
T H I C C T T R J G H R S I E I F R Y C R E E T N
I X T A A R O F A O D B E E Q W A Z P A E E T R I
F A P E A S Z P N C E V G U R G L E S D C R N A A
Y U R S P A C E G W N L R W E C B W U F N C I L M
N G T G I N D U S T R I A L S R E L D Q A B C D E
C O M M U N I T Y Y T R E B I L A K C I L S I H B
```

Answers on page 413.

Cryptoku

Answer the clues below to fill in the grid and discover the 9 different letters used in each 3-by-3 box. Just like a standard crossword, answers read across and down; numbers in parenthesis indicate how many letters are in the solution. And, like a code-doku, each letter appears only once in each 3-by-3 box. When complete, the shaded squares will reveal a mystery word.

ACROSS

1. Submarine: abbr. (3)
2. Nights and _____ (4)
3. Eliminate (3)
4. No moisture (3)
5. Baked roll (3)

DOWN

2. Expletive (4)
6. Eliminate (3)
7. Dawn to sunset (3)
8. Advertisement: abbr. (2)
9. Article (2)

H		N	¹		B	
N ⁶	U	R	² D	A		S
A		B			N ⁷	
B	D	U		S		A
U	³	⁸ A		⁴	R	
R	⁹	S		H	⁵ B	
S		R			A	
A	H	N		Y	R	B
R		S			D	

Answer on page 413.

Word Columns

Find the hidden quote from Samuel Johnson by using the letters directly below each of the blank squares. Each letter is used once. A black square indicates the end of a word.

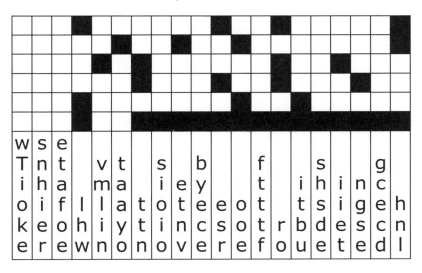

Mastermind

The goal of this puzzle is to replace the question marks with a correct sequence of numbers. The numbers you need for the answer are contained in the rows above the question marks. Follow these 2 guides: A black dot indicates that a number needed for the solution is in that row and in the correct position; a white dot means that a number needed for the solution is in that row but in the wrong position. Numbers do not appear more than once in the solution, and the solution never begins with 0.

3 6 4 2 ● ○ ○

4 6 8 5 ● ○

8 3 9 7 ● ○

5 7 9 3 ●

? ? ? ?

Answers on page 414.

Add-a-Letter

This puzzle is an anagram with a twist: Each word or phrase below is missing the same letter. Discover the missing letter, then unscramble. All the "before" AND "after" words can be found in the grid. They may be read either forward or backward.

ABLE HITS

ADD CIDER

BAT ARDOR

CUTE TOT INN

DIVORCE

HAD WOKEN

HAIR INTO

HELD OUR

HOPE ROWER

ICY TOE

ION HUG

LIT PROTÉGÉ

LUAU

MUD MIMER

NECTARY

NOW PITH

OPEN TOP

OUTER AMP

PERUSER

PIN THEM

RAINY ME

RENEW PAP

RUIN EVE

SEMI ION

SOUP MOUTH

STUD TAR

TABLE BALK

TART UP

TOW RINGER

TURNIP CAM

```
P Z S Q V F D B A T A R D O R V T N E M P I H S S
O S G X E P I H S N W O T O L L S T P N V T V F T
S N S N N W S E D R A O B R A T S S N T U U L F I
T Z P R A O C H S L Z D L G U H N O I O T T A Q H
P W A E E I A R A T D U T S S N H N M I E G Y U E
O U R T I V R E Q W A I N H U E O P T G C V R W L
N S T I H R D O N D I B A T L W U R K N R Y A B B
E T E R M Z E T T H M K L D P O A L T I O F T I A
B A S W A A D V A S E W O I S T A P U S V X C O B
B R U G Y T N I O D I U T N S B V N R U I N E V E
N D O N R D R U O C R H O P E H R W N O D U N X N
C U M O A I L W S P S I U L P Y E R I H L P I P U
O S C S N Z N L G C I I B O J R G E P U J T P J Z
N T R T I P D R A M R A D H W T N W C H E N M N J
S H O D M R S X E B T I O Z N S I O A G R O A E Y
T O K B E E M S F D T S P U I E R P M R U I R K T
I P I X S W X Y L O I E I T M C W E O N S S E O E
T E G E T O R P T I L C K E W N O S S C S S T W I
U N I V E R S E X I S D D S G A T R P U E I U D C
E T R L M E P I N T H E M D A R O O I A R M O A O
N O S S Y P M U D M I M E R A B E H H E P E K H S
T P E A N O P O S T H U M O U S P T M P U E P B K
F A I E I H D I C N E S C N S H O U L D E R R J O
T X H T A K P A P W E N E R C U T E T O T I N N F
B Z L B R L T W R E M M U S D I M W X C P T B R X
```

Answers on page 414.

Cryptoku

Answer the clues below to fill in the grid and discover the 6 different letters used in each 3-by-2 box. Just like a standard crossword, answers read across and down; numbers in parenthesis indicate how many letters are in the solution. And, like a code-doku, each letter appears only once in each 3-by-2 box. When complete, the shaded squares will reveal a mystery word.

ACROSS

1. Noxious rodent (3)

DOWN

2. Test (5)

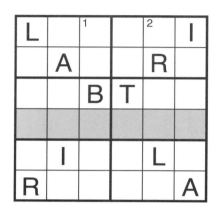

Cryptoku

Answer the clues below to fill in the grid and discover the 6 different letters used in each 3-by-2 box. Just like a standard crossword, answers read across and down; numbers in parenthesis indicate how many letters are in the solution. And, like a code-doku, each letter appears only once in each 3-by-2 box. When complete, the shaded squares will reveal a mystery word.

ACROSS

1. Magenta, say (3)

DOWN

2. Fish eggs (3)
3. Fishing implement (3)
4. Owing (3)

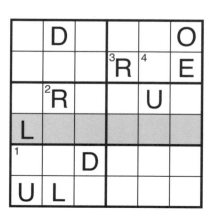

Answers on page 414.

Code-doku

Solve this puzzle just as you would a sudoku. Use deductive logic to complete the grid so that each row, column, and 3-by-3 box contains the letters from the word GODFATHER.

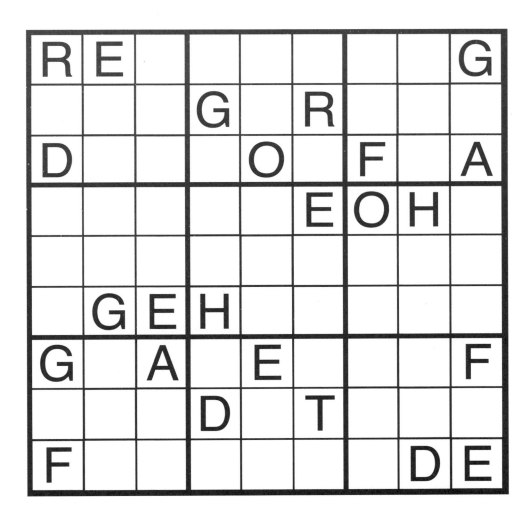

Answer on page 414.

Codeword

The letters of the alphabet are hidden in code: Each is represented by a random number from 1 through 26. With the letters already given, complete the crossword puzzle with English words and break the code.

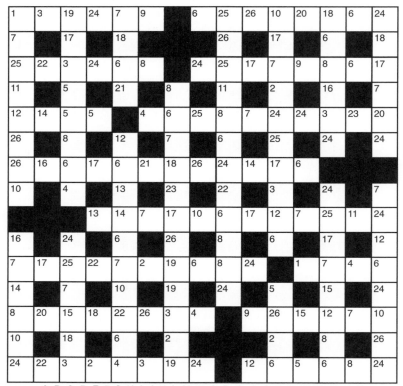

1	2	3	4	5	6	7	8	9	10	11	12	13
		I			E		L					

14	15	16	17	18	19	20	21	22	23	24	25	26
		V	P							S		

Answers on page 414.

Word Columns

Find the hidden humorous anecdote by using the letters directly below each of the blank squares. Each letter is used only once. A black square or the end of a line indicates the end of a word.

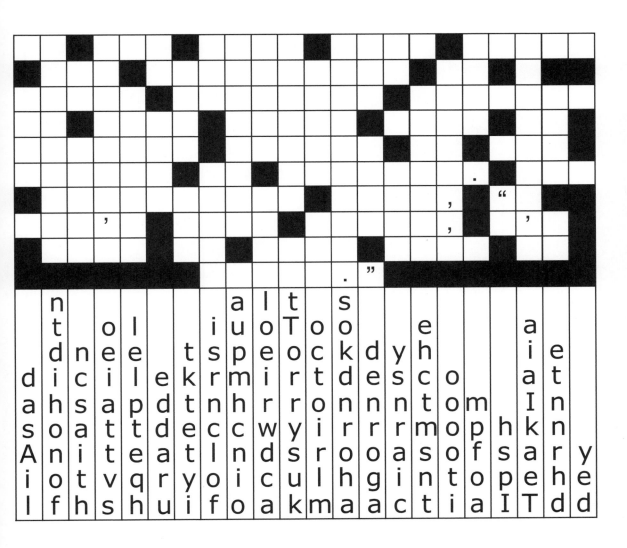

Answer on page 414.

Add-a-Letter

This puzzle is an anagram with a twist: Each word or phrase below is missing the same letter. Discover the missing letter, then unscramble. All the "before" AND "after" words can be found in the grid. They may be read either forward or backward.

AIM SIR	ID GAIT
ALE RAT	LOCATE BOAR
AM GIN	LUSH EDEN
APE ERUPT	NERVE TIC
BE RACER	NICE IN
BE TANK	NO RESCUE
CARVE IT	POD EVE
COD OIL	PREP LORE
CRY AIL	SARDINE
CUE SUN	SCENES IRK
DENSER	SECURE
EACH GLEN	STINGER
FAT CAR	TAU SHAM
HAM CITY	TITHES
HAT SAP	VIA LEG

```
U N S H E L L E D A P E E R U P T O B F O M L
Q I E R Y C H A L L E N G E N J X R A K D A A
W E R G T C E R E B R A L N O R E S C U E H C
W C U N I R T X E N I L C N I C A A T T K S I
O I C I C I S H R A O B E T A C O L L S Y U R
D N E L M R M U I R C V T R P O L E V E D A Y
E G S R A S A I M S I R E E E A W L B H R T L
N E D E H S U L L A T B O L N V I I R T T A B
S E E T M Q J A I W L L L C N C E O U I Y B T
E H L S L W C T T M S A E I V Y L D X T L E M
R R E G N I T S A J I L H R C B L O O V A S Z
P Q L D H B A L L I O S E T R I A C S P T U F
V V O T I C I Y P M W T S N T A T R B U E L T
E N Y Z T G A E R J S N R E D L C E W S R C I
K M B X N E R E D C G E V V Q E A T V Y A E E
N I G M A P K I F E D E E X T F R H A R L R V
A Y O C E P O N L N C R R S W I F L P F E U R
T K P T A L U A A U O C T P C H A D U S T N A
E K U S L C I L E L V S I H S D I G I T A L C
B A T O L V S S P D B K C X A E N I D R A S L
L A C E Y I U E C O L L A B O R A T E I F S G
H T U A L N R P T U V I L L A G E Q X B V W R
D S P R O P E L L E R S C E N E S I R K N M E
```

Answers on page 414.

Code-doku

Solve this puzzle just as you would a sudoku. Use deductive logic to complete the grid so that each row, column, and 3-by-3 box contains the letters from the word PUBLISHER.

P		B				H		R
	I					S		P
		R		P	U			I
			I	R				
				B				
				U	L			
B			E	H		P		
E		P					H	
L		U				I		E

Answer on page 415.

Codeword

The letters of the alphabet are hidden in code: Each is represented by a random number from 1 through 26. With the letters already given, complete the crossword puzzle with English words and break the code.

18	21	4	11	5	25	26	24		5	16	19	15
12		24		12		10				11		26
5	19	24	26	3		21	9	26	16	21	24	16
14		19		3		4			4			14
		6		21		2	26	8	26	16	21	10
8	26	5	12	5	21	5		26		6		11
4				5				24				4
11		4		19		23	11	21	9	26	21	15
11	21	8	19	11	5	21		20		24		
26		19				24		26		13		7
4	17	12	4	16	26	3		21	22	12	10	21
1		24				26		2		11		12
21	4	16	5		1	2	4	10	24	21	5	5

A B C D E F G H I J K L M N O P Q R S T U V W X Y Z

1	2	3	4	5	6	7	8	9	10	11	12	13
				S			M				U	J

14	15	16	17	18	19	20	21	22	23	24	25	26
H												

Answers on page 415.

Add-a-Letter

This puzzle is an anagram with a twist: Each word or phrase below is missing the same letter. Discover the missing letter, then unscramble. All the "before" AND "after" words can be found in the grid. They may be read either forward or backward.

ANY GAS	NERVE NET
BATONS	NO NATAL
CAD MACE	PAL TOM
CAR GLEN	PALE NUNS
CLIP TUBS	POET INDEX
COMET SOP	ROASTED
CONS CON US	SAVE CONVERT
DEEM ART	SHY ROT
DOING	SO SNAP
GO FERN	TASK ME
HOLDS ME	TOXIN ADO
IF FOCAL	TRUE MULL
MEAN ZAG	TRY TO ERR
MEN STIR	UNDID VIAL
MEND SET	UNIT TEST

```
Y L D D D I A M E T E R D N O I T A D I X O X N N
O R A X P C O N S E R V A T I V E I A T N R J Q O
P F O N C C L X R B V N R F M M U F T N E U V E I
P A F T O L L U M E U R T T D O B F S E R U X C S
G Q L I I I E L W K S T Y O E T Q O E M V P D A S
T N R E C R T A N V R N P X M L Y C T I E H K M A
P O I B N I R A R D I I L I O A A A T D N O P D P
Z S B O F U A E N I N M M N L P S L I E E L K A J
M I K O D O N L T H N A E A I C N T N S T D N C O
Y I N M I N I S T E R G A D S L I U U L A S T R B
A N S D C H W C Q Q Q A N O H O A M G T O M L X Q
S O T T I O I C C Y Y Z Z H N T G I S S Y E E F N
T I R K A V N S Z O K I A O O H L U U I N D I G O
E T Y I T K I C T Q M N G R C A N S H A N F I T U
R S T I X V E D U O J E Y R I O R Q L I V E G R M
O A O C A U P X U S R H T V C T U U T F R X O E E
I B E E E A N Y G A S Y D S W D S E I O D A F V N
D K R C N K S M K J L I N I O N O N F I S G E N D
T A R M V E S C A F D O O W I P A Y E T X O R O S
I Q K N Z N V A R N C B P N V C A Z E M S P N C E
G R G B O Z J R U C I M E D A C A D E Y J T R E T
V L A T A N O N E T M P M U I R U L L E T I C V U
H C A D E E M A R T C A R G L E N T A S K M E A A
G B Y I Z F R Q W I N S T I T U T E W J W A P S M
E T I S O P M O C O N I T S I C I L B U P L B C N
```

Answers on page 415.

Code-doku

Solve this puzzle just as you would a sudoku. Use deductive logic to complete the grid so that each row, each column, and each 3-by-3 box contains each of the letters DEFGHILOT in some order. When you have completed the puzzle, unscramble the letters to reveal "the path to self-development."

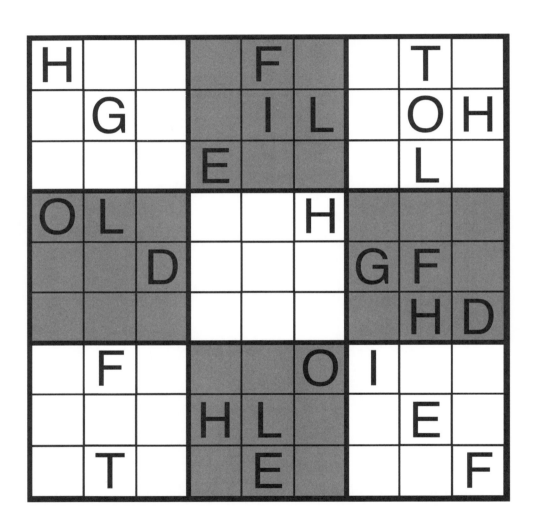

Hidden Message: _____

Answer on page 415.

Cryptoku

Answer the clues below to fill in the grid and discover the 9 different letters used in each 3-by-3 box. Just like a standard crossword, answers read across and down; numbers in parenthesis indicate how many letters are in the solution. And, like a code-doku, each letter appears only once in each 3-by-3 box. When complete, the shaded squares will reveal a mystery word.

ACROSS

1. Tent post (3)
2. Internet server (3)
3. _____ capita (3)
4. Hearing organ (3)
5. Space between (3)
6. Fish eggs (3)

DOWN

7. Knock (3)
8. Lily type (4)
9. Travel (2)
10. Goofball (3)
11. Mist (3)
12. Either/_____ (2)

O	⁸S	F	A	E		G
⁷	¹P		L		S	
	⁹G			E		O
	R	¹⁰	E	G		L	
L	A		¹¹F		O		S
	S	²		L	³	E	
⁴		R	¹²G				L
	O		R		S	⁵	A
S				A	⁶R		E

Answer on page 415.

LogiNumber

Determine the values of the variables below using 2 rules: Each letter is no greater than the numbers of letters in the puzzle; none of the letters are equal to each other. Use the grid to help keep track of possible solutions.

$$A + B + D = 6$$
$$2A = B - 1$$

	1	2	3	4
A				
B				
C				
D				

Crypto-Logic

Each of the numbers in the sequence below represents a letter. Use the mathematical clues to determine which number stands for which letter and reveal the encrypted word.

Hint: Remember that a / indicates divided by, and that all sums in parentheses must be done first.

8 1 4 4 3

Clues:

$R = 10$

$I = (R / 2) - 3$

$2I = E$

$E / E = W$

$E - W = T$

$2T = L$

$L + I = S$

Answers on page 415.

Chain Sudoku

Use deductive logic to complete the grid so that each row, each column, and each connected set of circles contains the numbers 1 through 7 in some order. The solution is unique.

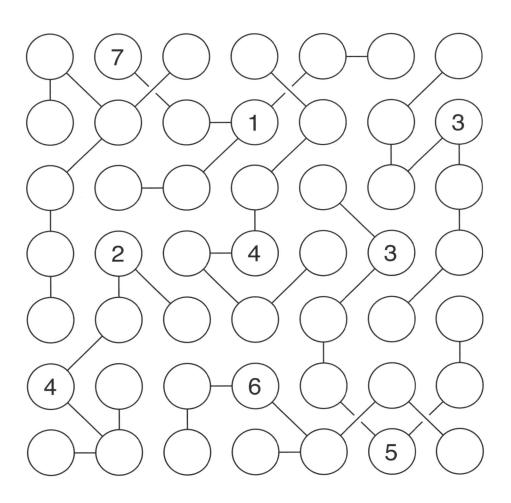

Answer on page 415.

Add-a-Letter

This puzzle is an anagram with a twist: Each word or phrase below is missing the same letter. Discover the missing letter, then unscramble. All the "before" AND "after" words can be found in the grid. They may be read either forward or backward.

ARTY EYES	NO SCENE
BUY STAIR	NOT SPICIER
CHOIR	NURSED TAN
CONIC NIECE	OAT CAVE
DIET ALE	OH VILE OIL
EBONY FIR	PENT NEED
EVICT TEE	RENT FIFE
EVIL BEE	RUNE CANE
FEW NOUN	SAVIOR
FISH RIPEN	USE DISCS
GLIB INN	VIA TOTEM
INCISE LIP	VOICERS
ION CUT	WORE DO
LOP EVE	YOUR BAN
MICA ACE	ZEE VISOR

```
U Q A S I G V S P I L E S I C N I Z T K G L R K W
C N I T C N B F E B O B D O O W D E R T Q V W D G
F I S H R I P E N I L P I C S I D H S O O O R I L
D A A N M D B C J V D N E I R F Y O B I R C O E I
E Y R A D N U O B E C A A C I M P N C E N O I T B
Z E L B P I G L V I E N E C S O N E D D E N V A I
I N G R K L H I D V N V D I H C R O C W W I A L N
S A Q U L B L E O V I M K E Z S W M B H F C S E N
R C T O N B N O I T P I R C S E D C X Y O N V E G
E E S Y E C E Z C F R I E N D S H I P S U I M V V
V N D E E O B E M O T I V A T E D H T W N E R E Q
O U O Y E S T E R D A Y A R T Y E Y E S D C C P R
D R O Q J E E A D D K E E U E E T T C I V E H O E
E L H A D U P W B I Y T Z D A F E W N O U N T L I
L V I A T O T E M S A C O N D U I T N E U P Z M C
I T L S L C H M F C U A R E P B T A J S N A R R I
A H E E C U A G O U Y R C O Z G T I B N R G O D P
T W V A O U X V U S A D D P S D G E Z E I K S I S
E E I N G V D Q E S E C O I E I L N V D F I I F T
D M L Q Q A Y B M E E E A S T I V O U N Y O V F O
B U Y S T A I R N D X D R D E Y C E Q O N L D E N
D U N D E R S T A N D U I V E S C H E C O Z A R A
O E F I F T N E R P N J E S I M B I U Z B R V E W
H T L I O E L I V H O D A D C Q I T Y M E Y L N E
S N D E P E N D E N T D U R L S B C U O U D I T L
```

Answers on page 415.

Cryptoku

Answer the clues below to fill in the grid and discover the 9 different letters used in each 3-by-3 box. Just like a standard crossword, answers read across and down; numbers in parenthesis indicate how many letters are in the solution. And, like a code-doku, each letter appears only once in each 3-by-3 box. When complete, the shaded squares will reveal a mystery word.

ACROSS

1. Aging horse (3)
2. Marsh (3)
3. Fallen tree trunk (3)
4. Taxi (3)
5. Grab (3)

DOWN

6. Charged atom (3)
7. To trick (3)
8. Alcoholic liquor (3)
9. _____ and behold! (2)
10. Droop (3)

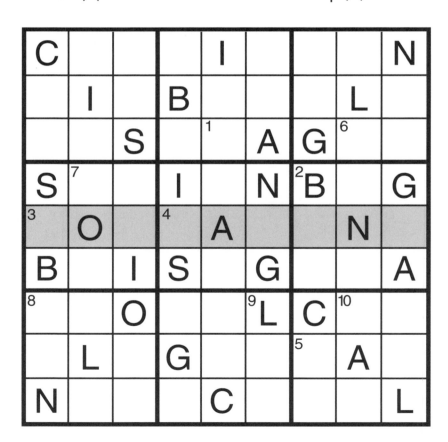

Answer on page 416.

Codeword

The letters of the alphabet are hidden in code: Each is represented by a random number from 1 through 26. With the letters already given, complete the crossword puzzle with English words and break the code.

8		14		24		21				8		7		16
21	2	9	20	8	9	19		9	4	18	19	12	5	20
6		11		21		11		22		8		9		9
12	15	3	21	1		25	8	12	6	5	7	4	9	2
15				15		9		16		20		8		23
3	19	16	23	11	9	20		17	7	16	13	19	8
16		9				7		9		6		19		4
	8	10	20	11	9	26	9	25	9	12	24	9	16
6		6		6		8		25				20		16
17	15	21	2	9	15		11	8	13	19	8	16	20
16		1		4		18		7		19				15
5	2	6	5	23	22	7	16	8		9	22	14	19	2
8		12		7		25		26		23		6		7
12	8	8	4	2	8	16		8	10	8	3	21	20	16
8		16		2				4		16		16		1

A B C D E F G H I J K L M N O P Q R S T U V W X Y Z

1	2	3	4	5	6	7	8	9	10	11	12	13
	L							A			N	

14	15	16	17	18	19	20	21	22	23	24	25	26
F		B	U		P	W						

Answers on page 416.

Add-a-Letter

370

This puzzle is an anagram with a twist: Each word or phrase below is missing the same letter. Discover the missing letter, then unscramble. All the "before" AND "after" words can be found in the grid. They may be read either forward or backward.

AFORE	MANIC PA
ALOE CLUE	MEN TIRE
ANTS DIN	NEAR END
CENSORS	ON TEAM
CORN EVE	OR YE ALL
COY RATE	PANT LEG
COYLY SHOP	RENT SIR
EVE RAN	RUINS TEA
FERN MAT	RULE HAT
HE HIT	SLOE ASH
HOT HOUR	THE COLONY
LASERS	THROW
LEANER	TRY EAST
LISTEN	WILT HARPY
LOAN IRE	ZERO NICE

```
R E N A E L T R U T A H E L U R W M E I E Q W N N
L G T N E M I G E R Y U F T A I V V K M W F U B S
A R X Z L J H V M Z D E H M L S E H S O L A G I R
R D J R H X E V G O G O L T A N E M N E K S P U O
E Y W C L R H C R A R O H P R N H R W R L E T D S
N R S O A Z O O T O A A T O A P I Q S R G N R N N
E E O N U P V N U N R R C R E N P C E G E T Z E E
G U S V G T O G I P O J H Y Y S T G P M N M F R C
O L V E H M H R Y F R I R F Y E N L G A G V H A J
P C G R T U E E T A Y B S C O A A A E J R L O E J
E E G G E I I S H T E P H O D N R S M G A O T N V
Z O P E R H N S R N A O O N T F H V T V V F H N Z
I L I L Q N Z I O R L C E H S X G C A T E G O R Y
N A A J A D G L W O L R S F S B Y T S J O Y U R Y
G U E A G Y C I G Z U Y Q S A Y L N P I P G R N E
O Z T L C N W Y A T R G X S T E L G N I S O O U T
C I S L L E D R A P M E G E Z R F Y K L H L J A S
E S N E H T G N I D M T Y G Z E S O O K O O M D E
R W I G R S G U C G L A C R K N R E R C Q N C A T
V F U O E I G H T H H R C A F T A O E A R H O N A
K A R R S L T O G D A T Z L I S G H N E G C N T R
W L B Y R E G N I R T S Q U H I T Q F I E E T S Y
E R Z F Y I Y X E V N O M R G R O W T H C T E D O
R E G I O N A L V M O Y R F U F J Q H E J E A I C
S T A N D I N G B H Z E U G A E L L O C X V M N B
```

Answers on page 416.

The Murder Castle

Cryptograms are messages in substitution code. Break the code to read the message. THE SMART CAT might become FVO QWGDF JGF if **F** is substituted for **T**, **V** for **H**, **O** for **E**, and so on.

V. V. VXNQJF CYJC ZJOXDJ VJ HIDTJC 35. YT VYF DJNSHYLJNU
FVXDH NYOJ, VJ GXQQYHHJC S TIQZJD XO QIDCJDF, HVXIPV
HVJ JRSGH TIQZJD YF ITKTXMT. YH QSU VSLJ ZJJT OJMJD HVST
10, ZIH YH QSU VSLJ TIQZJDJC QXDJ HVST 100. VXNQJF MSF
SNFX S ZYPSQYFH, QSDDUYTP HVDJJ CYOOJDJTH MXQJT.
VXNQJF MSF SGHYLJ SH HVJ HYQJ XO HVJ 1893 MXDNC'F
OSYD YT GVYGSPX, YNNYTXYF. VJ XMTJC S ZIYNCYTP HX
MVYGV VJ NIDJC LYGHYQF ITCJD HVJ PIYFJ HVSH YH MSF S
VXHJN; YH MSF NSHJD CIZZJC HVJ QIDCJD VXHJN STC HVJ
QIDCJD GSFHNJ OXD HVJ KYNNYTPF VJ GXQQYHHJC HVJDJ.

Duality

Cryptograms are messages in substitution code. Break the code to read the message. THE SMART CAT might become FVO QWGDF JGF if **F** is substituted for **T**, **V** for **H**, **O** for **E**, and so on.

XQOT QDJMHI EQPK BYQTKN EMYXKI, QON XQOT EQPK
BYQTKN RQJIMO—ZLJ ZHGJGIE QDJMH BQJHGDA XQDOKK
RQI MOK MU JEK UKR JM BYQT ZMJE HMYKI NLHGOV Q
YMOV DQHKKH! EK BYQTKN JEK DEQHQDJKH MU RQJIMO
MBBMIGJK HMVKH XMMHK QON DEHGIJMBEKH YKK. QON JM
DQB GJ MUU, GO 1984, EK BYQTKN Q DEQHQDJKH MO JEK
JKYKPGIGMO IEMR XQVOLX B.G. REM EQN Q NKYLIGMO JEQJ
EK RQI IEKHYMDA EMYXKI.

Answers on page 416.

Cryptoku

Answer the clues below to fill in the grid and discover the 9 different letters used in each 3-by-3 box. Just like a standard crossword, answers read across and down; numbers in parenthesis indicate how many letters are in the solution. And, like a code-doku, each letter appears only once in each 3-by-3 box. When complete, the shaded squares will reveal a mystery word.

ACROSS

1. Cooking container (3)
2. Cravat (3)
3. Hole in the ground (3)

DOWN

4. Garden tool (3)
5. Uppermost point (3)
6. Pronoun: fem. (3)

	I			H			P
	⁴			P	Y		
¹		⁵		E			C
R		O			C	⁶	
	²T	E		P			
			I		H		Y
	P			T			
O		Y		R	³		

Answer on page 416.

Answers

Game On! (page 4)

M	E	G	A
G	A	M	E
A	G	E	M
E	M	A	G

Code-doku (page 5)

T	O	H	U	M
H	U	M	T	O
M	T	O	H	U
O	H	U	M	T
U	M	T	O	H

An Actor's Bio (page 6)

He won back-to-back Oscars for "Captains Courageous" and "Boys Town." He also starred in "Father of the Bride." Who is he? Spencer Tracy

A Place in the United States (page 6)

This top city has the Gateway Arch and the Missouri Botanical Garden. What is it? St. Louis

Petalgrams (page 7)

officer, magnify, alfalfa, uniform, refusal, leaflet
BONUS WORD: formula

Confused? (page 8-9)

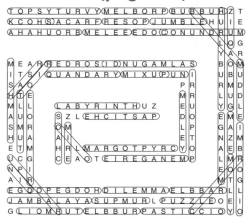

Zen in a Nutshell (page 10)

"Be here now. Be someplace else later. Is that so complicated?"

2 Rules (page 10)

There are two rules for ultimate success in life. Never tell everything you know.

Sum It Up (page 11)

The future comes one day at a time.

One for the Ages (page 12)

Betty is 7, Billy is 6, Bobby is 10, and Bonny is 9.

Who's There? (page 13)

Well, if I called the wrong number, why did you answer the phone? —James Thurber

Pardon My French (page 13)

What's the French for fiddle-dedee? —Lewis Carroll

Cryptoquotes (page 14)

1. "Debt, if owed to ourselves, is not debt but an investment."—Franklin D. Roosevelt
2. "Let us endeavor so to live that when we come to die even the undertaker will be sorry."—Mark Twain

Plus Code (page 15)

1. child, 2. extol, 3. event, 4. white, 5. byway, 6. ionic, 7. kudos, 8. zones, 9. usurp, 10. cycle

Animal Riddles (page 16)

1. What's black and white and "red" all over?
A zebra wearing lipstick.
2. Why did the police arrest the bird?
Because it was a robin.

Space Savers (page 17)

Look before you leap.
Waste not, want not.

Mind Bender (page 17)

Read the message backward—and put spaces in the right places—and you'll see that it says "Stifle is an anagram of itself," a bit of self-referential humor that really is a mind-bender!

Countdown (page 18)

"When angry, count ten before you speak; if very angry an hundred."
—Thomas Jefferson
"When angry, count four; when very angry swear." —Mark Twain

Letter Lesson (page 19)

"Now, in English, the letter which most frequently occurs is E. Afterward, the succession runs thus: A, O, I, D, H, N, R, S, T, U, Y, C, F, G, L, M, W, B, K, P, Q, X, Z. E predominates so remarkably, that an individual sentence of any length is rarely seen, in which it is not the prevailing character."
—Edgar Allan Poe

Bird Wisdom (page 19)

1. A bird in the hand is worth two in the bush.
2. Birds of a feather flock together.
3. The early bird gets the worm.

Is That a Fact? (page 20)

A business is too big when it takes a week for gossip to go from one end of the office to the other.
Keep in mind that even if you are on the right track, you will get run over if you just sit there.
A reckless driver is a person who races past you when you are going sixty-five miles per hour.

Cryptoquote (page 21)

"Put all your eggs in one basket— and watch that basket." —Mark Twain

Instant Cure (page 21)

"When I told my doctor I couldn't afford an operation, he offered to touch-up my X-rays." —Henny Youngman

Word Columns (page 22)

I believe for every drop of rain that falls, a flower grows, a foundation leaks, a ball game gets rained out, a car rusts and...

Word Columns (page 22)

In some societies, they beat the ground with clubs and yell. It is called witchcraft. Other societies call it "golf."

World Capitals (page 23)

A=D; B=L; C=B; D=M; E=H; F=O; G=J; H=N; I=A; J=P; K=R; L=G; M=C; N=I; O=E; P=K; R=T; S=W; T=Y; U=S.
1. Oslo, Norway; 2. Stockholm, Sweden; 3. New Delhi, India; 4. Cairo, Egypt; 5. Belgrade, Serbia; 6. Amsterdam, Netherlands; 7. Madrid, Spain; 8. Tokyo, Japan; 9. Santiago, Chile; 10. Phnom Penh, Cambodia

Rules of Thumb (page 24)

1. Energy: One BTU equals roughly the energy of one average candy bar or one blue-tip wooden match. 2. Poker rule: Look around the table and find the victim. If you can't tell who it is, it's you. 3. How to mix a proper oil-and-vinegar salad dressing: Three parts oil, one part vinegar. 4. What to bring to summer camp? A good rule of thumb: If you care about the item, leave it at home.

Word Columns (page 24)

A husband said to his wife, "No, I don't hate your relatives. In fact, I like your mother-in-law better than I like mine."

Crypto-Animal Families (page 25)

1. Chicken, goat, cow, horse, goose, duckling, sheep, swine, rabbit, hound.
A=C, B=I, C=G, D=N, E=O, F=A, G=R, H=E, I=S, J=W, K=T, M=H, N=K, O=D, P=U, R=L, S=P, T=B.
2. Hippopotamus, rhino, tiger, giraffe, elephant, gorilla, zebra, kangaroo, snakes, lion.
A=P, B=F, C=B, D=M, E=H, F=I, G=O, H=T, I=A, J=U, K=S, L=R, M=N, N=E, O=L, P=G, R=Z, S=K.
3. Whale, seal, turtle, stingray, dolphin, lobster, oyster, starfish, jellyfish, shark.
A=T, B=R, C=E, D=G, E=A, F=W, G=U, H=I, I=S, J=Y, K=N, L=H, M=O, N=P, P=L, R=D, S=B, T=F, U=J, V=K.

Name Calling (page 26)

Money is the root of all wealth.

Famed Fabulist (page 26)

This man was, by tradition, a slave who lived in mid-sixth century B.C. ancient Greece. His stories are still taught as moral lessons. Some of his most familiar stories are "The Tortoise and the Hare" and "The Boy Who Cried Wolf." He is known as Aesop.

Wacky Wordy (page 27)

Once in a blue moon

Classic Lit (page 27)

"It is a truth universally acknowledged, that a single man in possession of a good fortune, must be in want of a wife."
—Jane Austen, *Pride and Prejudice*

Triangle Trial (page 28)

There are 35 triangles:
ABC; ABD; ABE; ABF; ABG; ABH; ACD; ACE; ADE; AEF; AEG; AFG; AEJ; ADH; ACJ; BCD; BCE; BCG; BCH; BCI; BDE; BDF; BEI; BGH; CDE; CDH; CDI; CDJ; CEG; CHI; DEF; DEI; DEJ; DIJ; EFJ

Name Calling (page 28)

He who blows his stack only adds to the world's pollution.

Acrostic Anagram (page 29)

1. cabin; 2. symphonic; 3. level;
4. typing; 5. warhead; 6. pecan;
7. finalize; 8. chore; 9. aviator;
10. wearily; 11. booze; 12. output
"People who cannot recognize a palpable absurdity are very much in the way of civilization."

Wacky Wordy (page 30)

Blue in the face

Crypto-Wisdom (page 30)

1. A rolling stone gathers no moss.
2. A penny saved is a penny earned.
3. Kind words linger in the heart.

Acrostic Anagram (page 31)

A. iodine; B. flowery; C. furious;
D. wispy; E. country; F. school;
G. nominee; H. snore; I. tornado;
J. siege; K. reunion; L. shiny
"Writing is the only profession where no one considers you ridiculous if you earn no money."

Acrostic Anagram (page 32)

1. catamaran; 2. thereabout; 3. leaflet;
4. succumb; 5. bench; 6. façade;
7. haggle; 8. convergence;
9. telephone; 10. hyphen
"Change the changeable, accept the unchangeable, and remove yourself from the unacceptable."

Name Calling (page 33)

It is difficult to make predictions, especially about the future.

Wacky Wordy (page 33)

Change in the weather

Crypto-Game Families (page 34)

1. basketball, polo, golf, croquet, volleyball, tennis, football, bocce, baseball, soccer
A=R, B=V, C=L, D=T, E=I, F=O, G=Q, H=P, I=B, J=U, K=S, L=A, M=C, N=E, O=Y, P=F, R=K, S=G, T=N
2. bridge, euchre, pinochle, canasta, gin rummy, crazy eights, poker, hearts, solitaire, baccarat
A=I, B=G, C=E, D=U, E=H, F=P, G=N, H=D, I=O, J=R, K=A, L=S, M=K, N=Z, O=T, P=L, R=C, S=B, T=M
3. Chess, Scrabble, Checkers, Monopoly, Battleship, Game of Life, Chinese Checkers, Parcheesi, Clue, Sorry
A=Y, B=R, C=L, D=U, E=A, F=O, H=M, I=B, J=S, K=E, L=K, M=P, N=T, O=H, P=C, R=N, S=I, T=G, U=F

Word Columns (page 35)

"The first man to compare the cheeks of a young woman to a rose was obviously a poet; the first to repeat it was possibly an idiot." —Salvador Dali

Acrostic Anagram (page 36)

A. incapacitated; B. perished; C. usefulness; D. survey; E. forehead; F. fishing; G. witting; H. willow; I. sorority
Virtue is its own reward. There's a pleasure in doing good which sufficiently pays itself.

Acrostic Anagram (page 37)

A. counterbalance; B. dossier; C. goldfish; D. thornier; E. heartaches; F. thereafter; G. wafts; H. venue; I. without
"A hurtful act is the transference to others of the degradation which we bear in ourselves."

Big Top Code-doku (page 38)

A CAMPY PACHYDERM PARADE

Name Calling (page 38)

Victory goes to the player who makes the next-to-last mistake.

Classic Lit (page 39)

A=13, B=4, C=23, D=19, E=9, F=24, G=21, H=18, I=6, J=14, K=10, L=26, M=11, N=1, O=15, P=5, Q=22, R=8, S=20, T=3, U=25, V=12, W=17, X=7, Y=2, Z=16

"It is a truth universally acknowledged, that a single man in possession of a good fortune, must be in want of a wife." —Jane Austen, *Pride and Prejudice*

Word Columns (page 40)

Sometimes I lie awake at night and ask, "Where have I gone wrong?" Then a voice says to me, "This is going to take more than one night." —Charles Schultz

Wacky Wordy (page 40)

Neon sign (KNEE on SIGN)

Letterbox Colors (page 41)

1	2	3	4	5	6	7	8	9	10	11	12	13
N	U	O	B	L	A	C	K	Q	F	X	J	S
14	15	16	17	18	19	20	21	22	23	24	25	26
Z	G	P	W	H	I	T	E	R	M	V	D	Y

Fiery Lyrics (page 42)

The time to hesitate is through; no time to wallow in the mire. Try now we can only lose, and our love become a funeral pyre. —The Doors

Comedy Faster than a Speeding Bullet (page 42)

"In England, if you commit a crime, the police don't have a gun and you don't have a gun. If you commit a crime, the police will say 'Stop, or I'll say stop again.'" —From his "Live at the Met" performance in New York, 1986

Acrostic Clues (page 43)

A. Somerset Maugham; B. Fenimore;
C. flamenco; D. cremation; E. fortieth;
F. Robin Hood; G. affair; H. inoculating;
I. confound

"I can imagine no more comfortable frame of mind for the conduct of life than a humorous resignation."

Code-doku (page 44)

ONE SMALL STEP ON A PALE MOON

O	A	L	T	M	E	N	S	P
E	T	S	N	O	P	M	A	L
P	M	N	A	L	S	E	O	T
T	S	M	E	P	N	A	L	O
N	O	A	S	T	L	P	M	E
L	E	P	O	A	M	S	T	N
M	N	T	P	S	O	L	E	A
A	L	E	M	N	T	O	P	S
S	P	O	L	E	A	T	N	M

Trick Question (page 44)

If they squeeze olives to get olive oil, how do they get baby oil?

Crypto-Quote (page 45)

"The first and most important thing of all, at least for writers today, is to strip language clean, to lay it bare down to the bone." —Ernest Hemingway

Crypto-Wisdom (page 45)

1. Worry is a misuse of the imagination.
A=F; B=I; C=R; D-M; E=H; F=W; G=U; H=A; I=N; J=O; K=E; L=S; M=Y; N=G; O=T

2. The worst thing about mistakes in the kitchen is that you usually have to eat them.
A=U; B=E; C=H; D=O; E=B; F=A; G=W; H=T; I=S; J=N; K=R; L=I; M=G;
N=K; O=C; P=M; R=Y; S=L; T=V

3. Don't forget that appreciation is always appreciated.
A=T; B=O; C=G; D=R; E=H; F=A; G=N; H=D; I=F; J=P; K=C; L=E; M=I; N=S; O=W; P=Y; R=L

The Man with the Toothbrush Mustache (page 46)

"We all want to help one another. We want to live by each other's happiness, not by each other's misery."

Frankly, My Dear... (page 46)

He gave his Oscar for It Happened One Night (1934) to a child who admired it, telling him it was the winning of the statue that had mattered, not owning it. The Oscar was returned to the actor's family after his death.

Letterbox Valuables (page 47)

1	2	3	4	5	6	7	8	9	10	11	12	13
J	A	D	E	C	N	Q	K	V	R	U	B	Y
14	15	16	17	18	19	20	21	22	23	24	25	26
M	Z	T	L	G	X	F	S	O	P	H	I	W

Hashi (page 48)

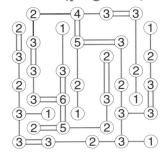

Crypto-botany (page 48)

Tomato (name of plant). There are more varieties of tomatoes than of any other vegetable. Originally, people thought tomatoes were poisonous and grew them as ornamental plants. Thomas Jefferson began to grow them in 1781, but they weren't considered to be edible until 1834. Tomatoes have also been called garden apples, gold apples, and love apples.

Name Calling (page 49)

What food these morsels be!

What Did He Mean By That? (page 49)

Most people are bothered by those passages of Scripture they do not understand, but the passages that bother me are those I do understand. –Mark Twain

Word Columns (page 50)

No one knew who was attacking the castle until we learned it was the forces of Sir Nymbas of Cumulus, the legendary Dark and Stormy Knight.

Crypto-Logic (page 51)

The word is NEAT. If S is 5, I is 10. If I is 10, T is 1. Therefore N is 4. 4 - A = 1, so A is 3. Therefore E is 9.

Movie Title and Director Cryptogram (page 51)

1. *North by Northwest*: Alfred Hitchcock
2. *The Shining*: Stanley Kubrick
3. *Citizen Kane*: Orson Welles
4. *Raging Bull*: Martin Scorsese

The Sopranos (page 52-53)

A. The Sopranos; B. additive; C. Junior; D. patted; E. Janice; F. violent; G. shrink; H. gutted; I. Gambino; J. nitwit; K. outlaw; L. night owl; M. vendetta; N. ambition; O. renovated; P. geranium
"I am living in the moral Never Never Land with this patient. Not wanting to judge but to treat. But now I've judged. I took a position, and I am scared."

Code-doku (page 54)

CAMBRIDGE

M	B	C	D	E	R	G	A	I
D	A	I	C	G	M	E	B	R
G	R	E	I	A	B	D	C	M
I	C	D	A	R	G	B	M	E
R	M	B	E	I	D	A	G	C
A	E	G	B	M	C	I	R	D
E	D	R	G	C	A	M	I	B
B	G	M	R	D	I	C	E	A
C	I	A	M	B	E	R	D	G

Cross Count (page 55)

^{2}t	^{9}r	^{5}e	^{5}s	17
^{5}w	^{1}a	^{9}i	^{2}t	17
^{1}a	^{3}c	^{9}r	^{5}e	18
^{1}s	^{5}e	^{5}e	^{4}m	15
9	18	28	12	

Crypto-Logic (page 56)

GENIUS. If A is 8 then B is 2, and 21 is therefore 2, making I value 1. E is thus 4, and so G is 6. R is hence 10, and so U is 5, and N is 9. 9 - 2 = S which is therefore 7.

Name Calling (page 56)

Not to have felt pain is not to have been human.

Code-doku (page 57)

PEARL BUCK

```
A U L K C P B E R
E K R L B A C P U
C B P R E U A L K
K P U E A B R C L
L E B U R C P K A
R A C P L K E U B
U R A C P L K B E
P L E B K R U A C
B C K A U E L R P
```

Cross Count (page 58)

¹s	³c	¹a	²t	7
¹a	³u	⁹r	¹a	14
¹s	³l	⁹i	⁴m	17
¹s	³l	¹a	⁷p	12
4	12	20	14	

Word Columns (page 59)

Did you hear about the herb who was an all around great guy, did loads of charity work, and was always there to help? He was a Tarragon of Virtue.

Record High (page 60)

Rob (John Cusack): "Now, the making of a good compilation tape is a very subtle art. Many dos and don'ts. First of all, you're using someone else's poetry to express how you feel. This is a delicate thing."

Revolutionary Crypto-quote (page 60)

"A lie told often enough becomes the truth." —V. I. Lenin

Code-doku (page 61)

CLARINETS

Cross Count (page 62)

²t	⁹r	⁹i	⁷p	27
⁹r	⁶o	⁴d	⁵e	24
¹a	³l	⁵e	⁵e	14
⁷p	³l	¹a	⁵n	16
19	21	19	22	

Word Columns (page 63)

"A man's first care should be to avoid the reproaches of his own heart, and his next to escape the censures of the world."

Maiden Voyage (page 63)

From carpet to chandeliers, most of the decor on the ship was either reconstructed by or under the supervision of the original companies that furnished the *Titanic*.

Code-doku (page 64)

A BAWDY PARODY ON BROADWAY

Codeword (page 65)

five or less (therefore 1, 2 and 3). U is less than I and I is less than T. So T is 3, I is 2, and U is 1. 3Y is 12, so Y is 4. Therefore C is 6, and hence S is 8. Therefore R is 5, and P is 45, and N is 9. So I is 2.

Mastermind (page 66)

178

Unconventional Genius (page 66)

"My momma always said life was like a box of chocolates. You never know what you're gonna get."

Codeword (page 67)

Crypto-group: Comic Book Heroes (page 68)

Batman, Daredevil, Black Widow, Iron Fist, Cyclops

Crypto-Logic (page 68)

SCRUTINY. If F is 10, then 10 - T - U - I = 5, making the value of T plus U plus

Code-doku (page 69)

DREAMINGS

Code-doku (page 70)

John Tyler

Word Columns (page 71)

Now that we have reached the moon and flown beyond the stars, maybe we should take another try at getting pigeons off public buildings.

Best Day Ever (page 71)

Groundhog Day was not filmed in Punxsutawney, Pennsylvania, but in Woodstock, Illinois. Bill Murray was bitten by the groundhog twice during shooting.

Party Time (page 72)

Several historical figures were invited to a party. Einstein said it would be relatively easy to attend. Schubert said he'd come, but there was something he had to finish first. Dr. Jekyll was of two minds...

Maxims to Ponder (page 72)

1. Eagles may soar but weasels don't get sucked into jet engines.
2. Never argue with a spouse who is packing your parachute.
3. Never moon a werewolf.

Codeword (page 73)

Codeword (page 74)

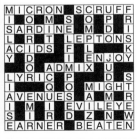

Crypto-Logic (page 75)

Concealed

Mastermind (page 75)

7102

Acrostic (page 76-77)

A. Moth; B. Epitaph; C. Narcissus;
D. Chart; E. Kowtow; F. Easily;
G. Nabbed; H. Marplot; I. Impost;
J. Noted; K. Offertory; L. Rosy;
M. Irate; N. Tossing; O. Youthful;
P. Rangy; Q. Ethical; R. Proffer;
S. Overshot; T. Rashly; U. Ties

"The fact that I have no remedy for all the sorrows of the world is no reason for my accepting yours. It simply supports the strong probability that yours is a fake."

Name Calling (page 78)

Ask about your neighbors, then buy the house.

Crypto-group: European Cities (page 78)

Nice, London, Barcelona, Venice, Berlin

Cross Count (page 79)

⁶f	¹a	⁹r	⁴m	20
¹a	³l	⁶o	⁵e	15
¹s	⁷p	⁶o	²t	16
²t	⁶o	²t	⁵e	15
10	17	23	16	

Life's Little Mysteries (page 80)

1. Whose cruel idea was it to put an "s" in the word "lisp"?
2. If swimming is so good for your figure, how come whales are so fat?
3. What happens if you get scared half to death twice?

Mastermind (page 80)

4150

Code-doku (page 81)

MAGELLAN'S ATTEMPT SPANS PLANET

Code-doku (page 82)

FINE PRINCE KISSES PRINCESS

Codeword (page 83)

1	2	3	4	5	6	7	8	9	10	11	12	13
X	R	F	Q	B	M	K	G	V	A	D	Z	S

14	15	16	17	18	19	20	21	22	23	24	25	26
H	N	C	L	P	T	U	O	Y	W	I	J	E

A World Upside-Down (page 84-85)

A. Tobey Maguire; B. fought; C. Mary Jane; D. toffee; E. Church; F. Green Goblin; G. white; H. sweethearts; I. honest; J. Stan Lee; K. shoe shine; L. honcho; M. Fantasia

"These are the years when a man changes into the man he's going to be for the rest of his life. Just be careful who you change into."

Codeword (page 86)

1	2	3	4	5	6	7	8	9	10	11	12	13
L	P	K	N	I	A	J	T	D	S	C	H	X

14	15	16	17	18	19	20	21	22	23	24	25	26
E	Q	F	U	R	M	B	O	Y	Z	W	V	G

Number Code: 5 Months (page 87)

1. 15 + 10 = 25 M
   3 + 16 = 19 A
   4 + 8 = 12 Y
2. 2 + 4 = 6 J
   7 + 6 = 13 U
   14 + 7 = 21 L
   6 + 6 = 12 Y
3. 1 + 5 = 6 J
   11 + 2 = 13 U
   6 + 2 = 8 N
   5 + 6 = 11 E
4. 4 + 15 = 19 A
   12 + 14 = 26 P
   8 + 1 = 9 R
   9 + 8 = 17 I
   6 + 15 = 21 L
5. 12 + 13 = 25 M
   3 + 16 = 19 A
   2 + 7 = 9 R
   7 + 8 = 15 C
   15 + 8 = 23 H

Shrouded Summary (page 88-89)

Superstitious porcine veneration barbarizes group dynamic amongst stranded youth. "Lord of the Flies" by William Golding.
ANAGRAMS:
ANT SMOG (7) = AMONGST
BIZARRE ABS (10)= BARBARIZES
INN OVERHEAT (10) = VENERATION
OUTSTRIP ISSUE (13) = SUPERSTITIOUS
PIG MUD CRAYON (5,7) = GROUP DYNAMIC
RIP ONCE (7) = PORCINE
THUNDERY TOADS (8,5) = STRANDED YOUTH

```
O V S A N T A S N V A S N
V O U T S T R P E N S U E
E F P O R C I N E E U V U
R S E O C Q C W L W E M
E A R U B R R L I S S U E
A U S M A I A W U M S N D
T L T T R A Z Y U P E U Z
L D I E B G E A O N C E A
D O T I A E M G R N J D R
N F I G R O U P S R Y E R
A G O C I M A N Y D L D E
O V U F Z A R M A X N P
F B S P E D F N O O K A L
S C A E S T O A D N U R Q
A U P G H M D H P K G T I
U M H Z D E N D A R T S H
L E N W I G Z S T N U L T
```

Beauty Products (page 90)

1	2	3	4	5	6	7	8	9	10	11	12	13
M	A	N	I	C	U	R	E	T	Z	W	P	B
14	15	16	17	18	19	20	21	22	23	24	25	26
F	K	O	S	Y	V	D	G	L	H	J	Q	X

Titan of Terror (page 91)

Alfred Hitchcock was not only the master of suspense, but the maestro of witty retorts. To a woman who complained that the shower scene in *Psycho* so frightened her daughter that the girl would no longer shower, he said, "Then Madam, I suggest you have her dry-cleaned."

Mastermind (page 91)

7930

Codeword (page 92)

1	2	3	4	5	6	7	8	9	10	11	12	13
I	W	Q	O	P	G	F	T	H	E	V	L	M

14	15	16	17	18	19	20	21	22	23	24	25	26
U	J	R	A	Z	B	D	N	X	C	Y	K	S

Gemstones (page 93)

1	2	3	4	5	6	7	8	9	10	11	12	13
G	A	R	N	E	T	Z	X	U	Y	B	H	K
14	15	16	17	18	19	20	21	22	23	24	25	26
O	S	D	I	M	P	C	F	J	L	Q	V	W

Timeless Truths (page 94)

1. Advertising: The fine art of making you think you've longed for something all your life that you never heard of before.

2. "He that does good for good's sake seeks neither praise nor reward, but he is sure of both in the end." —William Penn

Wise Words (page 95)

1. Most of us are loyal—when we reach a certain age we like to stick to it.
2. The things most people want to know are none of their business.
3. Nothing is impossible to the man who does not have to do it himself.
4. Thinking well is wise; planning well is wiser; doing well is wisest and best of all.
5. You can keep your head above water if you hold your chin up.
6. Success is knowing the difference between cornering people and getting them in your corner.

Searching for Evidence (page 96-97)

J	I	M	I		L	A	B	O	R		L	E	A	N
A	V	E	R		A	L	A	M	O		U	R	G	E
X	E	N	O		N	I	N	E	S		C	R	E	W
			U	N	I	T	E	D	N	A	T	I	O	N	S
		Z	E	N			R	E	A	L	T	Y
S	E	N	I	O	R		E	N	Y	A		
B	R	A	N	D	N	A	M	E		R	I	P	E	R
L	A	I	D		S	N	A	R	E		M	A	X	I
I	T	F	O	R		K	I	D	N	A	P	P	E	D
		O	V	A	L		A	L	S	A	C	E
A	T	E	A	S	E		N	B	A		
R	E	D	N	A	I	L	P	O	L	I	S	H
I	S	I	N		L	E	A	S	E		W	A	R	D
A	L	F	A		E	A	G	E	R		A	T	O	N
S	A	Y	S		D	R	E	S	S		B	E	T	A

Batteries Not Included (page 98)

1. Some assembly required.
2. Use only as directed.
3. As seen on TV.
4. Avoid contact with skin.
5. Apply only to affected area.
6. You must be present to win.
7. Harmful or fatal if swallowed.
8. No purchase necessary!

Codeword (page 99)

1	2	3	4	5	6	7	8	9	10	11	12	13
P	O	Q	W	R	J	Y	I	M	X	K	H	A

14	15	16	17	18	19	20	21	22	23	24	25	26
N	T	S	D	L	C	Z	V	G	U	F	E	B

Codeword (page 100)

1	2	3	4	5	6	7	8	9	10	11	12	13
N	O	L	G	P	U	D	X	R	B	W	K	E

14	15	16	17	18	19	20	21	22	23	24	25	26
S	Z	F	C	Q	Y	I	J	M	T	A	H	V

Ancient Wisdom (page 101)

"Better a diamond with a flaw than a pebble without." —Chinese proverb

Grape Expectations (page 101)

"Penicillin cures, but wine makes people happy." —Alexander Fleming

Shoes (page 102)

1	2	3	4	5	6	7	8	9	10	11	12	13
C	L	O	G	S	A	I	X	N	R	P	B	F

14	15	16	17	18	19	20	21	22	23	24	25	26
K	H	E	M	U	V	Z	W	T	D	Y	J	Q

Women's Jobs (page 103)

1	2	3	4	5	6	7	8	9	10	11	12	13
H	U	N	T	E	R	X	A	S	V	W	O	B

14	15	16	17	18	19	20	21	22	23	24	25	26
G	K	L	I	D	F	C	M	P	J	Q	Y	Z

Code-doku (page 104)

ABSURDITY

A	U	T	D	I	S	Y	R	B
D	B	S	T	R	Y	I	A	U
R	Y	I	U	B	A	T	D	S
S	D	Y	B	A	U	R	I	T
T	I	U	Y	D	R	B	S	A
B	R	A	I	S	T	U	Y	D
Y	S	B	A	T	I	D	U	R
I	A	D	R	U	B	S	T	Y
U	T	R	S	Y	D	A	B	I

Word Columns (page 105)

The fellow that owns his own home is always just coming out of a hardware store.

Missing Connections (page 105)

H	O	C	K	E	Y		T	U	B
A			I		E		I		E
T	U	R	N		W	O	N		A
C			G	A	S		T	A	R
H	O	P		X		S			N
		E	X	I	S	T			D
P	E	N		S		E	D	E	N
R		C			W				S
E		I	R	A	T	E			
P	A	L			D	A	R	T	

Made Ya Laugh! (page 106)

1. "Why do they call it a 'building?' It looks like it's finished. Why isn't it a 'built?' " —Jerry Seinfeld
2. A Freudian slip is when you say one thing but mean your mother.
3. Her vocabulary was as bad as, like, whatever.
4. "I planted some bird seed. A bird grew. Now I don't know what to feed it." —Steven Wright
5. Where do forest rangers go to get away from it all?

Wacky Wordy (page 107)

One thing after another

Wacky Wordy (page 107)

Indigo (In DEE, GO)

Acrostic Anagram (page 108)

1. anyway; 2. arctic; 3. watery;
4. tower; 5. chain; 6. annoys;
7. ozone; 8. utility; 9. heaved;
10. flank; 11. layout; 12. vivid
"You can't say that civilization don't advance…for in every war they kill you a new way."

Acrostic Anagram (page 109)

1. trends; 2. branded; 3. clasps;
4. bungler; 5. honey; 6. refine;
7. rushing; 8. morning; 9. angry;
10. disdain; 11. details; 12. orient
"Humor brings insight and tolerance. Irony brings a deeper and less friendly understanding."

Word Columns (page 110)

You should always try to keep a smile on your face and a melody in your heart. Once you master that, try patting your head and rubbing your belly at the same time.

Code-doku (page 111)

ALL'S WELL THAT ENDS WELL

T	D	N	H	W	S	A	L	E
L	E	H	T	N	A	S	D	W
S	A	W	E	L	D	T	N	H
N	L	S	W	D	T	E	H	A
A	T	D	S	E	H	L	W	N
H	W	E	N	A	L	D	T	S
D	N	L	A	S	W	H	E	T
W	S	T	D	H	E	N	A	L
E	H	A	L	T	N	W	S	D

Name Calling (page 111)

My poor mind works like lightning: one brilliant flash and it is gone!

Queen of Song (page 112)

Ella Fitzgerald won thirteen Grammy awards, more than any other jazz performer. Her nickname was "First Lady of Song."

Cryptogram (page 112)

"When she started to play, Steinway came down personally and rubbed his name off the piano." —Bob Hope, on Phyllis Diller

Code-doku (page 113)

DOVETAILS

T	D	E	I	L	V	O	A	S
I	A	S	E	O	T	L	D	V
O	V	L	S	A	D	I	E	T
S	E	I	A	V	O	D	T	L
V	T	D	L	S	I	A	O	E
A	L	O	D	T	E	S	V	I
L	I	V	O	E	A	T	S	D
D	O	T	V	I	S	E	L	A
E	S	A	T	D	L	V	I	O

Acrostic Anagram (page 114)

A. breathless; B. thermometer; C. foregoes; D. fortify; E. euthanasia; F. faction; G. eunuch; H. chunky; I. widowed

"More firm and sure the hand of courage strikes, when it obeys the watchful eye of caution."

The First Lady of Cinema (page 115)

"Why slap them on the wrist with feathers when you can belt them over the head with a sledgehammer?"
—Katharine Hepburn

Wise Words from a *Star Wars* Queen (page 115)

"The best part about being friends with your parents is that no matter what you do, they have to keep loving you."
—Natalie Portman

Code-doku (page 116)

EDINBURGH

Codeword (page 117)

Name Calling (page 118)

"Push" and "Pull" are written on the door of success.

Name Calling (page 118)

A pessimist, confronted with two bad choices, chooses both.

Acrostic Anagram (page 119)

A. acerbic; B. repetitive; C. gushes; D. entity; E. overjoys; F. navigational; G. enviable; H. belonged; I. follower

"If your job is to leaven ordinary lives with elevating spectacle, be elevating or be gone."

The Greatest (page 120)

"A man who views the world the same at fifty as he did at twenty has wasted thirty years of his life." —Muhammad Ali

Breaking the Baseball Color Line (page 120)

"The right of every American to first-class citizenship is the most important issue of our time."—Jackie Robinson

Word Columns (page 121)

"Nature is indifferent to the survival of the human species, including Americans." —Adlai Stevenson

Dial Tone (page 121)

We waited for 4 hours for tickets to the hottest show on broadway.

Codeword (page 122)

1 2 3 4 5 6 7 8 9 10 11 12 13
P F C K O Z I X G U S M A

14 15 16 17 18 19 20 21 22 23 24 25 26
Y L N V Q D E W R J T B H

Code-doku (page 123)

Set a thief to catch a thief

Acrostic Anagram (page 124)

A. preparedness; B. flophouses;
C. motions; D. pontoon; E. adaptation;
F. forehead; G. ravenously; H. diffused
"To depend upon a profession is a less odious form of slavery than to depend upon a father."

The Big Dipper (page 125)

"When you go out there and do the things you're supposed to do, people view you as selfish." —Wilt Chamberlain

Who Is...? (page 125)

In 1997, he hosted "Wheel of Fortune" while Pat Sajak took over "Jeopardy!" The switcheroo was an April Fools' Day joke.

Codeword (page 126)

1 2 3 4 5 6 7 8 9 10 11 12 13
C F N U Z D K X W T Y Q B

14 15 16 17 18 19 20 21 22 23 24 25 26
A O P S E L M I H V G R J

Name Calling (page 127)

America had often been discovered before Columbus, but it had always been hushed up.

Crack the Code (page 127)

The diagonal sum is 9. Star = 5, Diamond = 3, Circle = 2, and Arrow = 1

Acrostic (page 128)

A. Leonardo da Vinci; B. daydreams;
C. dived; D. vested; E. desktop;
F. fungus; G. disbands; H. windiest;
I. offensively; J. immensely
"As every divided kingdom falls, so every mind divided between many studies confounds and saps itself."

Acrostic Anagram (page 129)

A. macabre; B. anthrax; C. whammed;
D. westerns; E. thinnest; F. cataracts;
G. alarmists; H. hotheaded;
I. hoodwinks
"The world embarrasses me, and I cannot dream that this watch exists and has no watchmaker."

Headline Hoots (page 130)

1. If strike isn't settled quickly it may last a while.
2. Queen Mary having bottom scraped.
3. Stolen painting found by tree.
4. Federal agents raid gun shop, find weapons.

Name Calling (page 131)

The sea has a soothing effect. Did you ever see a nervous clam?

Mastermind (page 131)

2359

Codeword (page 132)

1	2	3	4	5	6	7	8	9	10	11	12	13
H	Y	S	M	V	I	L	J	B	R	P	E	N
14	15	16	17	18	19	20	21	22	23	24	25	26
K	O	C	X	Z	F	G	W	Q	U	T	A	D

Codeword (page 133)

1	2	3	4	5	6	7	8	9	10	11	12	13
V	A	E	H	Y	J	I	X	U	O	T	N	C
14	15	16	17	18	19	20	21	22	23	24	25	26
D	W	K	S	Z	G	B	L	F	R	M	Q	P

Kitchen (page 134)

1	2	3	4	5	6	7	8	9	10	11	12	13
C	U	P	B	O	A	R	D	S	Z	V	T	K
14	15	16	17	18	19	20	21	22	23	24	25	26
E	H	F	N	W	M	L	X	G	J	Y	I	Q

Acrostic (page 135)

A. tableware; B. hyphenate; C. nooks; D. wittingly; E. continuous; F. housewarming; G. ratatouille; H. oaths
"A woman is like a tea bag, you cannot tell how strong she is until you put her in hot water."

Code-doku (page 136)

N	A	Y	I	T	O	P	S	L
L	S	T	A	P	N	O	Y	I
I	P	O	S	L	Y	N	T	A
S	T	P	L	O	A	Y	I	N
Y	I	A	N	S	P	T	L	O
O	N	L	Y	I	T	A	P	S
A	Y	S	P	N	L	I	O	T
P	O	I	T	A	S	L	N	Y
T	L	N	O	Y	I	S	A	P

French Women (page 137)

1	2	3	4	5	6	7	8	9	10	11	12	13
M	A	R	I	E	B	T	Z	U	S	O	L	J
14	15	16	17	18	19	20	21	22	23	24	25	26
D	C	F	Y	V	Q	N	P	H	G	K	W	X

Codeword (page 138)

1	2	3	4	5	6	7	8	9	10	11	12	13
K	S	Y	X	F	H	C	L	P	D	O	B	J
14	15	16	17	18	19	20	21	22	23	24	25	26
R	W	U	V	M	Z	E	T	N	A	Q	I	G

Dial Tone (page 139)

After breaking up with your boyfriend, comfort foods such as ice cream can really help!

Altared States (page 139)

"I love being married. It's so great to find that one special person you want to annoy for the rest of your life." —Rita Rudner

Code-doku (page 140)

A	H	R	S	T	U	E	N	B
B	S	N	A	H	E	U	T	R
E	T	U	B	R	N	A	S	H
H	A	B	U	N	T	S	R	E
N	R	E	H	B	S	T	A	U
S	U	T	R	E	A	B	H	N
T	N	S	E	U	R	H	B	A
U	B	A	N	S	H	R	E	T
R	E	H	T	A	B	N	U	S

Stores (page 141)

1	2	3	4	5	6	7	8	9	10	11	12	13
D	I	S	C	O	U	N	T	E	A	J	Y	W

14	15	16	17	18	19	20	21	22	23	24	25	26
Q	L	H	F	B	K	P	R	V	G	M	X	Z

Beyond *Clueless* (page 142)

"I don't want to be known as the Aerosmith chick, but it's fun to put on the boots and makeup and act like a tough girl." —Alicia Silverstone

Good Eats Up North (page 142)

Poutine, a popular comfort food in Canada, is French fries topped with fresh cheese curds, then covered with brown gravy.

Codeword (page 143)

1	2	3	4	5	6	7	8	9	10	11	12	13
H	A	K	X	D	G	Z	R	N	J	U	V	I

14	15	16	17	18	19	20	21	22	23	24	25	26
E	T	O	C	B	S	Y	M	P	Q	F	L	W

Shrouded Summary (page 144-145)

juvenile adventuring; anthropomorphic; semantics; advisory; assist; marvelous. Anthropomorphic advisory semantics assist marvelous juvenile adventuring. "Alice's Adventures in Wonderland" by Lewis Carroll.

Code-doku (page 146)

O	I	S	N	U	E	F	M	V
N	V	M	F	S	O	U	I	E
F	U	E	M	I	V	S	O	N
S	E	I	V	O	M	N	U	F
V	N	O	U	E	F	M	S	I
M	F	U	I	N	S	V	E	O
U	S	V	E	F	I	O	N	M
I	M	N	O	V	U	E	F	S
E	O	F	S	M	N	I	V	U

Word Columns (page 147)

Life isn't fair. If it were, my running shoes would keep me running right past all those doughnut shops.

Word Columns (page 147)

My career counselor tells me I'd be perfect working for the airlines since I am always late and lose stuff.

Grid Fill (page 148)

F	U	R	T	A	D	O
	M	I	S	S	Y	
J	E	S	S	I	C	A
		E	V	E		
E	L	L	I	O	T	T
	N	E	L	L	Y	
S	I	M	P	S	O	N

About One of Her Own (page 148)

"I'd have to say that, in general, models take themselves too seriously. Basically, they are genetic freaks who spend a couple of hours in hair and makeup."
—Rebecca Romijn

Out of Africa (page 149)

1	2	3	4	5	6	7	8	9	10	11	12	13
C	O	U	N	T	R	I	E	S	H	Y	Z	K

14	15	16	17	18	19	20	21	22	23	24	25	26
J	G	P	A	D	V	Q	B	L	M	W	F	X

It's a Fortnight (page 150)

1	2	3	4	5	6	7	8	9	10	11	12	13
S	O	M	E	D	A	Y	I	U	N	R	T	P

14	15	16	17	18	19	20	21	22	23	24	25	26
C	H	W	L	K	X	V	G	B	F	J	Q	Z

Codeword (page 151)

1	2	3	4	5	6	7	8	9	10	11	12	13
X	W	B	L	F	I	V	E	K	M	U	C	Z

14	15	16	17	18	19	20	21	22	23	24	25	26
Q	T	Y	H	A	O	S	P	J	G	N	R	D

Happy Christmas (page 152)

1	2	3	4	5	6	7	8	9	10	11	12	13
G	H	Y	T	I	N	S	E	L	P	B	O	D

14	15	16	17	18	19	20	21	22	23	24	25	26
V	X	W	Z	U	M	A	J	K	Q	C	F	R

Codeword (page 153)

STANLEY CUP

Codeword (page 151)

1	2	3	4	5	6	7	8	9	10	11	12	13
S	T	Q	K	F	R	D	U	V	G	H	N	M

14	15	16	17	18	19	20	21	22	23	24	25	26
Y	J	I	O	E	W	B	X	L	A	C	P	Z

Cryptogram (page 154)

"I came here tonight because when you realize you want to spend the rest of your life with somebody, you want the rest of your life to start as soon as possible." —Billy Crystal, *When Harry Met Sally*

Grid Fill (page 154)

S	P	R	I	N	T
A	C	C	E	S	S
K	E	T	T	L	E
A	C	H	I	N	G
C	L	O	T	H	S
E	R	O	D	E	S
L	E	A	G	U	E

Have a Ball (page 155)

1	2	3	4	5	6	7	8	9	10	11	12	13
C	U	R	V	E	S	B	A	L	K	Z	Q	O

14	15	16	17	18	19	20	21	22	23	24	25	26
H	W	J	G	P	N	M	I	F	D	T	Y	X

Codeword (page 156)

1	2	3	4	5	6	7	8	9	10	11	12	13
H	E	L	K	B	G	D	Z	W	F	T	R	C

14	15	16	17	18	19	20	21	22	23	24	25	26
S	X	J	A	U	Q	I	Y	P	V	M	O	N

Acrostic (page 157)

A. tyranny; B. mothball; C. pshaw; D. segregation; E. evidently; F. hit and run; G. White House; H. eighteenth; I. buoyant

"When you have got an elephant by the hind leg, and he is trying to run away, it's best to let him run."

Code-doku (page 158)

FACTORIES

C	F	E	T	S	R	O	A	I
T	S	R	O	A	I	E	C	F
A	I	O	C	F	E	T	S	R
I	O	A	F	E	C	S	R	T
F	E	C	S	R	T	A	I	O
S	R	T	A	I	O	C	F	E
E	C	F	R	T	S	I	O	A
R	T	S	I	O	A	F	E	C
O	A	I	E	C	F	R	T	S

Mastermind (page 159)

LEAF

Mastermind (page 159)

MOIST

Order in the Court (page 160)

1	2	3	4	5	6	7	8	9	10	11	12	13
T	R	I	A	L	S	E	Z	X	J	N	M	Y

14	15	16	17	18	19	20	21	22	23	24	25	26
U	Q	D	B	O	P	C	F	G	H	V	W	K

Codeword (page 161)

1	2	3	4	5	6	7	8	9	10	11	12	13
W	G	Z	X	S	V	Q	C	A	N	J	E	Y

14	15	16	17	18	19	20	21	22	23	24	25	26
H	F	T	K	I	P	M	R	L	U	O	D	B

Code-doku (page 162)

O	E	R	W	M	C	V	I	A
C	W	I	V	R	A	O	E	M
V	A	M	O	E	I	R	W	C
I	R	A	M	V	E	W	C	O
E	C	O	A	W	R	I	M	V
W	M	V	C	I	O	E	A	R
R	V	E	I	A	M	C	O	W
M	I	C	R	O	W	A	V	E
A	O	W	E	C	V	M	R	I

Calcu-doku (page 163)

4	1	2	6	5	3
3	2	4	5	1	6
1	6	5	3	4	2
5	4	6	2	3	1
2	3	1	4	6	5
6	5	3	1	2	4

Trade Secret (page 164)

Ruth Reichl, restaurant critic for the *New York Times*, used multiple disguises when she visited restaurants. The disguise kit included twelve wigs, rubber cement to create wrinkles, phony eyeglasses, and "bad clothes from thrift shops."

Sight Unseen (page 164)

"I have no interest in the Grand Canyon; I prefer unnatural wonders, like Mall of America or Madonna." — Columnist Norman Chad

Thirteen States? (page 165)

1	2	3	4	5	6	7	8	9	10	11	12	13
W	Y	O	M	I	N	G	T	Z	D	A	P	K

14	15	16	17	18	19	20	21	22	23	24	25	26
V	U	E	C	S	L	X	J	B	R	F	H	Q

What's That? (page 166)

Don't count your chickens before they hatch.

Symbol Solution (page 166)

B. The first 9 symbols are being repeated, except that a symbol is removed from the end of the sequence each time.

Code-doku (page 167)

DALLY A BIT BY LADY LIBERTY

I	T	B	E	D	R	L	Y	A
Y	A	R	T	I	L	E	D	B
L	D	E	Y	A	B	T	I	R
T	B	A	I	R	E	Y	L	D
D	E	L	B	T	Y	R	A	I
R	I	Y	A	L	D	B	E	T
E	Y	I	D	B	T	A	R	L
A	L	T	R	Y	I	D	B	E
B	R	D	L	E	A	I	T	Y

Mastermind (page 168)

DAISY

You Could Look It Up (page 168)

Yes, "The Bible Cure for Irritable Bowel Syndrome" and "The Thermodynamics of Pizza" are the titles of actual books.

Codeword (page 169)

PREDATORS

1	2	3	4	5	6	7	8	9	10	11	12	13
P	U	J	T	W	H	Y	V	R	A	L	N	S

14	15	16	17	18	19	20	21	22	23	24	25	26
I	E	F	D	G	X	B	K	Z	Q	M	O	C

Chain Sudoku (page 170)

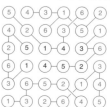

LogiNumber (page 171)

A = 4, B = 6, C = 8, D = 2, E = 7, F = 3, G = 1, H = 5

Code-doku (page 172)

S	L	I	A	T	Y	N	O	P
O	N	T	L	P	S	I	A	Y
P	Y	A	O	I	N	T	L	S
A	P	N	T	Y	L	O	S	I
I	O	Y	N	S	A	L	P	T
T	S	L	P	O	I	A	Y	N
Y	A	S	I	N	O	P	T	L
L	I	P	S	A	T	Y	N	O
N	T	O	Y	L	P	S	I	A

Crypto-Logic (page 173)

INTRIGUING

Crypto-Logic (page 173)

PACE

Cryptoku (page 174)

M	E	C	H	T	Y	I	S	R
I	T	R	S	E	M	Y	C	H
H	S	Y	C	R	I	E	T	M
Y	M	I	T	C	R	S	H	E
C	H	E	M	I	S	T	R	Y
S	R	T	Y	H	E	C	M	I
E	I	H	R	S	C	M	Y	T
T	C	M	E	Y	H	R	I	S
R	Y	S	I	M	T	H	E	C

Pray, But Keep Your Eyes Open (page 175)

When the missionaries came to Africa they had the Bible and we had the land. They said, "Let us pray." We closed our eyes. When we opened them we had the Bible and they had the land.
—Bishop Desmond Tutu

Mastermind (page 175)

17548

Crazy Calculator (page 176)

The upper left/upper right and the lower left/lower right segments are the faulty pairs.

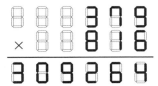

No Extra Charge for Groaners (page 176)

Question: What's the difference between mashed potatoes and pea soup? Answer: Anyone can mash potatoes.

Acrostic Anagram (page 177)

A. amalgamates; B. confinements;
C. hounding; D. whenever; E. cherubim;
F. audibly; G. toothache; H. civilian;
I. holiday
"Men hate the individual whom they call avaricious only because nothing can be gained from him."

LogiNumber (page 178)

A = 3, B = 4, C = 2, D = 1

Christmas Dinner Fit for a King (page 178)

In the year 1213, King John of England ordered about three thousand capons (chickens), a thousand salted eels, four hundred hogs, one hundred pounds of almonds, and twenty-four casks of wine for his Christmas feast.

Code-doku (page 179)

Cryptoku (page 180)

Royal Fellows (page 181)

1	2	3	4	5	6	7	8	9	10	11	12	13
G	E	N	T	R	Y	V	I	D	P	A	U	K

14	15	16	17	18	19	20	21	22	23	24	25	26
W	Z	M	F	C	B	O	J	L	Q	S	H	X

Codes and Ciphers (page 182-183)

Find the Codebreakers (page 184-185)

Before Man (page 186)

1	2	3	4	5	6	7	8	9	10	11	12	13
L	A	S	T	M	E	N	U	I	D	Q	C	W

14	15	16	17	18	19	20	21	22	23	24	25	26
K	Y	V	H	Z	F	X	J	R	B	O	G	P

Toppers (page 187)

1	2	3	4	5	6	7	8	9	10	11	12	13
H	A	T	S	F	O	R	M	E	N	W	C	P

14	15	16	17	18	19	20	21	22	23	24	25	26
Z	L	X	Y	G	B	U	J	D	V	I	K	Q

Codeword (page 188)

1	2	3	4	5	6	7	8	9	10	11	12	13
Y	K	J	F	I	B	A	G	H	L	V	C	P

14	15	16	17	18	19	20	21	22	23	24	25	26
M	E	O	Z	S	D	U	W	X	N	R	T	Q

Flowers (page 189)

1	2	3	4	5	6	7	8	9	10	11	12	13
O	R	C	H	I	D	J	Z	X	W	T	S	E

14	15	16	17	18	19	20	21	22	23	24	25	26
A	B	K	N	Q	U	Y	P	L	G	M	F	V

Codeword (page 190)

1	2	3	4	5	6	7	8	9	10	11	12	13
S	M	F	T	E	V	Q	A	I	R	D	Y	B

14	15	16	17	18	19	20	21	22	23	24	25	26
C	O	L	K	U	W	P	H	Z	J	X	N	G

Cryptoku (page 191)

W	T	R	D	A	R
A	D	O	T	W	R
R	A	D	O	T	W
T	O	W	A	R	D
D	R	A	W	O	T
O	W	T	R	D	A

Geometry (page 192)

1	2	3	4	5	6	7	8	9	10	11	12	13
S	H	A	P	E	V	X	Z	L	M	K	I	U

14	15	16	17	18	19	20	21	22	23	24	25	26
B	O	T	G	D	Q	C	N	R	Y	W	F	J

Slingin' the Slang (page 193)

In the colorful world of slang, cornbread is an "Arkansas wedding cake," a raccoon bone is a "Tennessee toothpick," and chewing tobacco is "West Virginia coleslaw."

Loopy Laws (page 193)

According to Rich Smith in "You Can Get Arrested for That," it's illegal to fall asleep in a cheese factory in South Dakota.

Decipher This! (page 194-195)

Codeword (page 196)

1	2	3	4	5	6	7	8	9	10	11	12	13
B	X	Q	W	C	O	H	R	N	Y	Z	L	K

14	15	16	17	18	19	20	21	22	23	24	25	26
M	U	G	V	J	T	P	I	A	D	E	S	F

What's On? (page 197)

1	2	3	4	5	6	7	8	9	10	11	12	13
T	V	N	A	M	E	S	G	X	Z	I	D	P

14	15	16	17	18	19	20	21	22	23	24	25	26
O	C	U	H	R	K	J	W	Y	L	F	B	Q

Women (page 198)

1	2	3	4	5	6	7	8	9	10	11	12	13
G	I	R	L	S	A	X	D	T	U	W	M	N

14	15	16	17	18	19	20	21	22	23	24	25	26
F	J	Q	B	C	E	H	K	O	P	Y	V	Z

An Ancient True Crime (page 199)

Gilles Garnier died in 1573, burned at the stake. A hermit, he was accused of being a werewolf—specifically, of killing and eating four children. He lived in France.

Lewis Hutchinson (page 199)

This killer was born in Scotland but moved to Jamaica, where he set up an estate called Edinburgh Castle. Travelers who approached the castle too closely tended to disappear. He reportedly tossed his victims into a sinkhole. He was called the Mad Master or the Mad Doctor of Edinburgh. He eventually shot a soldier who had been sent to capture him. He then tried to flee the area, but was caught, tried, and hanged.

Interception (page 200)

Take the second letter of each word and you reveal: BUCHAREST

Everybody and His Brother (page 200)

Actor Christopher Lee played the famous detective in the 1962 movie *"Sherlock Holmes and the Deadly Necklace."* In 1970, Lee played a Holmes again—Sherlock's brother Mycroft, in the movie *"The Private Life of Sherlock Holmes."* He had also played Sir Henry Baskerville in an earlier film adapted from *"The Hound of the Baskervilles."*

Where It's At (page 201)

1	2	3	4	5	6	7	8	9	10	11	12	13
S	E	C	T	I	O	N	A	U	Y	M	R	Q

14	15	16	17	18	19	20	21	22	23	24	25	26
B	V	H	F	P	Z	L	W	J	D	K	G	X

Add-a-Letter (page 202-203)

The missing letter is X

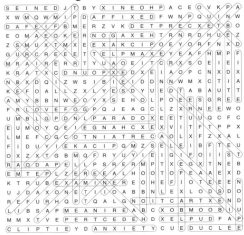

Codeword (page 204)

1	2	3	4	5	6	7	8	9	10	11	12	13
O	A	Q	U	J	H	F	I	K	N	V	X	S

14	15	16	17	18	19	20	21	22	23	24	25	26
Z	G	B	D	R	T	C	P	E	M	Y	L	W

An Alphabetical Phrase (page 205)

A pangram is a sentence that includes all letters of the alphabet. Most people have heard the sentence, "The quick brown fox jumps over the lazy dog."

A Mysterious Event (page 205)

The year 1911 involved a notable case of art theft—the Mona Lisa was stolen from the Louvre by an employee. He was caught two years later and the painting was returned to its home.

A Surprising Viewpoint (page 206)

"I consider that a man's brain originally is like a little empty attic, and you have to stock it with such furniture as you choose. A fool takes in all the lumber of every sort that he comes across, so that the knowledge which might be useful to him gets crowded out, or at best is jumbled up with a lot of other things so that he has a difficulty in laying his hands upon it. Now the skilful workman is very careful indeed as to what he takes into his brain-attic. He will have nothing but the tools which may help him in doing his work, but of these he has a large assortment, and all in the most perfect order. It is a mistake to think that that little room has elastic walls and can distend to any extent. Depend upon it there comes a time when for every addition of knowledge you forget something that you knew before. It is of the highest importance, therefore, not to have useless facts elbowing out the useful ones."
Bonus answer: Sherlock Holmes is the speaker in "A Study in Scarlet"

Perfection (page 207)

A man named Joseph Grizzard was one of the legendary jewel thieves of his age. In 1913, he stole a famous string of precious pearls from a sealed box while they were in transit. Adding insult to injury, he replaced the pearls with sugar cubes before sealing the box and leaving the theft to be discovered.

Han van Meegeren (page 207)

This Dutch painter began as an artist of original work, gaining some success. However, his work was sometimes critiqued as derivative and unoriginal. He eventually turned to forgeries, including of Dutch painter Johannes Vermeer. During World War II, one of the forger's paintings ended up in the hands of Nazi Herman Goring. Van Meegeran was arrested after the war for collaboration with the enemy—until he explained that he hadn't sold a real Vermeer, but a forgery. He was given a lesser sentence for fraud, though he died before he served time in prison.

Code-doku (page 208)

REVELRY EVERY NEW YEAR'S EVE

Code-doku (page 209)

GREEN IGUANA MARGARITA

Add-a-Letter (page 210-211)

The missing letter is H

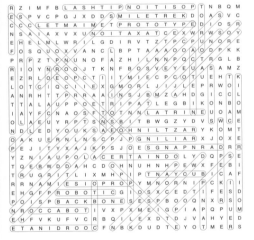

Add-a-Letter (page 212-213)

The missing letter is O

Festive Fare (page 214)

1	2	3	4	5	6	7	8	9	10	11	12	13
H	D	O	V	L	Z	F	S	N	W	A	I	Q
14	15	16	17	18	19	20	21	22	23	24	25	26
C	P	X	T	U	R	K	E	Y	J	G	M	B

Cryptoku (page 215)

G	N	V	O	Y	I	T	E	L
E	L	O	N	V	T	G	Y	I
Y	I	T	E	L	G	V	N	O
I	G	Y	L	T	N	E	O	V
L	O	N	G	E	V	I	T	Y
V	T	E	I	O	Y	L	G	N
T	Y	I	V	N	E	O	L	G
O	E	G	Y	I	L	N	V	T
N	V	L	T	G	O	Y	I	E

Endearment (page 216)

1	2	3	4	5	6	7	8	9	10	11	12	13
L	O	V	E	R	X	S	A	G	C	D	M	T
14	15	16	17	18	19	20	21	22	23	24	25	26
U	Y	K	H	B	F	I	N	P	W	J	Q	Z

Composers Letterbox (page 217)

1	2	3	4	5	6	7	8	9	10	11	12	13
H	O	L	S	T	N	D	U	J	P	F	G	Y
14	15	16	17	18	19	20	21	22	23	24	25	26
V	X	Z	K	B	A	C	I	R	E	M	W	Q

Add-a-Letter (page 218-219)

The missing letter is R

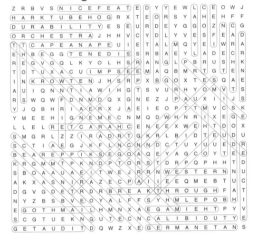

No Man's Lands (page 220)

1	2	3	4	5	6	7	8	9	10	11	12	13
I	S	L	A	N	D	U	Y	E	O	B	T	J
14	15	16	17	18	19	20	21	22	23	24	25	26
Z	M	F	R	V	H	P	C	W	G	X	K	Q

Cryptoku (page 221)

K	R	W	O	N	H	B	E	C
B	N	C	E	R	K	H	W	O
O	E	H	W	C	B	R	N	K
H	K	B	N	W	C	E	O	R
W	O	R	K	B	E	N	C	H
E	C	N	H	O	R	W	K	B
R	B	O	C	E	W	K	H	N
N	W	K	R	H	O	C	B	E
C	H	E	B	K	N	O	R	W

Cryptoku (page 222)

M	R	O	G	T	I	S	H	A
A	H	G	M	S	R	T	I	O
T	S	I	A	H	O	M	G	R
O	M	A	R	I	H	G	T	S
H	I	S	T	O	G	R	A	M
G	T	R	S	A	M	H	O	I
S	G	T	O	R	A	I	M	H
R	A	H	I	M	T	O	S	G
I	O	M	H	G	S	A	R	T

Separated Cities (page 223)

1	2	3	4	5	6	7	8	9	10	11	12	13
U	R	B	A	N	S	P	L	I	T	F	E	O
14	15	16	17	18	19	20	21	22	23	24	25	26
Y	M	K	V	H	D	C	G	J	W	Q	X	Z

Add-a-Letter (page 224-225)

The missing letter is U

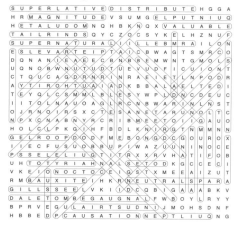

Add-a-Letter (page 226-227)

The missing letter is A

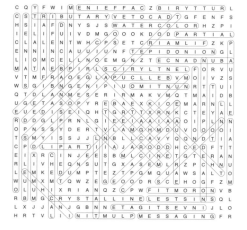

Not a Hack (page 228-229)

The leftover letters spell: He won an Oscar for his role as Jimmy "Popeye" Doyle in *The French Connection*.

Where the Heart Is (page 230)

1	2	3	4	5	6	7	8	9	10	11	12	13
A	B	O	D	E	S	I	Y	U	R	T	F	C
14	15	16	17	18	19	20	21	22	23	24	25	26
N	P	H	M	W	K	L	V	G	Q	J	X	Z

Codeword (page 231)

1	2	3	4	5	6	7	8	9	10	11	12	13
R	J	B	E	S	X	W	Y	F	O	M	C	P

14	15	16	17	18	19	20	21	22	23	24	25	26
Q	A	I	T	G	H	Z	U	V	N	K	L	D

Forever Jung page 232-233)

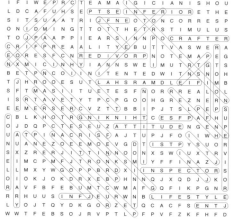

Codeword (page 234)

Code-doku (page 235)

Word Columns (page 236)

"Getting back with an old boyfriend is like going to a garage sale and buying your own stuff back."

Word Columns (page 236)

"The United States has become a place where entertainers and professional athletes are mistaken for people of importance."

Acrostic (page 237)

A. Thomas Paine; B. blitz; C. dwelt; D. Hoover; E. forthright; F. Kong; G. inequities; H. Delhi; I. nephew; J. fleshy; K. unity
"When men yield up the privilege of thinking, the last shadow of liberty quits the horizon."

Code-doku (page 238)

Mastermind (page 239)

23461

Cipher Trivia (page 239)

With book ciphers, both sender and receiver use the same book as the key to the cipher. The Bible and particular editions of the dictionary are sometimes used because they have many words available. Other people might use a more obscure book for an extra layer of security.

Codeword (page 240)

Code-doku (page 241)

They Are the Champions (page 242)

A. Bohemian; B. One Vision; C. soothes;
D. A Kind; E. Hijack; F. Pressure;
G. starves; H. Deacon; I. Stone Cold;
J. Elvis; K. speakers; L . attempt
"To avoid complications she never kept
the same address. In conversation, she
spoke just like a baroness."

LogiNumber (page 243)

A = 1, B = 3, C = 2, D = 5, E = 6, F =4

LogiNumber (page 243)

A = 5, B = 1, C = 3, D = 2, E = 4, F = 6

Cryptoku (page 244)

S	U	M	O	R	P	E	T	A
E	R	A	T	U	S	P	M	O
O	T	P	M	A	E	U	R	S
P	S	E	R	M	A	T	O	U
M	O	U	S	E	T	R	A	P
T	A	R	P	O	U	M	S	E
U	E	O	A	T	M	S	P	R
R	M	S	U	P	O	A	E	T
A	P	T	E	S	R	O	U	M

Code-doku (page 245)

R	E	A	S	L	C	W	O	K
S	L	O	K	A	W	E	R	C
W	K	C	R	O	E	L	A	S
E	C	L	O	K	A	S	W	R
O	S	R	W	C	L	K	E	A
K	A	W	E	R	S	C	L	O
A	W	K	C	E	O	R	S	L
L	R	S	A	W	K	O	C	E
C	O	E	L	S	R	A	K	W

Acrostic (page 246)

A. Susan Sontag; B. Hirohito;
C. campsite; D. prevented;
E. worthwhile; F. prophets; G. chamber;
H. Einstein; I. hotter; J. typhoon
"In America, the photographer is not
simply the person who records the past,
but the one who invents it."

Codeword (page 247)

SLASHING

Codeword (page 248)

Code-doku (page 249)

L	F	O	D	S	E	U	T	I
E	T	D	I	U	L	O	S	F
I	U	S	T	F	O	D	L	E
F	L	E	O	D	T	S	I	U
D	S	I	F	L	U	E	O	T
T	O	U	S	E	I	F	D	L
O	I	F	U	T	S	L	E	D
S	D	L	E	I	F	T	U	O
U	E	T	L	O	D	I	F	S

Dial Tone (page 250)

Essential items for your purse include a
makeup bag, cell phone, and comb!

Wisdom of the Moors (page 250)

Every beetle is a gazelle in the eyes of its mother. —Moroccan proverb

Codeword (page 251)

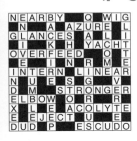

Cryptoku (page 252)

D	R	U	S	A	I
A	I	S	D	R	U
S	U	I	A	D	R
R	A	D	I	U	S
I	D	R	U	S	A
U	S	A	R	I	D

Word Columns (page 253)

Two farmers each claimed to own a certain cow. While one pulled on its head and the other pulled on its tail, the cow was milked by the lawyer.

Crypto-Logic (page 253)

NOSTALGIC

Code-doku (page 254)

MARCO POLO ROAMS ACROSS ASIA

Codeword (page 255)

Code-doku (page 256)

E	R	O	S	F	I	A	T	V
I	F	V	R	A	T	E	S	O
A	T	S	O	V	E	F	R	I
S	E	T	I	R	O	V	A	F
V	I	A	F	T	S	R	O	E
R	O	F	V	E	A	T	I	S
F	S	R	A	I	V	O	E	T
O	A	E	T	S	F	I	V	R
T	V	I	E	O	R	S	F	A

LogiNumber (page 257)

A = 1, B = 5, C = 6, D = 2, E = 3, F = 4

LogiNumber (page 257)

A = 3, B = 1, C = 5, D = 2, E = 4

Sequence (page 258)

QRSTU. The sequence progresses A BC d EFG hi JKLM nop QRSTU

Sequence (page 258)

1/11. This really 2 sequences in one. The first sequence is 1/2 2/3 3/4 4/5 and 5/6; the second is 1/3 1/5 1/7 1/9 and 1/11.

Magazine Rack (page 259)

YELTSIN = INSTYLE
QUERIES = ESQUIRE
ORAL GUM = GLAMOUR
TEN-FOUR = FORTUNE
RATIFY IVAN = VANITY FAIR
ORLON SNIGLET = ROLLING STONE

Codeword (page 260)

1	2	3	4	5	6	7	8	9	10	11	12	13
J	X	Q	Y	L	W	E	M	P	S	A	B	I

14	15	16	17	18	19	20	21	22	23	24	25	26
T	F	O	U	H	R	G	N	Z	C	D	K	V

Code-doku (page 261)

P	O	M	A	L	E	U	D	K
D	A	U	K	P	M	O	E	L
K	E	L	O	U	D	M	P	A
E	M	A	U	O	P	L	K	D
U	K	P	E	D	L	A	M	O
O	L	D	M	A	K	E	U	P
A	D	O	P	M	U	K	L	E
M	P	E	L	K	A	D	O	U
L	U	K	D	E	O	P	A	M

Tourist Attractions (page 262)

1. Betsy Ross House, 2. Alcatraz Island, 3. Empire State Building, 4. Epcot Center, 5. Franklin Institute, 6. Getty Museum, 7. Golden Gate Bridge, 8. Liberty Bell, 9. Willis Tower (was Sears Tower), 10. Space Needle, 11. Statue of Liberty, 12. White House

Bungle Gym (page 262)

BROW CLOTH = BLOWTORCH
CRUCIAL WARS = CIRCULAR SAW
I SAW CHAN = CHAIN SAW
WEB ATLAS = TABLE SAW
LOGIC SPRINKLE = LOCKING PLIERS
CAR BROW = CROWBAR

Music (page 263)

1	2	3	4	5	6	7	8	9	10	11	12	13
G	H	P	I	A	N	O	J	W	T	X	K	F

14	15	16	17	18	19	20	21	22	23	24	25	26
D	R	U	M	Z	L	S	B	E	C	V	Y	Q

Girls' Names (page 264)

1	2	3	4	5	6	7	8	9	10	11	12	13
J	X	K	Z	B	S	H	Q	W	F	P	G	U

14	15	16	17	18	19	20	21	22	23	24	25	26
Y	D	V	E	R	O	N	I	C	A	L	T	M

Codeword (page 265)

1	2	3	4	5	6	7	8	9	10	11	12	13
G	N	M	D	H	X	S	P	Y	T	A	V	W

14	15	16	17	18	19	20	21	22	23	24	25	26
C	Q	R	E	F	L	U	K	I	O	J	B	Z

Code-doku (page 266)

D	C	N	A	U	E	O	I	T
U	A	I	T	C	O	N	E	D
T	O	E	I	N	D	A	C	U
A	E	D	U	O	C	T	N	I
I	N	C	E	T	A	D	U	O
O	U	T	N	D	I	E	A	C
E	D	U	C	A	T	I	O	N
C	T	A	O	I	N	U	D	E
N	I	O	D	E	U	C	T	A

4-Letter Anagrams (page 267)

1. odor, door; 2. lids, slid; 3. runt, turn; 4. part, rapt; 5. ring, grin; 6. lamp, palm; 7. form, from; 8. pace, cape

Queen Ana Gram (page 267)

There are two common words that are anagrams of "itself": filets and stifle. Laity is an anagram of Italy.

Letterbox Big Screen (page 268)

1	2	3	4	5	6	7	8	9	10	11	12	13
M	X	N	S	J	O	L	I	E	V	A	W	F

14	15	16	17	18	19	20	21	22	23	24	25	26
Y	B	T	P	G	C	R	U	Z	H	D	Q	K

Cryptoku (page 269)

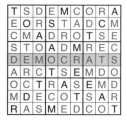

T	S	D	E	M	C	O	R	A
E	O	R	S	T	A	D	C	M
C	M	A	D	R	O	T	S	E
S	T	O	A	D	M	R	E	C
D	E	M	O	C	R	A	T	S
A	R	C	T	S	E	M	D	O
O	C	T	R	A	S	E	M	D
M	D	E	C	O	T	S	A	R
R	A	S	M	E	D	C	O	T

Codeword (page 270)

V O B H N A
COUPLE USEFUL
L A S G C N
QUILTING KITE
M D E L I
FEMALE DIADEM
M C
JEWELS CREEPS
L T H O R
BOTH ANTIQUES
P Y W T U F
VESSEL ORIGIN
S T S N Z X

1	2	3	4	5	6	7	8	9	10	11	12	13
Q	I	G	V	X	O	P	Y	M	U	H	B	N

14	15	16	17	18	19	20	21	22	23	24	25	26
C	T	E	D	W	K	Z	L	R	A	S	J	F

Chain Sudoku (page 271)

One Out of Three Ain't Bad (page 272)

Getting a hit three times out of ten at bat is considered an excellent average. George Schaller and other naturalists have observed that lions and cheetahs are also successful only about a third of the time in capturing their prey.

Word Columns (page 272)

"The secret of managing a team is to keep the guys who hate you away from the guys who are undecided."

Codeword (page 273)

A E S B B F
ONYX CORSAGES
G I A U B L
LEOTARDS UGLY
L V H S O
ASHAMED SHAWL
Q S P K
GROUP PAJAMAS
E A S P P
FAIR TWEEZERS
S I A R E O
COQUETTE RING
N M E D O S

1	2	3	4	5	6	7	8	9	10	11	12	13
E	G	Z	H	J	T	O	W	A	B	V	L	Y

14	15	16	17	18	19	20	21	22	23	24	25	26
C	M	X	P	N	R	I	Q	U	D	S	K	F

Add-a-Letter (page 274-275)

The missing letter is B

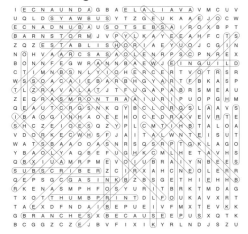

Code-doku (page 276)

C	A	D	E	I	T	M	Y	N
I	Y	M	D	C	N	A	T	E
T	N	E	Y	A	M	C	D	I
M	E	C	A	N	Y	D	I	T
A	T	Y	I	D	C	E	N	M
D	I	N	M	T	E	Y	C	A
Y	C	T	N	E	A	I	M	D
E	M	I	T	Y	D	N	A	C
N	D	A	C	M	I	T	E	Y

What's Next? (page 277)

B. In each pair of diagrams, the middle planet makes a half turn around the big planet. The small planet makes a whole turn around the middle one.

Sleigh Bells (page 277)

C (Dasher, Dancer, Prancer, Vixen, Comet, Cupid, Donder, Blitzen)

Add-a-Letter (page 278-279)

The missing letter is W

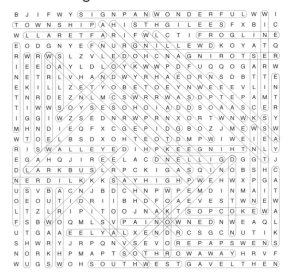

Codeword (page 280)

Code-doku (page 281)

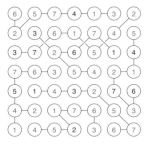

Fashionable Anagrams (page 282)

designer/resigned/redesign

Backyard Barbecue (page 282)

WET SIGNS = SWING SET
HOSS HEROES = HORSESHOES
THICK TRIO = TIKI TORCH
TOAST PIE = PATIO SET
EAGLE CUSHION = CHAISE LONGUE
CLONE HELP = CELL PHONE
RUM LABEL = UMBRELLA
NO HBO CONCERT = CORN ON THE COB
PRESCRIBE MAD HUB = BARBECUED SHRIMP
TO CHOKE SKIS = KISS THE COOK

Chain Sudoku (page 283)

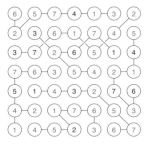

Interception (page 284)

Take the first two letters of each place name: The meet will take place in "The city of Austin in a big hotel."

Addagram (page 284)

The missing letter is Y.
Typhoon, hysteria, asylum, mainstay

Codeword (page 285)

1	2	3	4	5	6	7	8	9	10	11	12	13
K	H	S	V	R	C	W	J	Y	F	Q	Z	D

14	15	16	17	18	19	20	21	22	23	24	25	26
P	B	X	I	T	N	E	M	U	A	L	O	G

Code-doku (page 286)

Baseball Teams Letterbox (page 287)

1	2	3	4	5	6	7	8	9	10	11	12	13
A	N	G	E	L	S	Y	K	U	R	P	B	D

14	15	16	17	18	19	20	21	22	23	24	25	26
M	X	I	W	J	H	C	V	T	O	F	Q	Z

Chain Sudoku (page 288)

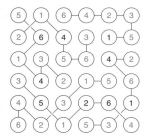

Codeword (page 289)

1	2	3	4	5	6	7	8	9	10	11	12	13
I	H	J	Q	K	G	W	E	B	M	X	C	R

14	15	16	17	18	19	20	21	22	23	24	25	26
F	Z	Y	T	P	U	V	S	A	D	L	O	N

Cryptogram (page 290)

"All hockey players are bilingual. They know English and profanity." —Gordie Howe

LogiNumber (page 290)

A = 3, B = 1, C = 2, D = 4

LogiNumber (page 291)

A = 3, B = 1, C = 4, D = 2

Baseball Quirks (page 291)

"Say 'Dodgers' and people know you're talking about baseball. Say 'Braves' and they ask, 'What reservation?' Say 'Reds' and they think of communism. Say 'Padres' and they look around for a priest." –Tommy Lasorda

Boys' Names (page 292)

1	2	3	4	5	6	7	8	9	10	11	12	13
P	I	J	C	H	A	R	L	E	S	U	F	W

14	15	16	17	18	19	20	21	22	23	24	25	26
M	X	D	Q	B	K	Z	T	O	N	Y	G	V

World Cities Letterbox (page 293)

1	2	3	4	5	6	7	8	9	10	11	12	13
H	J	O	C	P	A	R	I	S	D	V	F	K

14	15	16	17	18	19	20	21	22	23	24	25	26
Q	Y	N	Z	E	U	T	B	X	M	G	W	L

Codeword (page 294)

Henrik Sedin

1	2	3	4	5	6	7	8	9	10	11	12	13
C	S	J	Q	Z	U	Y	P	H	A	L	I	D

14	15	16	17	18	19	20	21	22	23	24	25	26
V	B	K	T	F	E	W	R	X	N	G	M	O

Code-doku (page 295)

What Comes Next? (page 296)

C. The arrow turns 90 degrees clockwise from one shape to another.

Visual Sequence (page 296)

B. The digits of the sequentially increasing numbers 13, 14, 15, and 16 are conjoined. The next number in the sequence would be 17, so the answer is B.

Living Large Anagram (page 297)

HOT GAIL = GOLIATH
THE PLANE = ELEPHANT
CNN TONITE = CONTINENT
OSTRICH MELT = STRETCH LIMO
LEO MUSIC = COLISEUM
SUSIE CHIRP = CRUISE SHIP
NO EMOLLIENT FLAB = FOOTBALL LINEMEN
MEOW RUSTLERS = SUMO WRESTLER

NANCY DRAGON = GRAND CANYON
END BATTALION = NATIONAL DEBT

Codeword (page 298)

1	2	3	4	5	6	7	8	9	10	11	12	13
G	K	H	C	J	U	I	B	Y	P	R	Z	F

14	15	16	17	18	19	20	21	22	23	24	25	26
L	T	S	M	W	D	X	O	A	Q	E	N	V

Codeword (page 299)

1	2	3	4	5	6	7	8	9	10	11	12	13
V	G	M	P	S	X	J	L	H	F	C	Y	B

14	15	16	17	18	19	20	21	22	23	24	25	26
E	D	T	A	Z	W	K	I	R	Q	O	N	U

Chain Sudoku (page 300)

Code-doku (page 301)

E	Y	I	H	S	M	R	T	C
T	M	R	I	C	E	Y	S	H
S	C	H	Y	R	T	M	I	E
C	H	T	S	Y	I	E	R	M
R	E	S	C	M	H	T	Y	I
Y	I	M	E	T	R	C	H	S
H	S	C	R	E	Y	I	M	T
I	T	Y	M	H	C	S	E	R
M	R	E	T	I	S	H	C	Y

On That Note (page 302-303)

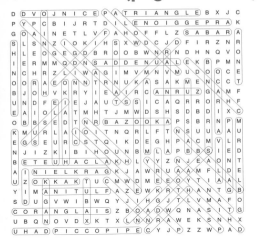

LogiNumber (page 304)

A + 3, B = 6, C = 1, D = 7, E =4,
F = 2, G = 8, H= 5

LogiNumber (page 304)

A = 5, B = 4, C = 7, D = 6, E = 2,
F = 8, G = 3, H = 1

Codeword (page 305)

Code-doku (page 306)

Addagram (page 307)

They mystery letter is M.
Flamingo, platinum, comedy, remnant

Addagram (page 307)

The mystery letter is U.
Umpire, figure, insurance, revenue

Honeycomb (page 308-309)

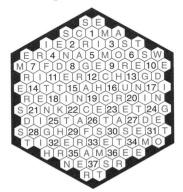

Group Dynamics (page 310-311)

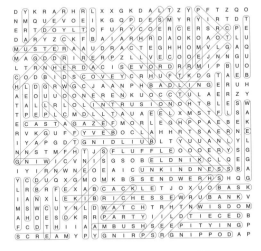

Mastermind (page 312)

6047

Crypto-Logic (page 312)

DONE

Code-doku (page 313)

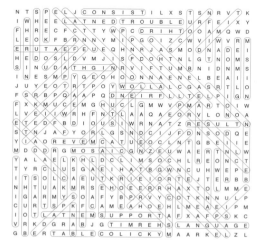

M	C	S	U	R	P	O	E	T
R	T	E	O	C	M	S	U	P
U	P	O	T	S	E	M	C	R
T	R	P	M	E	S	U	O	C
C	O	M	P	U	T	E	R	S
S	E	U	R	O	C	T	P	M
O	U	T	S	P	R	C	M	E
E	S	R	C	M	U	P	T	O
P	M	C	E	T	O	R	S	U

Variety Pack (page 314-315)

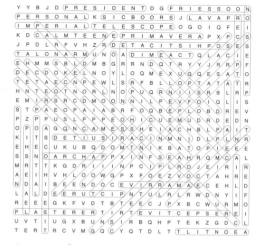

Add-a-Letter (page 316-317)

The missing letter is P

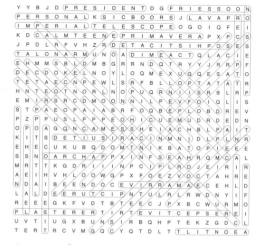

Cryptoku (page 318)

Mystery word: Bank heist

I	B	T	H	E	N	A	K	S
E	K	A	S	B	I	H	T	N
N	H	S	T	K	A	B	E	I
K	E	I	A	T	S	N	B	H
B	A	N	K	H	E	I	S	T
S	T	H	N	I	B	K	A	E
A	N	E	I	S	K	T	H	B
H	I	B	E	A	T	S	N	K
T	S	K	B	N	H	E	I	A

Codeword (page 319)

1	2	3	4	5	6	7	8	9	10	11	12	13
K	T	X	J	E	U	V	F	L	S	H	D	G

14	15	16	17	18	19	20	21	22	23	24	25	26
N	Y	W	I	Q	B	A	M	Z	R	C	O	P

Add-a-Letter (page 320-321)

The missing letter is E

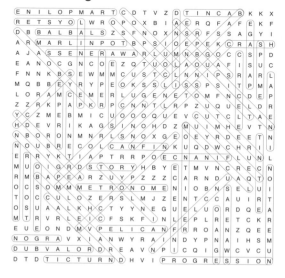

410

Code-doku (page 322)

C	E	R	A	I	Y	M	H	N
N	H	M	R	C	E	A	Y	I
Y	I	A	N	M	H	C	R	E
A	Y	E	I	R	N	H	C	M
H	N	C	Y	A	M	I	E	R
M	R	I	E	H	C	N	A	Y
I	A	Y	H	N	R	E	M	C
E	C	H	M	Y	I	R	N	A
R	M	N	C	E	A	Y	I	H

Astrological Discovery (page 323)

"My wife's an Earth sign. I'm a water sign. Together we make mud." —Henny Youngman

Word Columns (page 323)

If a trio of doctors who specialized in tonsillectomies formed a singing group with no instruments they could call themselves "Ahhh Capella."

Chain Sudoku (page 324)

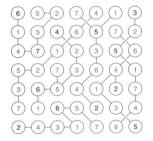

Codeword (page 325)

Add-a-Letter (page 326-327)

The missing letter is F

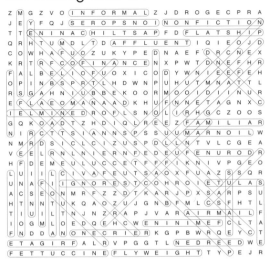

Cryptoku (page 328)

A	K	R	T	P	I	D	C	H
I	T	P	D	C	H	K	A	R
H	D	C	K	A	R	T	P	I
K	R	A	P	I	T	C	H	D
P	I	T	C	H	D	A	R	K
C	H	D	A	R	K	P	I	T
D	C	H	R	K	A	I	T	P
T	P	I	H	D	C	R	K	A
R	A	K	I	T	P	H	D	C

LogiNumber (page 329)

A = 4, B = 2, C = 1, D = 7, E = 6, F = 5, G = 3

LogiNumber (page 329)

A = 7, B = 2, C = 1, D = 5, E = 6, F = 3, G = 4

Add-a-Letter (page 330-331)

The missing letter is N

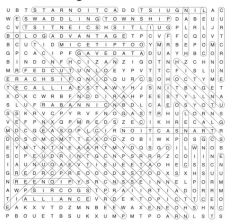

Code-doku (page 332)

Cryptoku (page 333)

Mystery word: Customize

T	S	C	U	I	E	O	M	Z
O	I	Z	M	S	T	E	C	U
U	M	E	C	Z	O	S	I	T
E	T	O	I	C	Z	M	U	S
C	U	S	T	O	M	I	Z	E
M	Z	I	E	U	S	C	T	O
S	O	U	Z	M	C	T	E	I
I	C	T	S	E	U	Z	O	M
Z	E	M	O	T	I	U	S	C

Codeword (page 334)

M	A	T	C	H	B	O	X	E	S		Q	U	I	T
S	C	R	A	P	H	E	A	P	S		G	I	V	E
T	E	A	S	P	O	O	N	F	U	L	S
H	A	C	K	S	A	W		E	X	C	I	T	E	R
R	U	N	W	A	Y	S		P	E	R	J	U	R	E
E	N	U	N	C	I	A	T	I	O	N	S
B	E	E	F		B	I	R	T	H	S	T	O	N	E
E	A	S	Y		I	M	P	R	E	S	A	R	I	O

1	2	3	4	5	6	7	8	9	10	11	12	13
Y	V	C	T	E	O	R	K	B	M	L	A	J

14	15	16	17	18	19	20	21	22	23	24	25	26
N	I	U	Q	D	G	S	P	Z	W	X	F	H

Mastermind (page 335)

85692

Addagram (page 335)

The mystery letter is G.
Grenade, allergy, midget, and longitude

Add-a-Letter (page 336-337)

The missing letter is V

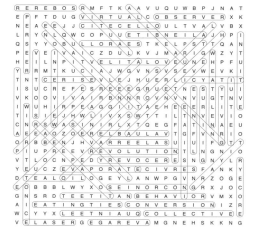

Futoshiki (page 338)

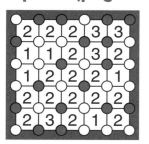

SquarO (page 338)

Codeword (page 339)

| O | Z | C | J | G | Q | I | M | V | X | R | H | Y |
| 1 | 2 | 3 | 4 | 5 | 6 | 7 | 8 | 9 | 10 | 11 | 12 | 13 |

| D | P | U | B | T | E | N | W | S | L | K | A | F |
| 14 | 15 | 16 | 17 | 18 | 19 | 20 | 21 | 22 | 23 | 24 | 25 | 26 |

Add-a-Letter (page 340-341)

The missing letter is C

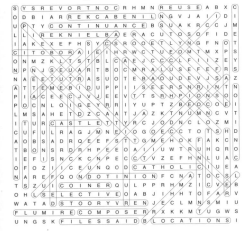

Code-doku (page 342)

TRAVEL TO VISIT RELATIVES

LogiNumber (page 343)

A = 5, B = 4, C = 3, D = 2, E = 1

LogiNumber (page 343)

A = 4, B = 3, C = 5, D = 1, E = 2

Codeword (page 344)

| T | B | F | H | W | P | J | I | R | Y | D | E | L |
| 1 | 2 | 3 | 4 | 5 | 6 | 7 | 8 | 9 | 10 | 11 | 12 | 13 |

| A | C | V | S | X | G | O | N | Z | K | M | Q | U |
| 14 | 15 | 16 | 17 | 18 | 19 | 20 | 21 | 22 | 23 | 24 | 25 | 26 |

Code-doku (page 345)

G	C	A	I	N	P	H	R	E
P	R	E	A	C	H	I	N	G
H	N	I	R	E	G	C	P	A
E	I	R	H	A	C	P	G	N
N	P	C	G	R	E	A	I	H
A	G	H	N	P	I	R	E	C
R	E	P	C	H	N	G	A	I
C	A	G	E	I	R	N	H	P
I	H	N	P	G	A	E	C	R

Add-a-Letter (page 346-347)

The missing letter is T

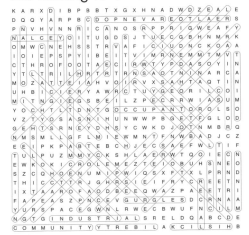

Cryptoku (page 348)

D	H	Y	A	N	S	U	B	R
N	B	U	R	H	D	A	Y	S
S	A	R	Y	B	U	H	N	D
B	N	D	U	Y	R	S	H	A
H	U	S	B	A	N	D	R	Y
R	Y	A	S	D	H	B	U	N
U	S	N	D	R	B	Y	A	H
A	D	H	N	U	Y	R	S	B
Y	R	B	H	S	A	N	D	U

Word Columns (page 349)

"The vanity of being known to be trusted with a secret is generally one of the chief motives to disclose it."

Mastermind (page 349)

8623

Add-a-Letter (page 350-351)

The missing letter is S

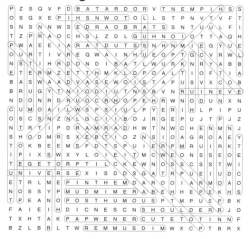

Cryptoku (page 352)

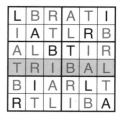

L	B	R	A	T	I
I	A	T	L	R	B
A	L	B	T	I	R
T	R	I	B	A	L
B	I	A	R	L	T
R	T	L	I	B	A

Cryptoku (page 352)

E	D	R	U	L	O
O	U	L	R	D	E
D	R	E	O	U	L
L	O	U	D	E	R
R	E	D	L	O	U
U	L	O	E	R	D

Code-doku (page 353)

R	E	H	T	A	F	D	O	G
A	F	O	G	D	R	T	E	H
D	T	G	E	O	H	F	R	A
T	A	D	F	G	E	O	H	R
H	R	F	O	T	A	E	G	D
O	G	E	H	R	D	A	F	T
G	D	A	R	E	O	H	T	F
E	H	R	D	F	T	G	A	O
F	O	T	A	H	G	R	D	E

Codeword (page 354)

1	2	3	4	5	6	7	8	9	10	11	12	13
J	N	I	D	Z	E	A	L	W	T	K	B	Q

14	15	16	17	18	19	20	21	22	23	24	25	26
U	M	V	R	P	G	Y	X	H	F	S	C	O

Word Columns (page 355)

An old lady once asked the dispatcher of a local trucking company if they could ship an antique mirror to her sister in Toronto. The dispatcher says, "I don't know madam, I'd have to look into it first."

Add-a-Letter (page 356-357)

The missing letter is L

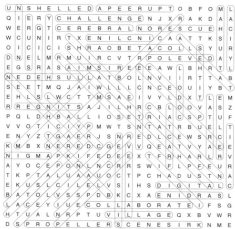

Code-doku (page 358)

Codeword (page 359)

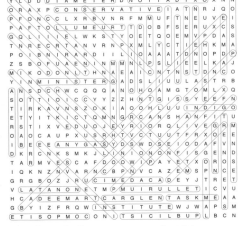

Add-a-Letter (page 360-361)

The missing letter is I

Code-doku (page 362)

EIGHTFOLD

Cryptoku (page 363)

Mystery word: Leap frogs

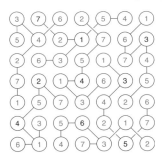

LogiNumber (page 364)

A = 1, B = 3, C = 4, D = 2

Crypto-Logic (page 364)

SWEET

Chain Sudoku (page 365)

Add-a-Letter (page 366-367)

The missing letter is D

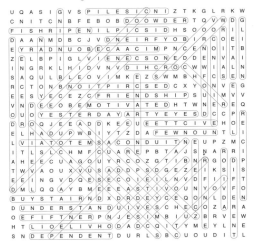

415

Cryptoku (page 368)

C	G	L	O	I	S	A	B	N
A	I	N	B	G	C	S	L	O
O	B	S	L	N	A	G	I	C
S	C	A	I	S	N	B	O	G
L	O	G	C	A	B	I	N	S
B	N	I	S	O	G	L	C	A
G	A	O	N	B	L	C	S	I
I	L	C	G	S	O	N	A	B
N	S	B	A	C	I	O	G	L

Codeword (page 369)

E	F	Z	P		E	I	S	
P	L	A	T	E	A	U		A	D	J	U	N	C	T
O		R		P	R		W		E		A			A
N	Y	M	P	H		G	E	N	O	C	I	D	A	L
Y		A			Y	A	S		T	E	K			I
M	U	S	K	R	A	T		B	I	S	Q	U	E	
S		A		I		A		O		U			D	
	E	X	T	R	A	V	A	G	A	N	Z	A	S	
O		O		E	G		T			S				
B	Y	P	L	A	Y		R	E	Q	U	E	S	T	
S			H		D		J	U		Y			Y	
C	L	O	C	K	W	I	S	E		A	W	F	U	L
E			N		I		G		V		K		O	
N	E	E	D	L	E	S		E	X	E	M	P	T	S
E		S		L		D			S		S		H	

A B C D E F G H I J K L M N O P Q R S T U V W X Y Z

1	2	3	4	5	6	7	8	9	10	11	12	13
H	L	M	D	C	O	I	E	A	X	R	N	Q

14	15	16	17	18	19	20	21	22	23	24	25	26
F	Y	S	B	J	U	T	P	W	K	Z	G	V

Add-a-Letter (page 370-371)

The missing letter is G

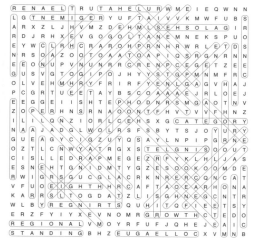

The Murder Castle (page 372)

H. H. Holmes died before he turned 35. In his relatively short life, he committed a number of murders, though the exact number is unknown. It may have been fewer than 10, but it may have numbered more than 100. Holmes was also a bigamist, marrying three different women. Holmes was active at the time of the 1893 World's Fair in Chicago, Illinois. He owned a building to which he lured victims under the guise that it was a hotel; it was later dubbed the Murder Hotel and the Murder Castle for the killings he committed there.

Duality (page 372)

Many actors have played Holmes, and many have played Watson—but British actor Patrick Macnee was one of the few to play both roles during a long career! He played the character of Watson opposite Roger Moore and Christopher Lee. And to cap it off, in 1984, he played a character on the television show *Magnum P.I.* who had a delusion that he was Sherlock Holmes.

Cryptoku (page 373)

Y	I	C	R	O	H	T	E	P
E	H	R	T	P	C	Y	O	I
P	O	T	I	E	Y	R	H	C
R	E	O	Y	T	I	C	P	H
H	Y	P	O	C	R	I	T	E
C	T	I	E	H	P	O	Y	R
T	R	E	P	I	O	H	C	Y
I	P	H	C	Y	T	E	R	O
O	C	Y	H	R	E	P	I	T